Gideon

THE SOUND AND THE GLORY

Gideon

THE SOUND AND THE GLORY

A Tale of Jerubbaal

BY JOSEPH GANCI

Gideon: The Sound and the Glory
A Tale of Jerubbaal

For information about this title or to order other books and/or electronic media, contact the publisher:

Joseph Ganci
gzepe@rumradio.org

ISBNs:
978-0-9978032-0-4 Hardcover
978-0-9978032-42 Softcover
978-0-9978032-2-8 Mobi
978-0-9978032-3-5 ePub

Printed in the United States of America

Cover and Family Tree design: Fredrick Richard
Interior design: 1106 Design
Map design: Sascha Montgomery with Book Fuel
Editor: Windy Goodlow and Gerard Robins

Everything in this book is good, except for the things that are knot, and the knots are not so tight. If you can hang in there long enough, you will undoubtedly enjoy the flight.

To my sweet granddaughter and fifth-grade proofreader, Claire Wellborn; violinist, and philosopher extraordinaire.

I believe in God as I believe in the sun; not because I can see the Sun, but because I can see everything because of the sun. And so, to his Son: the Holy Messiah, the prince of peace, wonderful, counselor, the only begotten of the Father, my savior, my redeemer and my friend, Jesus the Christ

TABLE OF CONTENTS

Table of Contents

FOREWORD

Moses flew away, for his work was done upon the earth, and the full mantle of "prophet" fell on the broad shoulders of Joshua, who had chiseled the laws of God into stone; given to all of the people of Israel. The people of Israel were now on the outskirts of Canaan, just beyond the River Jordan in the plains of Moab. They were within sight of the Promised Land, approaching the border of the land God promised to Abraham and his descendants. To assert their spiritual legacy would not be an easy undertaking. They would have to proceed by faith and rely solely on the strong hand and outstretched arm of God. The land of milk and honey was peopled by mixed and hostile populations who were violently opposed to yielding a cubit of ancestral lands—they would not go without a struggle. Canaan controlled the fertile valleys and the coastline with its unfriendly strongholds of walled cities. The high valleys were the domain of the Amorites. The Hivites, (Neo) Hittites, Jebusites, and Perizzites peopled the villages, towns, and hamlets of the central lowlands. This was Israel's time of conquest and settlement, often by force of arms. Occasionally, an attempt was made to infiltrate peaceably.

Gideon: The Sound and the Glory

The dawning of the Age of Iron created tools and skills in the form of the Kenite heavy metal wagons of war. Superior weapons were forged to drive out the rapidly multiplying immigrants before they could lay claim to all the land of Canaan.

The three chapters, Six through Eight, of the Book of Judges, consist of exactly one hundred verses that speak of the adventures of Gideon. He is an unsung hero who has been hidden in plain sight for three thousand years.

The account starts with the Battle of Tabor in Judges Four, where the sons of Gideon's mother—or Gideon's brothers—are murdered by two princes, who were now the twin kings of the Midianite horde. The slaughter of brothers had planted the seed of a blood feud in a collision of wills. This was the dry kindling that took the spark of Gideon's confidence and ignited in him a firestorm of resolve; resulting in the toppling of kings, gods, and generals, and the finding of perfect love. Three ferocious battles conclude in the wake of two ruined cities. The determined pursuit of their enemies by Gideon and his men is a testament to their faith, after being refused the bread of life by both Succoth and Penuel. All this was for the redemption of Israel by the hand of God in the appearance of the least likely of heroes. Gideon was a man who was lost in the forest of fear and doubt, a weak thing of this world—who through faith became God's instrument of vengeance and determination—a mighty man of valor. Gideon, means *hewer,* a simple woodsman—one who chops and hacks and makes a path through trees. Abimelech was Gideon's willful love child, who grows to be a vengeful predator and personally kills his seventy brothers, a congress of judges, to claim to be the first king of Israel. Abimelech returns Israel to the worship of Baal, and the Ephod of Gold becomes his cornerstone. He is short-lived when his head is crushed in another attempted holocaust of fire. The Ephod of Gold is resurrected by Eli, the young priest who miraculously finds a home for it, first in Shiloh, and then in the house of God in Nob, where the shepherd boy-king David takes possession of the accursed artifact. Your eyes will be opened, and deeper understandings will be shouldered, for any and all who read these five episodes will have no doubt that there is a God in Israel.

Part One

MEDITERANNEAN SEA

KEDESH

HAZOR

SEA OF GALILEE

MT. CARMEL

KISHON WADI

KEDESH NAPHALI

MT. TABOR

JEZREEL
VALLEY

OPHRAH

JORDAN RIVER

MEGIDDO

KISHON RIVER

HAROSHETH

TAANACH

BETH-SHAN

CHAPTER 1

A Call to War from the High Plateau

B arak turned out of his red ceremonial cloak that doubled as a bedroll. He stood up in the dark silence, except for the snoring and heavy breathing of his ten captains. He trusted two things, God and his sword; these two priorities might as well have been written in stone. Barak's esteemed weapon was passed on from father to son—it had edged many men to the afterlife; it rested on the ground wrapped in cloth, was swiftly snatched up, and like an old and trusted friend, found a comfortable rest on hip and thigh. Barak bore the weight of many scars; his face boasted a deep furrow from ear to crown. His arms and legs were roadmaps of personal combat. A moment alone with his thoughts was the rarest of luxuries for a man addicted to the passion of action. Barak means "lightning flash," and so he was the son of Abinoam; he resided in Kadesh, a mountain man from the tribe of Naphtali. Barak knelt to the ground and prayed that his spark of flint would start a blaze; it did on the third attempt. Barak thrust into the night with his firebrand, assaulting the gloom as

3

he barked a command: "Rise up and stand! We race the dawn to the next sleepy hamlet." His order was met with breaking of wind, the scratch of fleas, and blurry eyes trying to adjust to the dark, lit only by Barak's handheld flare of smoke and light. Men quickly found privacy in the shadows of boulders for the relief of nature's call. Swords and scimitars were reattached at the girdle, waiting to extend the reach and enhance the grasp of deadly arms. A prayer of Thanksgiving was uttered by Barak and all his cadre, as was their custom. Every knee was bowed, and every tongue confessed in a groan of awe and respect as they chanted: "Adonai, the only real God! Thank you for another day of breath and life; bless our efforts with a successful march, and make us Your channel of righteousness." Satchels and sacks were quickly repacked with bedrolls; flints and olive oil were slung over strapping backs. The rations of food had long since been eaten; the next town was Ophrah, an oasis of recruitment, wine, and barley bread. Ten torches were put forth that consumed the glow of Barak's flame and his zeal for God, and his zest for battle.

Barak declared to his company of captains, "Ophrah is just ahead, at the end of the trail, the final mountain stronghold. Ophrah is the last harbor for our needed dock of ten thousand men; all others have turned us down. God will make do with the many or the few, but this crew should be effortlessly rounded up and counted ready for the coming fight." Barak issued a simple order. "Listen up, Keras; as we enter the gate, announce our advance with three mighty blasts from the ram's horn—the shock of the shofar's sound will rouse them from their beds."

Keras mumbled in a feeble attempt at reasoned speech, "General, another hour of rest would have helped my aching feet.

We have been on this recruitment drive for a month . . . now to be rudely shaken at the entrance to dreams . . ." He shook his head sleepily before adding, "When the only visible enemy is our fatigue." Barak's silence kindled Keras's sullen mood. He spoke again, saying, "General, by all that is correct and sacred, we have invited forty thousand with shield and spear. Zebulon took the leader's baton, and Naphtali rallied, while, 'After thee Benjamin' was the war cry that clung to the coattails of Ephraim—a tribe deeply rooted in the country of the Amalekites. Machir, the lawgivers of East Manasseh, agreed, but they were few. Deborah's princes of Issachar arrived with pure intent, and yet it seems we have too few to prevail against the spinning wheels of the man-reaping chariot-scythes." Keras looked at Barak and asked, "What excuses were offered by the rest of the tribes?"

Barak, in a tone edged with ridicule, explained the logic of those absent: "Each had their seasoned excuses. Reuben debated with heartfelt passion, finally opting for the security of the sheepfold and the bleat of inaction. Judah and Simeon required every man they had to secure their borders against the assault of the Philistines. Gad did not agree to proceed and made their intentions known with words left unspoken. Dan found safe harbor in the import of ships; Asher found refuge in the cracks and crevices, beached on the high tide of fear; and as for Meroz, the sons of Manasseh, they were worst of all . . . their location is vital to our campaign, but their feet had grown cold. Deborah was furious and cursed them for their absence." Both men stood brooding in silence for a while before Barak continued.

"It is your complaint, though, Keras, that echoes in my ears. Do we really have too few to prevail? Do you trust in God?"

Keras could see the fire's glint in Barak's determined eyes. Holding his commander's stare, he answered, "I do, my lord, but I was hoping you would hear the words falling from your own lips. Surely it is folly, this noble yet doomed attempt to subdue Sisera's vastly superior arsenal of ironclad monsters?"

Barak was firm and steadfast with his reply. "We are on a mission from God. A way has already been made. If you believe it, then see it, and it will come to pass. His will be done." Barak did not take complaint lightly. Holding his captain's eyes, he spoke in a straightforward manner: "I look to you, Keras, my standard bearer, friend, and keeper of the horn of shofar, to gauge the strength of other men. As do I rely on all my other captains, I expect you all to be cut from tougher grit and to have the stamina to slice through to its finish. Peaks and valleys are a soldier's lot; do not dwell on the failings of others. Try, rather, to accept worthy challenges others have shunned. Fear wears the dark disguise of imagination that enslaves the heart, freezes the feet, and numbs the mind.

"All faith is blind and all trust is placed with the rod of God, who has already witnessed our victory march. Take courage, my friend, for Providence pursues the valiant, and if you cannot find it in yourself, then receive mine, and let us not speak of the disease of weakness."

Barak took a deep breath and said, "Listen up. This dark night is our cloak. We could have just as easily been a cunning enemy, inflicting the ambush of rape and handily penetrating through their gate with the malice of carnage." Barak quipped, "That the whisper of gain and glory will be heard before the loudest call to duty and order; we march to strike fear in their hearts and then remedy them with the promise of glory and spoil."

The trudge proceeded with strong, silent caution, with torches held at arm's length to avoid scars and scorches. Footfalls in the dim had to be made sure and each step was placed to sidestep cracks, potholes, and injury from twisted ankles.

The eager group, now girded with their commander's enthusiasm, approached Ophrah's massive gate, the final barrier to the heart of the city. The columns had fixed bronze hinges on an imposing monument of layered polished stone; it had the sprinkled glint of mirrored black obsidian that sparkled back from the reflective light of handheld torches. It was built at great cost to provide both admission and protection but often was left unbolted and unattended because Ophrah had never been assaulted or molested. General Barak observed the unguarded citadel. "Men," he said, "divine intervention is with us, for nothing stands in our way. Nothing can stem nor stall the swift force of righteousness. God's word cannot come back void or His promise empty, so our momentum will not be found wanting or confounded."

Barak called a man forward, asking him for information: "Balsam, you grew tall and strong behind Ophrah's walls before becoming a warrior. Tell me about its layout and who the princes and elders of reckoning might be."

"Yes," Balsam replied, "Ophrah was the place of my cradle. My visits have been few, with years in between, but at this high altitude, things generally stay the same from birth to grave. Ophrah is a stronghold of natural dens and caves carved out of the solid rock. There are freestanding houses with slate roofs that share common garden walls of stone, forming a semi-circle opposite a sheer-rock-face obstacle. The built-in barrier created by this design ensures the shelter and protection of a walled-in metropolis. The space between the houses and the mountain creates an open field that is the center of town meetings and marketplace. The bazaar is the heart from where all gossip is hung with the ready exchange of rumors, tools, and the constant flies from fresh meat. There is always the sweet scent of garlic, herbs, and in its season, the aroma of new wine drifts in the air. It masks the lingering tang of raw sewage and the sour-milk odor of caked sweat given off by an army of perspiring farmers."

Balsam continued: "Joash is the man whose voice is most critical. A wealthy prince, his mansion dominates the landscape; it is set higher than the rest and has a presence of greatness. Joash came to the Amorites with gold bullion, with which he built his large home and purchased lands round about. He also established the Grove of Baal, with its finely chiseled altar of stone, and appointed himself warden and high priest. Using his wealth, he recruited a score of servants and, due to his elevated position, has assumed the position of both judge and jury. His grove has a practical application—the swift dispatch of any person branded a criminal. The city elders rely on Joash to dispense frontier justice. He reconciles petty squabbles but also handles the execution of killers, providing regular and ready sacrifices for the altar." Balsam spoke darkly of a murder of crows that grew fat from the feasting on fresh corpses.

"Tell me more about this abominable grove," Barak insisted. Balsam dutifully continued:

"The grove's boundaries are continuously enlarged, bringing Joash more power and authority. The grove is used for the seasonal festival of fertility at the altar of Baal. These rituals are met with a carnal delight from the ever-increasing size of the mob. Certain nights are set aside for secluded iniquity in the hopes of letting loose a barren womb. These carnal acts are said to be for the pleasure and amusement of their fertility god. The out-of-the-way nature of the grove enables Joash to cash in on the sacrificial rites of virginity, providing him with a regular and steady tide of income."

Barak nodded slowly while gripping this information. "Is there any other place where the town gathers?" asked Barak.

"Yes, there most certainly is, and it's my favorite place," replied Balsam with a smile. All the captains leaned in. "The wine-press is usually the scene of greatest activity. Everyday woes are often fermented into the vintage of merrymaking and laughter. The vines thrive this high up on the plateau while wheat and barley are grown down below in the valley and along the plain of Jezreel. All activity rises and sets with the sun, except for the night of the full moon, which is reserved for justice, reverie, and sacrifice. The grove is fitting, for Ophrah is known to plant sin and harvest vanity. The grove is Ophrah's only diversion, allowing the community an opportunity for worship, pleasure, and mayhem." Balsam waited for the general's next question.

"Is there an area where I can project my words to rise above the noise of the city?" inquired Barak.

"Yes," Balsam replied. "There are three patches of rough-cobbled stones laid in the very center of the town, where the ram's horn is hung in case of emergency. It is there that we can stage your sure tongue of recruitment."

It was only to the cohort standard bearer and the captain of one hundred that the great ram's horn could be entrusted, and that was the hot-tempered Keras. Captain Keras gave three mighty blasts from the knuckle-ribbed ram's horn of shofar, the signal to war, as was the custom. These three sudden violent gusts cleverly alarmed the slumbering populace of both raised-up prince and lowly pauper. General Barak and ten of his captains had completed their roundabout and winding mountain trek to Ophrah, an outpost town on the borderlands of Issachar. Their timing was perfect; it was a stroke before the crowing of the morning cock, signaling the waking of life and an end to dreams—only to be abruptly rocked into the nightmare realm from a bloodcurdling war cry at the crossroads of reality.

Torches blazed, sputtered, and crackled, dispelling the darkness in flashes of light and hope on the path to a new day's dawning. Barak and his combat-hardened cadre strode with the promise of passion through the narrow gate of Ophrah's sleepy hamlet. The general, nicknamed "the Rock" by friend and foe alike, was also known for his oratory skills. His words could impart and entice young men to fight and instill in them the willingness and courage to be ferocious in combat or to give up their last breath for Israel in the approaching squall of conflict.

Dawn broke over the steep mountain peaks, flooding the grove, the vineyard, and the town center, bringing with it a steely surprise. The thin air and the blazing morning sun drew up the mountain dew into an eerie blanket of shifting vapor that slowly settled into patches of thick fog, offering Barak and his squad the appearance of ghosts steadily pushing through a wall of haze and smoke.

Scores of men came by the dozens,

Some came running, and some came lame.

And some came only to break the monotony of another boring day.

The city of Ophrah gathered, for the harvest and the threshing were over, creating a chorus of coughs and sneezes. Bites from bed bugs were scratched raw while babies nursed on mothers' milk from up-turned nipples. Steam drifted high above cooking kettles, releasing the aroma of porridge, and a poor man busily chewed a stick of dried meat in his haste to ensure a place in the gathering stir of excitement.

The town's center quickly filled with the overflow of chatter. General Barak was known to rouse a drowsy town with his passionate call to action. Barak looked to Keras and Balsam and said, "You two, secure any available wood and stone, so I can step up to elevate myself over the gathering throng, both head and shoulders." A rough and ready pedestal was hastily thrown together. The general was arrayed in his formal battle attire, flanked by ten fearsome-looking captains, five on each side. They carried scarred shields and were strapped about with bloody combat badges. This scene was to cast weight to the gravity of coming events and the end result of having faith in God but not committing to any required action, for in just such a case, all would be dead, and all would be lost. The clamor of the milling crowd quickly eased to a slight murmur of reverence.

Barak took a step forward, and the unruly mob yielded their undivided attention. Having gained their commitment to silence, the general stepped up, dropping his weighty cloak of office, and began sparking his remarks with the firebrand of emotion, his hallmark. "Men of Ophrah, hear me now. Fate is calling you. I solemnly assure you that a great reckoning stands before you. The moment has come to put your weight not behind the plow, but behind the love of God . . . and for the very survival of Israel.

Gideon: The Sound and the Glory

The time is now; today is the day to seize the commitment to victory. Not tomorrow! Not next week. Conquest does not rest or pause in timid reflection. If you are faint of heart, fearful, or of a peaceful disposition, this glorious adventure is not what you seek. Realize, you valiant men, that there is nothing more important right now, other than to stand proud and be counted as warriors of our most high God. You may never find yourselves, men of Ophrah, in such a position again." Here, Barak paused, holding the tension for a moment of dramatic reflection. "In any case," he continued, "it is better to die once, esteemed as a hero, than to suffer the endless ridicule from the murmurs and whispers of a coward's death in a slow bleed from little pricks and piercing needles.

"Do you wish to, once again, be slaves, scourged and butchered? Has your memory so dimmed of our recent Egyptian captivity? Now only to be repeated by the Jabin of Canaan? Do not give way to evil counsel! Do not refuse to do these things you are called upon to do. Do not listen to the advocates. Do not shun my call or turn your back to a righteous cause. Do not fancy that, because you dwell in a city high on a mountain top, you will suffer no lasting harm. The prophetess, Deborah, the oracle who lives under the palms, has proclaimed that the Lord God of Israel will deliver a most certain victory. We are assured of both glory and spoil. Join me now! And make no mistake, for together we will shake the pillars of heaven and bring our shared enemy to ground. We gather for the Battle of Mount Tabor."

CHAPTER 2

The Sons of My Mother, Brothers-in-Arms

The buzz of war was now at the door, promising young men to rise up from their quiet desperation of scythe and plow. With the sharp sword of esteem and the pointed lance of prestige, a young man's destiny could reach the heights of acclaim or fall down dead on the naked edge of fortune's blade.

The call to war had arrived, delivered by the swift messengers of Barak, Israel's general. Deborah, the prophetess who lived under the palms—an oracle of God—had promised victory by the hand of a woman.

The three sons of Joash were princes of the tribe Manasseh, but resided in Ophrah, a city inside the borders given to the tribe of Issachar. The house of Joash could make no claim to their ancestral tribe's portion of lands; they were rich in Issachar but poor in Manasseh. Adam, the oldest and the tallest, was often looked up to for comfort and direction. Adam was the only one of the three to have ever challenged their tough-minded father Joash. The brothers knew that Adam was as strong-willed and as determined as their domineering father. Hosea was the largest and the strongest, but gentle to a fault, and always agreed with the plans of Joash. Joseph was small in stature but made up the distance with the resolve of youth and a polite and light-hearted manner. Adam answered the door when the messenger called for every able-bodied man to come forth and do their part.

The boys craved this rite of passage, eager to become fierce warriors who would find the respect of men and the admiration of women. They also sought relief from boredom, for they had never traveled far from their small town. They heard the beckoning cries of Barak, who had come to speak of the glory of spoil and their duty to God and to Israel. The brothers adjourned to quieter surroundings for some heart-to-heart negotiation.

Joseph had the rash eagerness of youth and was the first to speak: "Father will never consent to our absence or give us leave to join in any armed conflict! If he has his way, we will grow old and die here. He recently told me he would find a wife for me, just as he did for Adam, which means I will surely never have the opportunity to go anywhere else."

Hosea spoke next, but instead of the usual uncertainty that tempered his voice, he was talking with resolve and conviction. "I will go only if we all go. If one stays, we all stay! I have been a dutiful son, and I have labored without complaint, but now I feel a strange craving . . . a deep longing to be a part of something bigger."

The three brothers stood in silent amusement of Hosea's musings, but it was suddenly broken by a chorus of a good-natured horse laughter.

Joseph caught his breath and, with a mischievous smile, said, "Older brother, I can't think of anything bigger than you . . . but

I must confess. I am of the same mind, my dearest big brother," he added.

Adam settled his two siblings down with a raised hand and a smile before speaking his mind on the subject.

"The timing is right, as we have had a bountiful harvest, and father is pleased. We need to first present our case with a united front, and then keep approaching him individually and at every opportunity. His resistance will be formidable, so our only hope is to wear down his steadfastness with our persistence."

The brothers approached Joash. They hoped that presenting a united front would help coax some sort of compromise from him, for they needed his agreement. Adam was their spokesman, for he carried the weight of logic and he was known for his ability to balance the scales of reason. The eldest son of Joash spoke first, addressing his father respectfully. "Father, we have sowed your land with good seed, and we have reaped a bountiful crop. We have harvested the horn of plenty—the storehouses overflow. Your vines have produced the promise of a sweet new wine. Now that our household is healthy and our warehouses are full, we implore you, Father, to give us your leave so we may experience the glory of battle in service to Israel."

Joash had never before been confronted by his sons in a state of such emotional charge and looking so determined. Joash paused and considered his response.

"I will consider your plea," he told them with a brisk nod. "For the moment, however, you must accept that I agree only to weigh your request, for there is much to mull over . . . heavy is the day that any father considers sending his sons to war." Joash abruptly dismissed his brood, with a few final words. "I have work to do . . .

as do you. Besides, it is best that we allow these heated moods to cool. Your emotions are heightened at the moment. Removing a boiling pot from the fire will ensure our discussion is influenced by reason rather than by the boil-over of feelings. We will take this to its foregone conclusion when all our heads are cooler." The combined stand had not produced the expected effect, but at least, they had not been refused outright . . . permission was still a possibility.

Joash was playing for time in the hope that this sudden rebellion within his household would be crushed with the distractions of work and wine. The brothers were familiar with this classic ploy and agreed to stick to their attempt at whittling down their father's resolve by taking turns at reminding him of their request, hoping to leave him no choice but to relent. This would be no easy task—Joash was the master of his household and the undisputed spiritual patriarch of the clan. Joash was, in effect, the leader of Ophrah, since he was the owner, as well as the self-proclaimed high priest, of the sacred Grove of Baal. Joash's word was as good as the law—not readily given, nor easily broken.

The three brothers took every effort to coax and convince their father because a chance like this could not be missed or recklessly abandoned to be counted among the warriors of Israel. It was one for all and all for one. The brothers had learned early on that the strength of the wolf was in the pack. Their accord would serve to ensure that they could prevail against any enemy attack and be confident in the union of brothers. They argued and pleaded with Joash, assuring him that they would return heaped with glory, and how their futures would be made lavish with gold. They finished every plea with the claim that they should not be denied this lawful rite of passage.

Joash had sinister reservations. He had experienced the brutality of battle and knew firsthand the grim menace of combat. But finally, he relented. The combined onslaught of his three determined sons eventually produced his acceptance in the giving of his patriarchal blessing. Joash summoned his sons. He looked Adam directly in the eye and said, "I will agree on one condition. Phurah will go with you. He will serve as your guardian and protector. He will act as my voice of reason and caution. Never have I encountered a more fearsome manservant. My trust in his judgment is without question. Into his strong hand, I place you for safe keeping." Adam nodded solemnly and then smiled as his father grasped his hand to seal their bargain.

Phurah was also chosen as a testament to his legendary strength. He had wrestled and restrained three men in one encounter at a local wrestling tournament. Phurah was orphaned by famine. Both parents had succumbed, and their final loving act was to place their last crust of bread into the hand of their only son. Rations were stark, and most were on the verge of starvation. Neither family nor friend made a claim for the youth. He was seen as yet one more mouth to feed. He was left to wander the hills without too much concern that, soon, he would become food for wolves—famine had a way of dulling even a mother's sympathy . . . especially when her own children lie at the brink of death.

The advent of divine intervention came in the form of Joash. He rescued the young pup on a wet and misty morning. Joash was out on the hunt when he heard a whimper coming out from the underbrush. It was a man-child, half-naked and faint from hunger. Phurah was immediately taken up and made secure in his savior's arms. A young boy of but five starving seasons, Phurah was adopted into the house of Joash and was given a place by the hearth. First, there were kitchen chores and then the work of farming. Phurah was as strong as any two full-grown men. He could easily continue without rest or pause from first light to well past eventide. In time, he became a trusted member of the clan and was given to the care of Joash's growing clutch of boys. His gratitude and loyalty knew no bounds—he would gladly have surrendered his life to ensure the safety of his adopted brothers. Phurah was summoned and given his grim commission. Joash explained to him in careful detail that he was to exercise all possible precaution. He was to help safeguard a satisfactory outcome in this impending and perilous enterprise.

Each son, in his turn, by age and rank, knelt before Joash with his head bowed in humble respect. Joash laid hands upon each boy's head individually and spoke reassuring words. "I, Joash, your father, and patriarch, bless you with courage that you might do your duty in the face of danger and not shrink away or shun your responsibility. That you tread with caution and forsake any harmful or foolhardy conduct; that you will look after your brothers and be made safe and protected; that you will find the strength and the determination to sustain your efforts to prevail, and that you find a victorious trail back to your home and loved ones. I ask these blessings and requests in the name of Yahweh, the God of Israel; and Baal, the god of the Amorite."

The boys who would be warriors and men could now be relieved from the everyday grind of tending fields and the milling of barley and wheat. With Joash's permission, they could join with all the other young men to prove themselves. No longer would they be just ordinary farmers but valiant warriors—men of stature and reckoning! The brothers were overjoyed at the prospect of adventure.

It was fate's unique chance to the men of Ophrah to confirm and attest to their willingness to participate in Israel's defense. The sons of Joash were born of Manasseh, but their home in Ophrah was in the borderlands of Issachar. This made them strangers in a strange land. Now, finally, they had a God-given occasion to be acknowledged as equals, as friendly neighbors. No longer would they be considered wandering immigrants. This alone was great motivation to join the men of the northern tribes of Zebulon and Naphtali; motivation to fight against the Canaanite mercenary, General Sisera, and his formidable army of trampling horses and iron wagons.

Adam and Hosea stood tall and forceful, like Joash, while Joseph, the youngest son, had a small frame and was of lesser stature—much like their slight-framed mother. Phurah—commissioned as an escort, chaperone, and bodyguard—led the way; encouraging his fledgling troop not to delay their departure for fear that Joash might recant his reluctant act of concession. Phurah looked to Joash on the day of departure; grasped his adopted father's hand, and announced: "I swear to you upon my life and by my will that I shall return with your brood—these, my adopted brothers—come mountains' height or the depth of hell's pit." Joash embraced Phurah and then each of his sons in turn.

The road was caked with long-dried dirt and parched with the dry heat of too many hot, sun-filled days. Ophrah's newest recruits kicked up clouds of fine, powdered dust, as they tramped away from their mountain stronghold. The road was filled with the blistering feet of young men seeking relief from the grind of mind-numbing boredom. Most were hard-pressed to recollect the memory of rain, as it had long since been washed away. Spirits were heightened as they lengthened their strides, and their lips double-timed with the prattle of wistful deeds and high-flying fantasies. Overhead, a troubled sky, with a cold draft from behind, sent a chill of death. Down they went on graveyard steps to the perils of man-to-man combat.

CHAPTER 3
Scythes, Prophecies, and the Flight of Crows

The Jabin, or the wise king of kings, was the overlord to all of the Canaan; he relied heavily upon the newly acquired foundry skills of the Kenite clan. The Kenites were first cousins to the Midianites. It was the Kenites who had conceived, built, and maintained the now infamous carriages of carnage in Harosheth, meaning the *smithy of the nations.* Canaan had nine hundred seemingly unstoppable chariots in their arsenal of terror. They were proving to be a curse—a stain on the landscape—that threatened to crush all the Hebrew tribes with hoof and wheel; grinding down into splinters a once-proud people. Wood and bronze could not withstand the strength of the iron tongue and the cunning of the mercenary general, Sisera. At every turn, he would outmaneuver and outfox the poorly led and ill-equipped collection of bickering and simple farmer tribesmen. Israel was at a loss. At every encounter, the chariots proved to be an irresistible force—striking fear and dread into all those who dared to oppose them. Only an act of God could relieve Israel's

Suffering; restore their lost confidence, and help to secure their unsure foothold in Canaan.

Absolute victory over Israel hung like a low-lying plum and was now ripe for the plucking. The Jabin, king of Canaan, supported by his hireling general Sisera and the Kenite foundries in Harosheth, was proving to gather together an overwhelming force. With the urging of Heber ringing in his ears, the Jabin's smile grew cruel. "Your Majesty," Heber began, "Midian has, for many seasons, been a sworn enemy of the tribes of Israel. They will create an unbreakable yoke to help you harness these sprawling immigrants that grow in population and in strength by the day. Combining their strength with your own could be the secret ingredient that brings these pesky Israelites to heel." Heber bowed submissively before the king.

The Jabin was impressed with Heber's timely advice. He hadn't considered adding Midian into the mix. He motioned to a servant to refill Heber's wine goblet.

"Thank you, my dutiful Kenite servant, for your wise and excellent counsel. A substantial amount of manpower will be required to round up these fractured and scattered tribes of Israel . . ." The Jabin's eyes acquired a far-off gaze as he allowed his imagination to complete the picture Heber's words had kindled. "Let it be so!" he ordered. And with a flick of his wrist, royal messengers were dispatched; sent to invite the young Midianite ambassadors, the twin princes, Zebah and Zalmunna, to hammer out the framework of an alliance. Messengers were dispatched far and away across the Jordan River to the wilderness caravan trail east of Nobah and Jogbehah and to the secure stronghold on Karkor. The twin princes were bored and at their leisure when their invitation arrived. A messenger caked with sweat and dust bowed humbly to the princess and said, "Your majesties I have an invitation from the Jabin, king of kings, and Lord of lords, to Join him at his fortress at Hazor." Zebah cast an approving glance at Zalmunna. The messenger then sheepishly uttered, "Will there be a reply?" Zalmunna with a smile said, "We will do better than that. We will depart with you at first light and answer this most gracious invitation with our presence."

The speedy arrival of the twin princes reflected their irresistible need to be involved in the Jabin's war of extermination. They had welcomed the invitation to make this powerful and beneficial coalition; their contempt for Israel was long-lived—increasing from generation to generation. The king spiced his political courting with the enticement of glory and spoil, saying, "I predict a beneficial outcome of lasting victory to our joint venture. This campaign will ensure the complete domination of our common foe so that Israel as a military force will be no more. We will gain the free labor of slaves, the one essential component necessary for the expansion of any empire." The princes of Midian nodded in agreement, encouraging the Jabin to continue spinning his web of conspiracy.

"We could make secure, once and for all, the fertile valley of Jezreel. With its plentiful bounty, we could supply many ranks of iron wagons, feeding their legions of swordsmen, spearmen, and archers. This strategic center-place of strength is like the hub of a wheel, the spokes of which extend out to the tribes in the north and those to the south. We could easily wreak havoc in all the unorganized Hebrew tribes and, once again, enslave them.

"We will return them to the familiar misery of their slavery, and those who refuse the rod and the yoke will be readily put to the sword—man, woman, or child. This will surely put an end to their growth as a nation and will bring them back into line so that we can bend them to our will now and for all time." The two princes of Midian nodded, acknowledging their appreciation of the Jabin's words with white-toothed grins.

They exchanged a quick glance, and then Zalmunna spoke on behalf of Midian. "We have heard of your many victories, O wise Jabin . . . but rumors remain. The Hebrews are a stubborn and determined lot, and we have heard they still have many warriors that will not be subdued or confounded by the might of your lethal carriages."

The Jabin took a deep breath. "I have restrained them for these twenty years." He spread his hands wide in a gesture meant to impress Zalmunna with the length of his rule. He smiled at Zalmunna, but there was no humor in his eyes. "The Philistines also continue to harass Judea and the tribe of Simeon. They are no more than a collection of squabbling and disorganized tribes who cannot even agree on a leader." He dismissed the tenacity of the Hebrew nation with a casual flick of his hair. "Their end as a free people will soon be a hard fact! They are right here . . ." He closed his fist on the empty air, "within my grasp . . . or should I say, at our fingertips." A humorless smile again returned to the prince's glance. "I have absolute confidence in my invincible army of iron-clad monsters. Together, we will overwhelm the feebleness of their bronze spears and wooden shields."

The Jabin invited Zebah and Zalmunna, along with their bodyguards of captains, to witness for themselves his latest achievements in a series of battles. It would be a tipping-point encounter. He would engage with an army of rough sod-tillers, but that was not important. He knew that, once the Midian princes had seen his chariots in action, it would be all that was needed to convince Zebah and Zalmunna to seal a bargain of a treaty for an axis of power.

In the Jabin's opinion, cordiality was the defining characteristic of royalty. He addressed the twin princes, saying, "We have ample time for our next encounter with the Hebrews. You will be in the reliable company of Sisera, my exceptional mercenary general. It is a three-day trip when taken at a leisurely pace or two days when compelled by the urgency of speed. We travel due south to Harosheth, the staging place of my next battle. You will both be my honored ambassadors, afforded all the privilege and protection of your station and rank. You will witness firsthand yet another decisive victory in the many I have amassed without a loss." The Jabin's eyes shone with deep-seated pride in his own achievements. "Alas, I will not be accompanying you, but please accept my apology in advance. I need to remain here in Hazor to command the defense of our impregnable walls and see to the leadership of our city."

Zalmunna bowed slightly before interrupting his host. "Your Highness, I must confess, and I do believe that I speak for both my brother and me." Zalmunna turned to Zebah, who nodded his approval, encouraging his brother to continue. "The walls of your fortress truly are magnificent! The thickness and their like we have never seen or even imagined as being even possible. And the gates . . ." He shook his head in awe, "their height, and girth . . . all covered in brass and bronze. Not only are they insurmountable, but a genuine work of art."

The Jabin, looking quite pleased with this praise of his accomplishments, betrayed his pride with yet another subtle flick of his wrist as if dismissing the skill of his artisans as a mere trifle. "I had it rebuilt from the ashes that the Hebrew, Joshua, destroyed with fire." An afterthought compelled him to add a line of smug assurance: "I can assure you, as long as I live, there will be no such reoccurrence."

The Jabin nodded sagely for a long moment before continuing on a lighter note. "There is a game of which I have grown quite fond. I would like to take this opportunity to match wits with my esteemed guests." Jabin motioned to his steward to retrieve his game board. Jabin could not hide his excitement at a chance to play with strangers, a rare opportunity for such a pleasurable challenge. The king continued, "The game of which I speak is known as the Royal Game of Ur, and I have had custom pieces made in your honor." He looked from one brother to the other, satisfied with seeing them both swell with vanity at his compliment.

"My pieces are iron chariots; yours, the sign of the Gemini. I hope you will be as delighted as I am to trade wits with fellow royalty." Having not said much during the entire exchange, Zebah jumped at the opportunity. "We certainly are enchanted by this amusement, O Jabin. What better grit to sharpen our intellects than challenging the mind of such a great king known for his standing and stature?" Zalmunna nodded his approval. "We are intrigued, indeed. Do tell us how the game is played and what rules govern the pieces."

In his element now, the Jabin began his explanation. "The game is played on this flat board placed before you. It has twenty decorated squares, arranged in two rows and then these three rows, here." He pointed to the rows being indicated. "A smaller square of six squares is connected by this bridge of four squares to the larger square of twelve squares." He looked at each brother. Both nodded in turn. "The game requires two players—I will be one and you two will be the other." Both princes bowed, enchanted at the idea of having pieces made in their honor. Jabin continued, "Move your pieces along a planned track, according to the throw of the dice of knucklebones. Twenty Squares is a racing game." The two princes were practically giddy with intrigue. The Jabin, having barely paused, went on with his explanation.

"Players take turns rolling the dice and moving around the board in opposite directions. And when they meet, briefly, and, might I add, dangerously, here, in the middle row . . ." He looked up from the board, lowering his voice dramatically, "and, by the way, this is my actual plan to catch the army of Israel—right here in the middle row." He raised one eyebrow for effect and kept talking in a slow, quiet monotone. "And this is how I devised our current strategy for the coming battle. It could very well mean victory or defeat!" The brothers stole a quick glance at each other, feeling both amused and slightly confused. Jabin went on without pausing between breaths. "If you land on a star, you get a second turn; if you fall on one of my chariots in the middle row, the piece is captured, and I am sent back to the starting point. The first player who moves all the pieces from the board wins the game."

The two princes were delighted to engage in such to-dos and commenced play with many toasts, holding their goblets of strong red wine aloft, glorifying their newfound friend and soon-to-be ally. The trio resembled a conspiracy of ravens hatching up an agreement of thieves.

《 《 《 》 》 》

Deborah was a prophetess, and a judge—esheth lappidoth—*a woman of light*. Deborah was an Oracle filled with the fire of God, where all knowledge, wisdom, and understanding resided. Deborah summoned Barak and said to him, "The word of the Lord has come unto me in the mystery of prophecy. You, Barak, General of Israel, will prevail against the formidable, and as yet, unstoppable might of the nine hundred chariots of iron—born of the anvil and baptized by fire." Deborah was decidedly resolute as she prophesied, before going on to proclaim: "Make no mistake, Barak, the glory will not be yours but will be found in the hand of a woman." Barak pondered her words, assuming to himself that the female she spoke of must be herself—Deborah, the prophetess. "No matter," he thought in the privacy of his mind, "as long as victory is assured!" As she continued, Deborah's prophecy became even more precise: "The Lord God of all creation has proclaimed, 'I will draw unto thee to the River Kishon—Sisera, the captain of Jabin's army, with his chariots and his multitude, and I will deliver him into thine hand." Barak bowed his head before Deborah, but she was not yet finished prophesying.

"Take ten thousand men of strength and valor and scale the heights of Mount Tabor; it is where Sisera's horse-drawn coaches will be stalled, and he will be deprived of the ability to maneuver."

Barak, the great general of Israel, acknowledged the prophetess Deborah's vision, for he knew she had confessed the will of God. Barak said unto Deborah the prophetess, "I will go if everything you say is true, but I need you to accompany me to Mount Tabor. If you come on this hard and dangerous journey, one woman among so many men, then I will go forth—but if you do not, then I will not proceed on a hunch and a wishful dream. Only in this way will I know that you have confirmed your sacred words with the faith to act."

Deborah relented and said, "You believe that I am the woman spoken of in the dream. Of this, I do not know with any certainty, but if this is what is required of me to move the army of God, I will hold high your banner of righteousness on the frontline. I, a woman, will take the lead if that is what is required of me."

In the sweeping shadow of a sundial's full round, the length of a day, Barak was in position with his ten thousand men, all armed with swords, spears, and shields. The men advanced with double-time speed, for the need was to be fleet of foot. They knew that they were most exposed when on the open road, for there they were easy prey to battle wagons and the thunder of hoofs. Their climb up the steep incline would ultimately provide relief and a safe haven. The army of Israel would be protected, once upon the high ground of Mount Tabor.

CHAPTER 4

The Heavens Dropped, and the Clouds Also Dropped Water

Heber the Kenite was a smithy of bronze and iron. He helped create the metal yoke, hinged scythes, spinning hubs, and the deflection plate, that were the hallmarks of advanced chariot design. Heber also attended to the Jabin's needs and whims as a go-between to Sisera and the foundries at Harosheth. He lived in a tent on the plain of Zaanaim, which was near Kadesh and within a day's journey to the protective walls of Hazor. He had been invited many times to live in the palace, but his wife, Jael, which means *wild mountain goat,* was ill at ease in walled cities and preferred the open-air tent of the Bedouin. Heber, aided by the wagging tongues and the loose lips of marketplace gossip, was alerted to the fact that Israel was gathering a formidable army. He witnessed the assembly of ten thousand men and the coming storm of war from the dust clouds they had kicked up. Heber could feel the road to Mount Tabor trembling under the pounding stride of so many soldiers, and he looked to the skies that had filled with dark clouds as the tears of heaven also gathered.

Heber hastened home and confided his lucky and fortunate happenstance to Jael, his childhood bride. Jael was plucking a brace of chickens when Heber entered the shade of his tent. He was still smiling at his good fortune, having heard in advance the rumor of Israel's approach. "My dear wife," he began, "love of my life, I bear news of good tidings."

Jael brushed the hair from her forehead, using a forearm to prevent smearing her face with blood and grease. "Whenever you engage me with endearments, it's usually to prepare me for some ridiculous plot you are hatching up." Jael narrowed her eyes at Heber. "Have out with it!" she snapped. "Can't you see I'm busy preparing our dinner?"

Heber fidgeted nervously with the hem of his robe before continuing. "I have witnessed the gathering of an army—Israel is on the march." He searched his wife's face for a sign of approval, but, seeing none, he pressed on. "This army will be the last hurdle to the Jabin's conquest of the Jezreel Valley and the end of all the gypsy Israelites. I will inform my king!" Heber thumped his chest with a callused palm. "In doing so, I will prepare him in advance, so he is ready for battle. A purse of gold will be my reward, perhaps even a promotion." He smiled broadly. "And the Kenite clan in Harosheth will be given future contracts to build more of our strong-wheeled, and very lucrative, heavy weapons of war."

Jael was having none of it! She rolled her eyes and began addressing Heber in a screech: "The Canaanites have never been our friends! They have only tolerated us because of your skill with hammer and tong . . . remember that the Lord God of

31

Israel precedes Barak into battle. I am dead set against this rash foolishness of yours. No good will come of it, and you will cause our undoing!" She turned back to the chicken she was plucking. "Consider yourself amply warned," she said and sarcasticly squealing, "my Dear and foolish husband!"

Heber pulled back his shoulders, straightening up to his full height, before replying. "Enough, woman! We make a good living. All our needs have been met for a score of years, and we want for nothing. I do what is best for the Kenite tribe and for our family." Dismissing his wife's opinion, Heber turned and strode briskly away, intent on conveying the message that Barak's two armed legions were marching against the Jabin's horde. Heber stretched his legs and doubled his pace, quickly arriving at the massive, walled fortress of Hazor. He banged at the bronze and brass doorway, demanding entry. "I am Heber!" he shouted, "a loyal and trusted servant to the Jabin, and I must see him immediately." His breathless persistence had the desired effect, prompting the guards to allow him an audience with the king.

The king was in the great hall, still completely absorbed in his game of twenty squares. He looked up at Heber in surprise. "What has brought you here with such urgency?" The king's voice echoed through the large chamber. "Your lungs resemble one of your bellows, and you're gulping for air." His eyes rested on Heber's exhausted form.

Feeling uncomfortable under the king's direct gaze, Heber caught his breath and blurted out his message without any further hesitation: "The army of Israel, my Jabin, with General Barak—your old adversary—is on the march. He has gathered, at the very least, two legions, fully armed! They are headed toward

Mount Tabor, ten miles north of the Kishon Wadi, and Barak marches his foot soldiers at a double-quick pace."

With apparent jubilation, the Jabin turned to his royal guests, having no concerns about disrupting the game they were playing. "Your Excellencies," he said, "my esteemed and honored guests, please excuse my intrusion—I have glad tidings and a simple request, but first, let me explain. It has just come to my attention that Barak, the general of the army of Israel, is rumored to have been on a recruitment drive, gathering together all the scattered tribes of his nation. Apparently, he now believes he has finally gathered strength enough and is on the march to Mount Tabor." The king paced the great chamber with eager anticipation. "My mercenary general, Sisera, who dwells in Harosheth with a host of men and chariots, must be alerted with all possible speed." Jabin blinked and then turned his eyes on Heber.

"My trusted servant, I need you to pull up your tent stakes, bring your wife and your forging tools, and meet these noble princes of Midian at the gate. I need you to accompany them to Harosheth, ahead of Barak, before he is able to engage with our army. Take heed, Heber, to the detail of my instruction. I made a promise to the regent of Taanach, in the realm where the soil is nothing but sand; and to the ruler of Megiddo, where fountains of water spring forth—I vowed that both would have a standing invitation to our next brawl with the Hebrews! Their hatred is greater than their need for silver and gold. They have no interest in money and are eager to lend me the use of their troops. Both Taanach and Megiddo are only a few miles out of your way—they are probably neither vital to our success, nor even necessary, but I did promise them, and my nobility gives me the obligation of keeping my word." He looked around with an air of smug pride at his own generosity of spirit. "And besides," he added, "there is no fee to negotiate, unlike with Sisera, whose service does not come cheaply." Focusing on Heber once more, the Jabin continued.

"Relay to Sisera: it is according to my wish that the forces of Taanach and Megiddo are to accompany him into battle. Furthermore, advise him to attack Barak with the greatest possible speed and savagery! I want him to mount an all-out offensive, that he may catch them flat-footed before they reach their destination. That way, we can hook them in between the mountain and the plain." The Jabin was excited at the prospect of what he believed would be one last clash with Israel. He addressed the twins: "It would greatly please me if our new friends, our brothers, Zebah, and Zalmunna, had a personal viewing of the killing fields . . . would you gentlemen be up for such an adventure?"

Taking the lead, Zebah addressed the Jabin. "Yes, of course! As Your Majesty commands. Our camels will easily keep up—in the long run, they can outlast any horse-drawn chariot, and much more so the pace of men." Zalmunna, fanatical glee etched into his well-kept features, added his voice to the excitement. "Wonderful! We will prepare to depart." With a flair for the dramatic, he turned over an hourglass and exclaimed, "Before the last grain of sand finds its rest on the bottom of the glass, we will be found ready to depart."

By the time Heber reached his tent, his enthusiasm had soured. He was no longer so sure of the circumstances in which he had become entangled, and was bracing himself for a hostile reaction from his wife. Jael was outside at the hearth, roasting a pair of plucked chickens. Heber's approach was a mixture of feigned confidence and stealth. He tiptoed up to the hearth, uneasy and anxious. He knew that his news would not be readily accepted. "Jael, my love," he began. "I, or rather, we, have been commissioned by the Jabin to pull up stakes." Jael's eyes squinted in contempt, but Heber swallowed hard and pressed on with what he had to say. "With all due haste, we are to accompany the princes of Midian and their caravan of camels back to Harosheth, ahead of Israel's approaching army. We are to leave within the hour. These men here . . ." He pointed to the Jabin's footmen, "are to see to our immediate departure. They were kindly sent to help pack our tent and all our worldly belongings into these speedy horse carts." Again, he gestured, this time toward the wagons attended by the footmen. "I have also been given the charge to remain with our Kenite clan at the foundries in Harosheth, with all the trappings of pay and rank due to the royal blacksmith." He allowed himself a generous smile. "You, my dear, will be reunited with your family, and you will no longer have to travel thirty miles for a reunion."

His feeble attempt at putting a positive spin on his news was immediately reversed when he uttered, his next sentence: "Your mother always said I would 'never amount to anything' . . . but this will show her. For now, I have become captain of the foundry." Jael's jawline tightened as she dropped her gaze back to the roasting chickens. Heber continued, "The porters will accompany us to Harosheth. They will assist us in the raising of our tent and setting up the household. You, my dear, will not be required to lift even your little finger." He allowed himself a generous smile in a vain attempt to put a positive spin on a losing argument.

Heber was hoping to ease the wrath of his wife's anger. Jael's eyes began to narrow, the hallmark of her inevitable outrage. She paused momentarily—the quiet before a storm—and then, in a fiery eruption, she let loose her anger. "What is wrong with you? Did I not tell you to avoid participating in the hearsay of gossip and rumor? Now we are dragged into a conspiracy with these warring armies, uprooted and moved into a place of the battle with the God of the Hebrews and the Canaan war machines. You idiot!"

The princes of Midian, along with their companions of captains and camels, were lightly packed. The practiced haste of their speedy nomadic routine earned Zalmunna's momentary bragging rights—they had beaten the hourglass. The forty miles drew in as fast as the wheels would turn, and the camels moved at a breakneck pace to keep abreast. Four miles from Harosheth, at a delightful clearing close to a shallow stretch where the river could be forded, Jael called out for the wagons to a halt. She surveyed the view. On the crest of a bank that sloped gently down to the swift-moving Kishon River, Jael chose her spot. It was surrounded by poplar trees and was far enough away from work and family to give her the peace she desired. The carts and camels were still jangling and jostling to a halt. Jael pointed. "This is my place of rest. This is our new home. The Jabin owes us this much. Besides," she added, "I cannot and I shall not attempt to abide city life, tribe or no. I will have our tent and home raised here." She aimed a frosty glance at her husband. "Leave the cart and the porters, and be about your business of Hebrew slaughter, Heber, and pray that this cold river chills my simmering aggravation."

Heber was glad for temporary relief from his wife's anger and, feeling more at peace, proceeded to Megiddo, a few miles to the north and east. The Canaanite king received him, overjoyed to hear of the next opportunity for battle. Addressing Heber, he said, "Please thank the Jabin, king of kings, for I have been practicing my warrior skills, and I chafe to perfect them in the arena of mortal combat. I will gather my army on the north side of the Kishon Wadi. We will be counted among the Jabin's force. We are prepared to join General Sisera."

Before taking his leave, Heber spoke a few polite words. "Thank you, Your Highness. Please forgive my hasty departure. I am pressed to inform your neighbor to the south and west, the King of Taanach, of the call to war. The Jabin has commanded it, and General Sisera awaits. He has not yet been made aware of the enemy's movements, and needs to prepare for his deadly offensive."

The reception at the court of Taanach was friendly and cordial. The king addressed Heber: "I will be assembled and ready for battle. Please inform the general I will meet him on the north side of the Kishon Wadi, at the entrance to the small plain of Tabor." Heber agreed to relay this message before departing.

The Midian prince, Zebah, struggled to keep his excitement in check as he commented, "This is too much fun! The excitement and the scheming are even better than drinking." Zalmunna laughed in agreement. "Yes, my brother, it is the call of high adventure. I can hardly wait to take on the next turn in this winding road." Before them lay the gates of Harosheth.

CHAPTER 5

Assemble All Who Would Fight Against Zion

Heber and the Midianite ambassadors sought Sisera, finding him in the charioteer stables. "Heber!" said Sisera, curbing his surprise when he saw the Kenite in the company of foreign gentlemen. "What brings you to my door?"

Heber straightened up to his full height and stature before addressing the general. "I have been sent by royal command. I am in the company of the twin princes, the ambassadors, Zebah and Zalmunna of Midian. The Jabin wishes them to witness our victory in the coming battle, in the hope of gaining an alliance against the Hebrews."

Sisera, looking a bit confused, responded briskly. "Come, come, Heber! What coming battle?"

To which Heber replied, "General Barak and ten thousand armed Hebrews are marching south from Kadesh on the road to Mount Tabor, even now as we speak."

"Why did you not speak up sooner, Heber?" replied Sisera, pausing before adding, "Why only ten thousand?" Sisera answered his own question. "The rest must be cowering in fear, feeling safe in their defenseless villages. I see an opportunity here that must not be wasted."

Wanting to complete his dispatch, Heber continued, "The kings of Megiddo and Taanach will be joining forces and meeting you on the north bank of the Kishon Wadi. They were excited and pleased to accept the king's invitation to participate. The Jabin has asked that you extend all due courtesy to their titles and rank."

Sisera scowled and expressed his frustration regarding the unwanted baggage of allies.

"You have been busy, Heber. Valuable time has been squandered! They are neither needed nor wanted, but I am at my lord's command, and it shall be so." Sisera immediately began barking commands. The stables bustled with the drone of whinnies and neighs, arms and legs.

The speed and destination of the enemy's advancing army were all Sisera needed to put his plans into motion. The wily general wanted to ensure a strategic outcome in the impending clash with Barak and the soldiers of Israel. Sisera hastened into the courtyard in a calculated rush, for he recognized an opportunity to crush the might of Israel once and for all. This chance opportunity had fallen neatly into his lap. Sisera addressed Zebah and Zalmunna. "Young princes, you are more than welcome to extend your visit, but my duty is pressing for the coming encounter. You can join me if you desire. You will be directly to the right of my command cohort of one hundred chariots. Each chariot has scythes that are hinged on every hub, which is extended just before battle formation. I will keep fifty hosts of infantry in reserve behind each century of carriages. My infantrymen will stand ready to dispatch the wounded and the dying to the next life. We show no mercy! We do not take prisoners." Sisera paused, gracing his visitors with a tight fist and clenched jaws.

"Unless they are women, and so the booty of conquest." His manner became brisk again. "It has not rained for many months, and the Kishon Wadi, only eleven miles away, is filled with sand and dust. We will cross the gully with minimal effort, entering the ten miles of flatland making up the small plain between the Wadi and the base of Tabor . . . a perfect killing field for prancing hooves and iron wheels." Sisera swirled his finger in an ever-tightening circle, exclaiming loudly, "We have them!" In a lighter tone, he continued, "I will assign a captain to make sure you have a full view of the coming devastation and that you both remain safe and out of harm's way. Please excuse me—the work of war is a demanding taskmaster. Captain Herkimer here will be your escort, and he will see to your needs."

Herkimer stepped in, saying, "Gentlemen, please follow me."

Sisera gathered his powerful professional army with a steely-eyed resolve. He marshaled his captains of chariots and his hosts of infantry, addressing them in his strapped and plumed battle attire from the platform of the general's lead chariot. The princes of Midian were also present atop their cohort of camels, giving the scene a surreal and exotic element. The city of Harosheth watched the grand spectacle, looking out from their windows and shops, and from the heights of balconies to cheer their hero on to victory. The commotion was filled with excitement and anticipation. The stables and the chariot support shook, barreling and bustling with a rush in preparation for the coming fight. Sisera raised both arms, keeping this stance until the only sounds were clattering hooves and anxious neighs from high-spirited war horses and the wind-whipped snap of battle banners.

Sisera paused in the silence where moments hang, and with a voice steeped in confidence, he declared, "We are an army of foreign fighters; we are a gang of brothers born to different fathers and different mothers. Our allegiance is not to cause or shifting political agendas, or to a homeland long since forgotten, but to each other and to the honor of our hire. Of our blood, we are a breed apart, soldiers of fortune swept together by the winds of fate and baptized by a tide of illegitimate and ill-conceived accidents. We survive and thrive by our skill and daring; we are an army of reckoning, armed with the latest and most deadly weaponry. We have been commissioned by the Jabin of Hazor to finally and decisively crush our enemy of twenty years—the Hebrews, who call themselves "Israel." Their outstretched arm now reaches for the road to Mount Tabor, ten miles north of the dry Kishon Wadi. We will give no quarter and show no mercy. Victory is ours for the taking! We will prevail as we have done many times before, and our final testament is that we will leave no Hebrew enemy left alive." The rousing cheer from the listening crowd was short-lived.

A brilliant flash of lightning, a bolt out of the blue, followed by an explosive clap of thunder, drowned out the cheering masses. The sky to the west had suddenly blackened during the general's speech, and now another flash of lightning from that direction produced an even louder thunderclap. An eerie silence that spoke of judgment was broken by a trumpet call to march. The army was off in a fanfare of dust, with the foreign caravan of camels in accompaniment on Sisera's immediate right. Nine cohorts in all, filling a contingent of fifty infantrymen fixed to each of the one hundred chariots, each chariot with its own driver and a platform to launch the lethally tipped shafts of the bowmen. Canteen wagons were assigned to every cohort of two hundred and fifty men and one hundred horses: rations, which included feed, oil, flints, bandages, sharpening stones, and bedrolls—it all moved right along, for an army eats its way across boundaries and borders. The long line of iron chariots, horses, and foot soldiers stretched due north to the Kishon River fording, and further on, to the dry wash of the Kishon Wadi, extending finally onto the small plain of Mount Tabor.

The crossing at the fording place was exceptionally shallow and proved uneventful, but a vicious storm was approaching, raging with violent, booming thunder and long fingers of lightning flashes, pressing in hastily from the west. The line of rally stretched on for miles; in some places, the road could accommodate the wheel ruts of only a single chariot.

The lesser kings of Canaan were true to their word and met Sisera and the Midian princes with their respective armies, wielding shields and spears on the north side of the Kishon Wadi—the entrance to Tabor's open, flat plain. Sisera welcomed the kings and applauded politely for their eagerness to do battle. He continued, saying, "Your Majesties, you honor me and my army of victorious soldiers of fortune . . . but please, bear with me while I explain the confidence I have in my victory—after all," smiled Sisera, "is not patience the virtue of kings?" He stopped smiling and regained his military bearing.

"When all the chariots and infantry have crossed over the Wadi, we will reform and organize into three separate spearheads. We are ten miles from Mount Tabor, and we will approach the enemy like unto a trident, the right and left flank in advance of the middle. This will draw the enemy into the center, and when they attempt to engage, we close in and spring the trap with my prearranged signal—a swirling red banner high overhead. We start circling in the direction of the battle ensign, catching Barak and his entire army under the spinning scythes of my iron blades. Our infantry will seal any empty gaps, finishing off all the survivors . . . the dead and the dying, with sword, spear, and javelin."

The kings could almost taste their imminent victory. The king of Megiddo stood up to say a few words of praise for Sisera. "A chief marshal of maneuvers you are, my good general! We are at your disposal."

Another bolt of lightning darkened the sky. The sun had lost its face. Missiles of rain exploded in the dust, and the heavens dropped, weighed down by the burst of fast-moving clouds. The last of the western sky had blackened, constantly lit by cascades of brilliant-white lightning flashes. The rearmost cohort of the last one hundred chariots had already filled the Kishon Wadi when a sudden blast of wind heralded the uproar from the surge of rushing waters. Sisera's fleet of iron chariots, his anxious hosts of infantrymen, and his archers were all caught in the eddy of a rising tide. Horse hooves broke, struggling for traction in a vain attempt to climb the slippery embankment. They were all swept away, abandoned to their grisly fate, washed away in the fast-moving rapids.

Sisera was not troubled, keenly aware that all combat is fluid. He maintained a heated but measured pace to the base of Mount Tabor. There, with its flat, open plain, the chariots would be an ideal weapon—an extremely sharp cleaver in the butchery of war. Sisera knew that, to successfully attack Barak, he needed to intercept the column of Hebrews before they reached the high ground of the mountain passes; forcing them out into the open flats of the small plain, he had to push both men and beast to their limit. The tremendous weight of Sisera's metal monsters was capable of squashing a man, especially given the sheer force of momentum. The scythes extending from the hub of their wheels could shear off a man's legs, slicing them cleanly from the torso. This battle was a critical event. A sign and a warning to all those who attempted to oppose Canaanite rule—they would be crushed under Canaan's iron heel.

The earth trembled, and the heavens dropped. And the clouds also dropped water. A hard rain continued to pelt the Canaanite host as the windows of heaven were opened. It stalled their advance, forcing them to trudge through mud. Sisera, against his best effort to move his host promptly into position, was just in time to witnesses the army of Israel complete their climb to the heights, as they disappeared behind boulders and rocks. He was too late! He had missed his moment by a whisker. This gave Barak and his ten thousand men-at-arms just enough time to secure the heights of Mount Tabor, where chariot scythes and iron-tipped arrows were blunted and made ineffective. Victory had been snatched out of Sisera's grasp for his lack of speed. The Canaanite war machine would have little or no effect. It was reduced to an idle siege, unable to make contact with the enemy infantry.

Sisera had sent Herkimer to scout a safe location to ensure that the Midianite princes were out of harm's way, yet in full view of where he guessed the battle would eventually erupt once the worst of the storm had passed. The two Midianite princes were still his valued guests, and their needs had to be met. Herkimer helped coordinate the raising of a portable pavilion to protect them from the rain and to keep them out of harm's way.

Sisera asked the counsel of the two Canaanite kings: "What say you, my two valuable allies? We have deployed—as we have done these many times before—but no good has come of our tactic. Do we continue to shiver, stiff and immobile in this endless squall, and wait them out? Or do we dismount and send up our infantry in an attempt to flush them from their secure perch in the pelt and piss of this wretched storm?"

The king of Megiddo was first to speak. "General, in my humble assessment, we are neither ducks nor goats! If we climb the mountain in this blinding downpour, the enemy can literally hurl rocks and stones, even dislodge huge boulders to rain havoc upon our heads. They have the advantage of height, and therefore, gravity."

The king of Taanach spoke next. "Going back is no longer an option. When the Wadi overflowed, it signaled that the Kishon River had spilled its banks, and this has closed any possibility of retreat. The Wadi has no fording place, and we will have to wait until it is bled dry. This will not happen until there is an end to this drenching curse. We have no retreat. Our only safe place at present is to keep to this tight spot of conspiracy, in the hope of resolving our dilemma." Taanach shook his head before continuing. "I would respectfully suggest, my General, that the logical option is to wait them out. It is raining on them as it is raining on us. They are neither sheep nor crows. They cannot eat grass nor fly away. We are already in position for a decisive victory, and I say we hold our ground and wait them out."

Sisera pondered and weighed all that he heard. Finally, in a tone of unaccustomed submission, he turned his head up in an attempt to face an unseen adversary, saying, "I have no appetite for patience! The stars in the heavens do conspire against us, but we will hold tight to the plain, and to the killing ground. I will curse the rain for every day we lose and for the soaking of our bones through these miserable nights."

The rain was relentless, its thick sheets framing every view in a watery screen. Mount Tabor was awash. Water spilled out from its peaks and summit; mud and rockslides melted from its sides like wax on a candle. Some of the Hebrews found partial relief from overhangs, cracks, and crevices, but for most, the misery was universal. There was nothing to report; the lookouts strained for even a faint glimpse, but because of the thick, dark, rain-filled clouds that had suddenly appeared and now surrounded the whole of the mountain and the plain down below, only vague, ghostly wisps and the outlines of smoke were evident. A call went out for volunteers to go down to the mountain's base to locate the Canaanite enemy, and to inform Barak of how they had been deployed. The scouts were to map out battle formations and the enemy's readiness to defend an assault on the small plain of Tabor.

Barak tried in vain to project his booming voice beyond a ten-meter radius. Even though his voice was trained to command, he was drowned out by the heavy, pounding drops of the relentless downpour. Even so, Barak shouted out to all those who were within the sound of his voice: "Who will go for us?"

Among those who heard their commander, some stood up in the hope of becoming heroes. Nine mighty men of valor stepped forward to undertake the perilous and covert mission set out by Barak—six stalwarts from Naphtali and the three overeager sons of Joash, who would not be separated or parted. Phurah protested at their intended participation in this short and reckless quest, and with the sternness of a responsible guardian, he tried to counsel them against it.

"The time is not yet ripe for us to fight. It is true that we are all tired of being wet and immobile, and at this moment, the appeal of a diversion may not seem like a foolhardy adventure, but it is ill-considered. I, too, am chilled, and my skin is weary of being wet. Just like you, I chafe at having to wait." Phurah paused, looking for inspiration. "Patience is bitter, but sweet are the fruits of discretion." The guardian's warning, however, was instantly rejected. The sons of Joash were tired of shivering. They craved the opportunity to try their hand at scouting. Phurah then insisted that he accompany the brothers, to honor his covenant with Joash, the patriarch, in the safeguarding of his sons. Thus, nine became ten.

Phurah took the lead as they made their way down below the rim. Through loose rock and slides of mud, they crisscrossed the jagged outcroppings, treading lightly on the rain-soaked earth. While the sons of Naphtali went east, the children of Joash headed west. They trudged on through the rainy haze until, out of nowhere, they happened upon a brightly colored pavilion. Just as suddenly, they were set upon by ghostly figures that quickly took on the form of flesh rather than fog; they were surrounded by a squad of slashing scimitars. Swords sparked against scimitars with the ferocity of metal hawking metal. Phurah proved himself well. With fury and skill, in the hope of cleaving the enemies' life and limb to pieces, he killed four and wounded two.

Adam was backed into a crevice, but he slew two of his attackers before he was stung and subdued. Hosea and Joseph made every effort with their slashing swords and fiery fists but were eventually overpowered and bound with strong cords by the ferocious bodyguards of Zebah and Zalmunna.

The sons of Joash were bound and gagged, and set before the two princes, their clothes proclaiming the status of their rank and privilege. The mark of this status spared their lives for the time being. Their manservant, Phurah, now bloodied and wounded on the face and neck, was tied to a tent peg and left out in the pelting rain. He was not deemed to be of sufficient rank to be taken into the presence of the royal twins.

Prince Zebah looked to his brother. "Are we not curious as to the schemes these men can impart? Surely they have information that could benefit general Sisera and his rain-weary complement? This godforsaken downpour, coupled with the steepness of this mountain ascent, has created a standoff of wills. Barak and the army of Israel occupy the impassable heights, while Sisera, with his men at arms, stand poised like statues in a storm, waiting to be restored by sunlight." The Prince Zalmunna directed his captain, Lexol, schooled in the art of both subtle and violent interrogation, to obtain any information that might be of practical benefit.

Pointing to the largest man, assuming him to be their leader, Lexol, using all the politeness of his elevated rank, asked, "Who are you, sir?"

"My name is Adam, son of Joash the Abiezrite. I am from Ophrah. I have come with my brothers three, one of whom has been wounded and not found worthy to be in your presence. He has been left out in the rain to bleed away his life."

Lexol frowned and then pointed his finger at Adam.

"You call him brother, but his attire proclaims the station of manservant? If you are forthright, and speak with truth and frankness, there we have some delicacies and hot roasted meats; you can warm your insides, and there is more than an even chance you will be saved alive and released unharmed."

Adam's answer was resolute. "We are here to help free Israel from the Jabin King, who desires the enslavement of my people."

Lexol smiled in a mock attempt at pleasantness. "Come, come . . . is not your life of greater value than the darkness of shifting politics? Tell us all what we need to know, so we can speedily end this quarrel and return safely to our homes."

Lexol, having already ordered the gag removed from Adam's mouth, ordered the same for all the brothers seated before the princes. Lexol observed, "You are soaked, and chilled to the bone. Before you fall ill, let us see to your wounds and take your fill of strong wine and ease your shudders." He said all this to lull his captives into a false sense of security, so they would relax into an idle conversation that might well induce the needed information. Lexol's ploy also was an attempt at judging the extent of the Israeli camp's supply of rations. He wanted to estimate the extent of time required for a prolonged siege sufficient to remove the enemy from the craggy peaks and high towers of Mount Tabor from starvation.

Adam sensed Lexol's intent, seeing through the deception. He was about to say that they had eaten well, but his little brother, Joseph, allowed his empty belly to speak, pleading in his weakness. "We have not eaten in three days, for rations are scarce, and we would delight in a hot meal." Adam shot a look of contempt

49

at his little brother, attempting to communicate his folly to him. Lexol focused in on the innocent lad.

"How many fellows do you have with you, so we might know how much food to prepare when your comrades yield to their plight of famine? We are willing to wait for Barak to surrender, no matter how long it takes. How many of your fellow warriors do you think we will need to feed? Ten thousand, more or less? Is that the correct number?"

Adam recognized Lexol's deceit and spoke up quickly on Joseph's behalf. "The mountain is seeded with as many warriors as is needed for the Jabin's defeat. We will prevail, for the Lord God of Israel has assured us that He will defeat all who oppose Israel."

Lexol laughed. "We will get nothing more of value from these three, Your Majesties. Regular torture would be a long and bloody event. Besides which, the tools needed to secure such information rest back at our stronghold at Kakor." Lexol addressed the twin princes, acknowledging their superior rank. "What is your command as to the disposition of these three? As a reminder to your royal highnesses, we are not here as enemy combatants, only as observers to the conflict. I suggest you either set them free or execute them, for we have no place to imprison them." The question was a mere formality, as they truly had nowhere to hold captives, and guards would be needed to secure them. Also, they had shed Midianite blood.

The only options were either to kill them or let them go, but because they had seen and heard so much, it was an easy decision . . . the presence of the Midian princes was better left a mystery. Prince Zebah, the younger and more bloodthirsty of the two, looked at his brother, Zalmunna, for the confirmation of a nod. Having received it, he commanded Lexol, "Take this band of ill-fated brothers and dispatch them to the grave and to whatever heaven awaits them. It is our only option, as these prisoners could otherwise confirm that we, Zebah, and Zalmunna, were friends to their enemy. They could very well seek revenge, and if, perchance or through some misadventure, Sisera fails to achieve his victory, we will be counted as allies to the defeated, and face the same fate as these unfortunates."

As the guards laid hands on them to take them out to the chopping block, the spirit of God came over Adam, and he spoke out from another realm, making a bold proclamation: "We, who are about to face our creator, hearken to my words. Our brother, Gideon, who will be the least regarded of all the sons of Joash, will be a hewer of forests and crush groves with his mighty ax. He will farm the poor man's grain of barley for Israel's bread. Gideon will become a mighty man of valor and with his double-edged sword. He will avenge our deaths. He will destroy the entire house of Midian so that your tents will no longer rise but lie along the ground . . . for the horde will be no more."

The murder of the three brothers took place on a flat rock. Their bodies were behind a blind between two boulders.

Phurah had managed to slip his bonds, aided by the slickness of his own blood. He disappeared into the rain-soaked mist. On his lips and in his heart, he spoke a vow to stand as a witness to this day's cruel execution of his beloved brothers by adoption. Phurah reclaimed the bloodless corpses of his three charges, remaining steadfast in his quest to take them back home, thus fulfilling his promised bond to Joash by returning the bodies of his adopted brothers.

CHAPTER 6
A Tent Peg Prophecy

Their bright polished metal dulled to red rust, their poise flecked and crumbled, the once-formidable Harosheth battle array was all but blunted. The war wagons stood idle on the flat, open plain at the foot of Tabor's steep mountain passes. Sisera now laid siege to the base of the high peaks. The downpour had slowed his advance and upset his plan to attack the army of Israel on the dry, open ground. The time that had been wasted in gathering up the armies of Taanach and Megiddo only added misfortune to his frustration.

All through the night, the shower pounded the army of Sisera, and they shivered in the chill and tribulation of harsh conditions. The River Kishon surged, swollen with the relentless downpour of heavy rain; the Wadi also overflowed and torrents spilled recklessly down the mountainsides. The Kishon had burst its banks, drowning the ten miles that were the small plain of Tabor, turning it into an inland sea littered with men and beasts that had been exposed too long to the elements. The field of battle was no longer fit to pilot as the chariots lost their ability to maneuver. The heavy iron chariots, once shields of protection, were now deadly millstones. At sunup, all but a few carts were hopelessly stuck hub-and-spoke in the bog, in spite of Sisera's struggle to pull them free from the vice-like grip of clay and mud, where they were fixed fast in the ooze of retribution.

The snap of whips and the neighs of pain from the trace-horses filled the air with screams. Despite repeated heaves, the worn-out animals were unable to budge their load even an inch. The mighty engines of war were now all but fixed monuments to the omnipotence of Adonai, the Lord God of Israel, the Decider of wars and the Bringer of storms.

From their safe and secure stronghold on the top of the mountain, the prophetess, Deborah, and General Barak witnessed the parting of the clouds. The sun broke through a solid blue sky to reveal the enemy stuck below, cemented in the concrete of sludge and mud. Deborah rallied the tribes of Israel with a pitched and urgent tone: "This is the time to attack! Hold nothing back because the Lord God of Israel goes before us. He has washed away the enemy's might with his tears."

The word of Adonai was in the hearts of a righteous army of ten thousand as they rushed down from the heights to the open plain far below. A vicious and brutal assault commenced—none was spared. In the fury of blood and the frenzy of battle, Barak shouted a command—"Save the horses!" The steeds received mercy, but all the men, in turn, suffered slaughter. No prisoners were taken. No quarter was asked, and none would be given! Mercy went wanting. Neither forgiveness nor pity could be found on the furious field of battle.

Gideon: The Sound and the Glory

Deborah remained above the fray as the army of God descended like birds of prey, talons and swords drawn. Two men, the same in every way and armed only with staffs and eyes of fire, seemed to materialize out of a deep cleft in the age-old rock. Deborah immediately dropped to her knees, sensing these were two heavenly beings. With open palms, she motioned three times for them to draw close to her side.

Their brilliance increased until they blotted out the sun, and she shielded her eyes with her fingers and her hands from the blinding glare of righteousness. One spoke for both as a nod of permission was given. His voice was like the sound of rushing waters, and he said, "Deborah, esheth lappidoth, you are a woman of light; you have used your gift of discernment wisely and have found favor with the Creator. You are blind to the lust of the eyes and made safe in the vision of faith, so God the Father can see only the rich radiance of your elegance from his priceless gift of grace.

"A memorial has been granted that will be enacted from generation to generation in the lighting of the two Shabbat candles struck by the matron of the hearth in the sacred moments before sundown. She will spark the wick and wave in the welcoming light three times before covering her eyes that God can see her in the glow alone and bless her—she who has the spark of the home in her heart and in her womb the spark of creation. This will be in everlasting memory of you, Deborah, esheth lappidoth, prophetess of Israel." The brightness had dimmed to daylight when Deborah uncovered her face. They were gone, and all that remained was a pillar of vanishing smoke and the battle that raged on far down below.

A Midianite sentry who had witnessed the carnage came bursting into the pavilion with dire urgency. "Your Majesties, we must depart immediately," he implored. "If your presence is made known, you will be caught up in the coming slaughter. No mercy is being shown. They massacre without discrimination. The Hebrews have come down the mountain in strength and have found Sisera's might swallowed up, sunk down into the mud . . . it is a bloodbath!"

Zalmunna sprang into action. "Our camels will, at least, be able to maneuver in this confounded sludge. Let us take our leave immediately!" The princes of Midian scrambled hastily, readying themselves to flee the battlefield. Their camels were the perfect beasts of burden to secure their route to safety. Neither man nor horse could keep up with their grueling pace over the long stretch of many hours. These ships of the desert were sure-footed, affording the royal Midianites a lifeboat in the newly formed swamp.

The army of Israel was now too busy with the business of butchery to notice the princes of Midian slipping away in the fog of battle. These princes, who at some point would be kings, could very well become a future threat to Israel. They could well emerge again, even more ravenous perhaps in their desire to swallow up the tribes of Israel. Today, however, their only concern was with stealth and the speed they could muster for a clean getaway.

Unable to defend against the onslaught of the Hebrew killing machine, Sisera witnessed, from his vantage point, the desperate and valiant effort put up by his infantry. Spearmen and swordsmen rallied to the aid of their charioteers, but without the chariot scythes, it was a lost cause. Sisera knew it was simply a matter of time before the tide turned. He knew that, soon, the battle would be lost, and Israel would overwhelm his army . . . down to the last spear, shield, and chariot wheel.

While Sisera sunk down, mired in the truth of his loss, an advance unit of Hebrews set upon him. He quickly dismounted his landlocked carriage, forced to engage in man-to-man combat. His bodyguards sacrificed their lives to give their captain a chance at survival. Sisera, with all the speed he could muster, proceeded on foot. Sisera was known for both his endurance and the swiftness of his feet. He left the battle in the midst of its fury. Harosheth was eighteen miles away, and the hours required to reach this haven of safety were being purchased for their general by those who stayed behind and fought to the death. The wrath of Israel was being vented as its tribesmen continued their relentless advance against the bits and pieces of Sisera's army. Finally, they made their way to Harosheth, considered by Barak to be a nest of vipers! Some of the lighter wagons managed to gain traction in the mud, and they raced back in the direction of Harosheth and safety.

A few of the Canaanite army's horses were unharnessed, so the charioteers could escape; several avoided the fray altogether, relieved to put behind them the bloodbath of carnage and mayhem. Each man would have to forge his own survival with the edge of his blade or by wily evasion. The army of Barak became a gathering of eagles, swooping down with hook and claw on helpless prey. The enemy ranks were valiant, but their desperate efforts caved and crumbled as the sun reached its zenith in the midday sky. None who stood to fight against Israel would live to see the close of day.

Barak pursued the chariots and the remaining host, but his ultimate goal, the main prize, was Sisera. The cunning general could not be found, neither dead nor alive, among the corpse-strewn battlefield. The Kishon Wadi had settled, but the river was not yet passable. Barak had commenced a running battle, forcing the chariots that were not bogged down to turn north and west, evidenced by the ruts of their wheels. The retreat of Sisera's army followed a scattered route, yet they ultimately headed south, to the shelter of the Harosheth stronghold.

Sisera, a general of the dead and the dying, was alone and on foot. He was hoping to reach the safety of Harosheth, where he could rest. Sisera was confident that, reaching Harosheth, he could reorganize a defense against the onslaught of Barak and his army, who were now wrapped in the blood of his mercenary brothers. The Canaanite kings of Taanach and Megiddo had been brutally slaughtered, ending their days as a portion for foxes.

Sisera's route back to the stronghold was a grueling journey. Fourteen miles by the straight-line flight of crows to reach the banks of the Kishon River, and then four short miles to Harosheth. By the time he arrived at the edge of the Kishon, his strength and endurance had reached their limit. He was led by fate, accident, or destiny to within a bow's shot of the encampment of Heber the Kenite. Jael's tent rested on the near shore of the flooded Kishon.

There was peace between Jabin, the king of Canaan, and the house of Heber. Heber was a trusted friend, an ally, and a servant. Had Heber not warned of the gathering of the army of Barak and their planned assault on the Jabin from Mount Tabor? This thought ran through Sisera's mind, as he stood wearily at the edge of Heber's camp. He felt safe and grateful for a momentary reprieve, his energy dwindling through extreme physical exhaustion.

Heber, however, on that particular day, had been unexpectedly called away to the foundry to oversee the relighting of its dampened fires. The wind and the rain had snuffed out the oven he had set to smelt the Jabin's iron weapons on which his wages and the waging of the war depended on. Heber was, in fact, engaged at that very moment in redesigning the chimney to prevent a recurrence of the now-extinguished furnace. Jael, Heber's wife of many years, had not a friend in Canaan and was still smarting from the forced relocation of her household. She was all alone in the tent of her new quarters when she glanced out of the flap, surprised at seeing the approach of a very spent Sisera.

He looked like a beggar at first glance, weather-worn and haggard. Sisera was near collapse and felt great relief in thinking he had escaped from the dogs of war—at least, for the moment. His strong-willed flight had temporarily put them back on their leash. He approached Heber's tent, confident of finding relief.

Craftiness was no stranger to Jael, and while it appeared that butter would melt in her mouth, her husband knew the truth of this matter! She smiled invitingly as she slyly approached Sisera, extending one soft, warm hand. "Turn in, my lord, turn in to me and have no fear. Come, find rest in the soft cushions of my tent." Her tempting sound produced the needed effect, and Sisera was encouraged by her artificial mantle of warmth and comfort.

"My throat is parched, and my lips are dry. A little water, I pray thee," Sisera pleaded.

"My lord," Jael purred. "I have something infinitely better, a fresh bottle of milk that has been cooled in the waters of the

Kishon River. It will quench your thirst and satisfy your hunger. It is an elixir of rest and dreams."

Sisera feared that Barak and his trackers might have picked up his trail. He knew that he was their prize, being the key to Canaan's survival. His downfall would leave Canaan with no military leadership, leaving his people defenseless against the onslaught of Israel. Harosheth, the home of his mother, would be set ablaze, ransacked, and plundered . . . his leadership was the crucial ingredient. Desperately in need of sleep, he pleaded with Jael.

"While I sleep, stand by the door of the tent. If anyone asks if there is someone here, tell them, 'No!' Say to them that you are alone. I must rest without disturbance. Having rested, I will pick up my feet, continue on to Harosheth, and regroup my troops for the protection of the city, my family, and for the Jabin, who is my benefactor and my king."

The sweet milk and Sisera's extreme exhaustion took its toll, and the sleep of the damned took its hold. Jael's prey was now caught in her silken web of milk and lies. Sisera lay helpless and defenseless. There was no hint of the mortal danger he faced. Little did the wily general expect treachery from the dainty hands of a woman, especially the wife of a friend.

The tent's pegs displayed the skill of her husband, Heber, fashioned through the technically advanced craft practiced by him in that day. They were made of iron, having a greater length than those made of wood. They could withstand harder blows. Having a much finer and sharper point, they sank more quickly to a greater depth even in the rockiest of hard ground, thus securing the tent against high winds. Jael removed a nail from the bag of spares in her tent—the sharpest one she could find. With a hammer in her hand, she paused, listening to the rhythmic breathing and the occasional snore that confirmed Sisera was sleeping. She glided quickly and silently, without any regret or hesitation, to where he lay on his side, tucked up like an infant child.

She took aim. The nail would penetrate the soft center of Sisera's left temple. She braced, took a breath, and swung the hammer in a full arc with all her might. The bone splintered on contact, snapping Sisera's skull with the sound of a sharp crack. For a moment, Sisera's eyes opened; for a split second, he was aware of what his attacker had accomplished. The sight unnerved Jael, prompting her to deliver a second and then a third blow of the hammer, until the nail went all the way through, puncturing Sisera's skull and locking his head to the floor. Once Jael had secured the general's head to the ground, a sense of relief pooled like the general's blood that was now all about her.

Meanwhile, Barak pursuing his quarry doggedly, had quickly made up the distance to the river's bank. He cautiously approached a solitary tent in the last moments of fading daylight. Hearing a slight sound, Jael looked out on the landscape of fading light. She saw Barak, his menacing cadre of captains following him, all streaked with blood and caked with sweat, their swords drawn. She threw back the tent fold, striding quickly out to meet them. "I know whom you seek," she told Barak. "He is now a permanent guest on the floor of my parlor. I have been expecting you. General Sisera has been still, quietly at rest while awaiting your arrival. Follow me, and I will show you the man you seek."

A Tent Peg Prophecy

Barak entered the dimly lit tent with his sword poised, keen for action. He was met instead by the stench of death that tugged at his nostrils. Sisera, his old adversary, lay dead, pegged through both temples, impaled upon the ground. He lay soaking in his own blood, his eyes wide open, ablaze with his final vision of treachery, done in by the delicate hand of a woman.

CHAPTER 7

The Deception of Horses and Chariots

Barak was both delighted and relieved to see his old nemesis lying crumpled at his feet. He turned to Jael and said, "You are blessed above women who live in the tent. For your courageous act, the Kenite clan, of which you are a part, will be spared the retribution of Israel's blade." With respect and gratitude evident in his voice, Barak honored Jael before all the company: "Jael, your name will be enshrined on the lips of time and in the verses of music sung to children, held forever in the memory of all future generations." Jael bowed her head, addressing Barak in all humility.

"You honor me, my lord. The sun has witnessed the glory of your day and now draws down the unfolding curtain of eventide. Please, be my guest. You and your band are welcome to stay and partake of my slender hospitality. Besides, the river remains impassable, and travel at night is treacherous and uncertain. There is time enough tomorrow to burn Harosheth to the ground with the fire of your righteous fury. And good riddance, I say, to that nest of vipers."

Barak accepted Jael's invitation. The time would be put to good use, allowing the rest of his army to make their way to this location. At daybreak, they would assemble for the coming battle, and the pillage of Harosheth would provide the bread and provisions needed to sustain his men.

The crack of first light saw the last of the stragglers arriving at the Kenite encampment, weary but hungry for the next brawl. Barak was reassured of God's providence and continued blessing—during the night the Kishon had dropped considerably, exposing the fording place only a few strides from their camp. "Gather on me!" Barak commanded, drawing the attention of his cadre of captains. Using the height of a convenient boulder, Barak stood tall to issue the day's marching orders. "Men! Warriors of our most high God. Yesterday, you witnessed His strong hand and outstretched arm in the final routing of our Canaanite enemy—a foe that has troubled us and crushed us at will and at their leisure, these past twenty years. Sisera, their esteemed general—the head of the snake—is crushed! He has been stripped of life and breath, and so shall he be stripped of his armor, his badges, and clothing. He will be left naked, to return to the earth, a feast for worms."

Barak straightened to his full height and raised his javelin with a clenched fist and an outstretched arm. "Our work is not yet done. Harosheth lies ahead while Hazor lies behind. Both will be destroyed! Harosheth will be plundered, and Hazor we will sack! The sacking of Hazor, the walled citadel of Jabin, the Canaanite king, was revealed to me in a dream . . . the details of which I will disclose to you atop the bones of Harosheth." Barak paused, allowing a murmur of moral approval to run its course. "As Adonai is our shield, we can and we will prevail!" Israel's commander raised his voice, shattering the early morning with a roar: "Captains . . . to your companies! We will cross the Kishon. We will form ranks on the far side. We will approach, clear as the moon and fair as the sun and terrible as an army with banners, for the Lord God is our banner!"

The soldiers cheered wildly, beating the flat of their swords against their shields while marching to the river, advancing in a murderous mood. They had only four miles to travel to the city walls, and a double-quick pace was set. Harosheth was in the slow process of waking up, not yet aware of the previous day's calamity or of the pending doom that approached them. The Canaanite host of infantrymen and fleeing charioteers who had survived the battle were, as yet, unable to cross the Kishon to alert the sleeping populace. They had decided—to a man—that they'd rather fade into the safety of the surrounding countryside. The element of surprise was on Barak's side, and he had timed his strategy well—the massive gates had been left open. To compound this gross arrogance, Harosheth's leadership had left only a small garrison to defend the city. They proved to be a disorganized rabble, having no apparent leader. Being of an insufficient number to trouble Barak's army, they were soon overwhelmed, extending beyond the Kishon a river of bloodshed that had started the day before on the small plain at the base of Mount Tabor.

Having secured the city, Barak took command of the next phase of his strategy. He addressed his captains, telling them to relay his orders. "Gather all the food first! Stuff your bellies with bread and cheese, but stash the wine for tonight's campfires. Load the carts with all the spoils and valuables you can carry. Strip every enemy soldier naked and take their uniforms, including all the clothes you find in their closets and lockers." Barak surveyed his loyal cadre of captains.

"Men, our work is not yet finished. Only when we have blunted all the Jabin's plans to enslave us, now and into the foreseeable future, will our work be done! Let us use this opportunity we have been given to wipe away the stain that Canaan has pressed upon our people. Let us rid Israel of Canaan's guile. Let us fulfill our destiny this day using the strength of our resolve, given to us by the one true God, Adonai." Barak passed a callused palm over his brow. "Go, my captains; relay to your troops my command concerning the food, spoil, and clothing. When you are done, rally to me yonder," Barak pointed, "under that broad oak. There, in the shade, I would share with you, my grand fellows, my plans and designs. Victory has been imparted to me in a vivid dream, the evidence of which will be made plain as our adventure unfolds."

The captains, having carried out Barak's command, returned to him in the shade of a giant oak tree. They stood ready, in a heightened state of anxious excitement. Barak knelt down on one knee. With an oak twig, he drew a map in the dirt. Carefully, he scratched out the route of his planned attack in the rich brown earth below the tree, clearly outlining the movement of troops and chariots. Barak lowered his voice, confiding in his trusted captains with the secrecy of a whisper. Every man leaned in closer; the only sound apart from Barak's voice was the crackling fires of the once proud city of Harosheth.

"I have grappled with caution, but even so, I have decided on a bold and daring plan. We will return to the small plain of Tabor, where God granted us victory. There, we will swap our clothes for the uniforms of the dead. Many of their war wagons will still be stuck fast in the mud. These we will dig up, releasing them for our own use. We will free those horses that are still attached. We will groom them and ready them for action. I have Sisera's uniform, helmet, and the badge of his rank. We will approach Hazor with Sisera's banners unfurled, signaling his complete and total victory. Deception and stealth will be the key to our success. Timing will be critical—long shadows will obscure our form, making recognition from a distance difficult, if not impossible. When the cloak of night swallows the last of the light, we will be in the process of entering the city gates. In twilight's gray coat we will mask our approach into the portal of the dragon's citadel. We will be given passage through its thick and impenetrable walls that go up to the heavens. Their massive bronze and brass doors will indeed open for us. Hazor's haste to swallow up the victorious Sisera, with his booty of spoil and his endless line of captured slaves—this will give us the access we desire."

The assembly was thunderstruck at Barak's brilliant proposal. It took a moment for his plan to sink in, but once it had, a collective cheer rang out from the circle of captains, followed by a chorus of flabbergasted laughter. Keras grasped Barak's shoulder, his eyes shining with admiration.

"My general, your plan is, at once, outlandish and courageous!" He looked at the men surrounding Barak with a wink and a smile. Turning back to his commander, Keras continued, "I, for one, believe that your plan just might be inspired! Either that or we will all be killed in our attempt to follow the detail of this divine blueprint."

Barak chuckled at Keras's quip, responding in kind: "Daring is the handmaiden of conquest! Envision the ending, even as we start the work of the beginning."

The army of Israel was feeling renewed and greatly inspired. They marched twenty miles back to the carnage on the plain of Tabor to be greeted by a sea of rotting corpses. The stench of decaying flesh and rotting carrion drifted on the breeze. Many hundreds of horses and chariots were stranded, still stuck in the mud that had now dried. Some of Barak's soldiers began to liberate the carriages while others worked at stripping the dead Canaanites of their uniforms. Most of the uniforms were caked with dry blood and were stained with the residue of dried gore. Barak was first to put on the costume of his deception. Its fit was perfect, making it strangely familiar. "Do all generals come in the same size?" Barak mused to himself. 'We as generals are inclined to be viewed larger than life, but death is the great leveler of men and, in the end, we seem to be all the same size."

Barak's saw his blood-stained uniform as a gift from his vanquished foe, General Sisera. He stood in the midst of his men when the day's work had been completed. "Men, warriors of the most high God, we must travel thirty-six miles to Hazor. We have this one night to feast and rest. Tomorrow night, you will receive specific instructions. The natural rhythms of night and day will set our pace—the rising and fall of two suns will bring us to the brink of victory. The second sunset will signal the end of the Jabin's of Canaan, on that day their dynasty will be left rotting and ruinous, and all but forgotten."

Dawn found the army of imposters working the harness and reins in trying to come to grips on horseback and in the maneuvering of heavy iron chariots. Twenty miles proved sufficient for them to gain a working knowledge of their newfound ability to jockey both steeds and chariot wheels. The day passed slowly. Thoughts remained guarded. Light conversation was lacking. The absence of horseplay marked the grim resolve of Barak's determined army.

In the dimming dusk, Barak rallied the vengeful host, surrounded by his faithful corps of captains. He outlined their final assault on the walled fortress. "Fill the chariot stands with swords and shields, with bows and the shafts of archers. Those unable to disguise themselves with enemy uniforms must hold tight to the long rope. Make sure you hang your heads down, eyes on the ground in the posture of defeat and humiliation. Your appearance must be the lament of slaves. Our approach will follow the formation of two hundred men behind each weapon's chariot and a single line of infantry along both flanks. Their enemy uniforms will bring security, adding to our disguise. I want every banner flying! Men in the forefront are to wait for my signal. When I unsheathe my sword—and not a moment before—then, and only then, take up your weapons with all due haste, for I will wait until the Jabin makes himself available inside the citadel." Barak surveyed his captains. "Are you all following my full instructions? If not, this is the time to dispel the haze of confusion with the torch light of reason," he said, receiving nods and grunts in the affirmative.

"Make your way quickly to the ropes and pulleys controlling the gate. Once the bulk of our chariots are inside, create a bottleneck of chariots within the entryway by dismounting, as this will prevent the massive doors from being closed. Be sure, however, to keep a full passage open through the chariots, permitting our infantry to penetrate the fortress threshold. I will take the lead in our formation as Sisera's armor will make our deception believable—the visor on Sisera's helmet will throw a shadow across my face. Our aim first to secure the massive doors. Once our trickery is made evident, they will attempt to shut inside all those who are through the portal, likewise locking outside the rest of our needed reinforcements. They will fight like wounded animals at this point, knowing the citadel has been breached. The first surge of their terror will be both deadly and desperate—we must quell this initial resistance swiftly!" Barak looked around, making sure his words had been made plain, for much depended on it.

"I will make it my personal mission to secure the head of the Jabin before he can find refuge in the protection of the keep. If I am confounded, I will not waste my energy—whether by my sword or by fire, the Jabin dies tomorrow! It matters not, for we will pillage and spoil to our hearts' content. And when all has been destroyed, and everything of value has been seized, then in the like of Joshua's wrath, Hazor, for the second time, will know the fire of Adonai! The city of Hazor will be reduced to hot cinders that will turn to cold ashes. We will give no quarter. We will show no mercy. Not one will be left breathing." Barak's face was still visible in the last light of day. "If there are any misunderstandings to assignments or to the timing . . ." He traversed the circle of eyes with his own, "now is the time to talk it out." Barak paused, but no questions were forthcoming, and no man made a comment. Every man knew his place, his duties fully understood. Barak spoke courage into the shadows at sundown. "This daring act will test our nerve, and restraint will count just as much as valor. We will be on the road for the first burn of dawn, to carve out our fate and create our just and rightful place in Canaan."

Barak, as was his custom, knelt upon the rough ground to petition God for his blessing. "Let us pray together for guidance and protection." Every knee was bent in supplication to the God of Israel. Barak prayed: "Adonai, Your will be done! I ask You to help us keep our wits about us in the coming conflict. Our victory and courage have already been tested. The last of our mutual enemy now stands before us. We affirm Your holy omnipotence, and we attest to the fact that it is by Your hand we would cleanse this scourge from our promised land. Bless our struggle in your holy name, forever and a day, Amen."

Israel's army was void of campfires, despite the chill of the desert night. Men huddled together, finding warmth in the zeal that burned within them. They felt assured of God's hand upon them and the righteousness of their mission. Every precaution was taken to evade detection. Men spoke in low whispers to avoid exposure to the possibility of roaming enemy patrols, liars who plied the highways, or even desperate travelers who risked death in the dark.

The long line of chariots extended for mile after mile. A caravan of this size was impossible to hide. Men, horses, and ration wagons dotted the distant landscape. Official word of their advance would be preceded only by the speed of gossip. Barak's army raced to keep pace with the arc of the sun; the building blocks of surprise were paved with blood, patience, and in the perfection of timing.

Watchful sentries saluted with upraised spear and javelin in utter amazement at seeing the army they thought belonged to

Sisera. They rejoiced at the return of Canaan's hero, in awe at the number of enemy soldiers he had captured for enslavement. The column turned onto the road leading to Hazor, finally headed toward the great, yawning threshold—the single, central access to the citadel. The darkening nightfall brought into sharp focus the streaming brightly lit torches, rousing and raising the crowded upper balconies. The massive doors remained closed until the very last possible moment slowly creaked open. Barak waved to the cheering throng that lined the entranceway in response to a sea of garlands and roses that began to shower down from the galleries and ramparts on high. The courtyard filled with the resounding chant of "Si-se-ra! Si-se-ra!" The lead chariot horses were reined in by the eager hands of well-wishers. Barak stood eerily unmoved by the uproar of applause; his helmet visor remained shut, in the attitude of imminent combat.

The Jabin made his grand entrance, sharing in the moment's glut of vanity and glory. A carpet was laid and a canopy hastily erected to assure the king of his majesty. The Jabin beckoned his costumed adversary. Barak stepped down on rose petals and red carpet, metering his approach until he was within striking distance. The king lifted his hand, the crowd hushed, and he spoke into the silence. "Hero of Canaan, reveal your face that I may look at the face of an old friend."

The snap of the trap! One hand on the visor's lip and the other on the hilt of his sword, in a single movement, a subtle flip, and a startled look froze in fear and misgiving . . . Barak's blade flew from its sheath to discover the flesh of the Jabin's neck, cleaving his head from his torso with one clean sweep. The crown rolled around until it came to rest on the king's crumpled corpse. A woman screamed as the army of pretenders flooded the stronghold; the gates were secured, and weapons, once hidden, were now fiercely wielded. The slaughter went on for most of that night; scorched earth was the rule—to ensure no future generational blood feud of vengeance would be forthcoming.

The spoils filled several caravans of overflowing carts; the chariots returned to the fires of their birth; the horses found favor in the future of farming. The hand of God prevailed, with the might of ten thousand warriors, a river, cunning, and a thunder cloud. God had subdued a dynasty—the Jabin of Canaan would rise no more, sealed on that day before all the eyes of Israel.

So let all thine enemies perish, O LORD: but let them who love Him be as the sun when he goeth forth in his might. And the land had rest forty years. Selah.

Part Two

CHAPTER 8
A Sacrifice for Love's Sake

Gideon had a meek and mild disposition. It did not match his rugged outward appearance—his thick, dark hair, wavy and untamed, resembled a lion's mane. He was kissed by the gods—deep, piercing eyes, flaring nostrils, and a beautiful forehead that was smooth and free of worry. Gideon was a handsome man; his firmly chiseled chin bore a deep cleft, giving him a noble expression that people readily trusted. He was thoughtful, rendered to long silences and dark brooding. His lips never spoke lies, and his mouth was not known to spill over with the malice of insult. Gideon was a patient listener, lending his ear to the fool as well as the wise, offering neither comment nor judgment. He carried his neck proudly, and though it appeared to be sculpted from iron, it had, without question, been bent to his father's will. He was pitifully unsure of himself and never spoke in his own defense; he was painfully dutiful.

Gideon carried his large frame with dignity, and all who first met him believed him to be a man of stature. He towered head and shoulders above all the men he encountered, both Hebrew and Amorite. His legs resembled the cedars of Lebanon, his arms, bulging with knotted muscle and sinew, were thick as the branches of the ancient oak affixed next to the winepress.

Gideon's gentle disposition enabled him to endure slights and insults without retaliation, even when they were spitefully crafted to intimidate him or stir him to anger. He was not a defiant man by nature. Already in his prime, in the approach to middle life, Gideon humbly refused to stand up to the giant and imposing shadow of his father, Joash, the domineering and overbearing patriarch of Manasseh. To secure the allowance of a wealthy dowry, Joash had arranged a loveless marriage for Gideon. His marriage to Ariel was terrible. She badgered him constantly, her piercing voice ringing out endlessly like the squeaking of a shrew. Their union was fruitful in the sense that she gave birth to a son, Jether which means *excellent surplus*. Father and son had the solace of blood, but both were cut from the cloth of self-doubt.

The sound of Gideon's sharp, double-bladed ax echoed through the valley at every splintering trunk on contact. Ever obedient, Gideon had been ordered by his father to open up a densely wooded patch. His mission was to enlarge the boundary of the sacred grove. The grove was owned by the House of Joash and dedicated to the worship of the Amorite god, Baal. Joash had adopted the ways of the Amorites, surrendering even to the worship of their foreign gods. All Israel had succumbed.

Enjoying the rhythm of his work, Gideon reveled in his strength, toning his body with every whack of his mighty ax. He paused to wipe away the sweat beading on his forehead when he instinctively felt a pair of eyes gazing at him. He looked up. There, upon a rocky outcropping, his eyes came to rest on a vision of loveliness. His breath caught in his throat. He swallowed hard, feeling suddenly bashful. The woman before him looked otherworldly, a vision of beauty impossible to describe. The early morning sun appeared to create for her a halo, forming a bright crown that sparkled through the leaves behind her. Spellbound, Gideon was unable to look away. He was bewitched.

The lovely vision before him was Drumah, a daughter of the house of Milo, sent to the sacred grove by Shechem, a sister town of Canaan. She was a child initiate, to be married to Lord Baal by the hand of sacrifice when she came of age. Her offering to Baal would seal a pact between the two cities, preventing either from attacking the other and ensuring mutually beneficial trade. Drumah had been a gangly and awkward girl when Gideon had first seen her washing at a nearby stream and then again a few years later, at the market. She stood before him now in the full flower of womanhood, filled with of grace and the promise of delight. Even though she was within arm's reach, Gideon knew she was off limits. Looking at her, Gideon's shyness melted, and he bounded up the rock face so that he might talk with the beauty standing before him. He wanted to know what had brought her to this place, and privately, he rejoiced at his good fortune in being given this heaven-sent opportunity.

"I am Gideon, son of Joash," he said with a newfound confidence. "I am in the process of enlarging the borders of my father's sacred grove so all the city's inhabitants might partake in the festival of the rising new moon. The sacrifice given unto Baal will ensure the fertility of our harvest from the earth, as well as the fertility of men and our beasts." He smiled at her, amazed at his own courage.

"I am Drumah," she spoke in a muted whisper, her head bowed at the thought of her impending doom. "I visit this place on the eve of my death, for I was chosen at birth to fulfill my destiny as a bride and be sacrificed to the great Lord Baal. I have come to see the altar of sacrifice where I am to enter into paradise as his handmaiden."

The young girl, now sixteen years old, was a virgin novice steeped in the lore of Baal. She had prepared her whole life for this one night of unabashed revelry—her praise offering to Lord Baal of the Amorites in ceremonial sacrifice. According to the lore of Baal, he was the giver of rain and all fertility. The night of revelry and sacrifice was all done in the dark, orchestrated by Baal, the ruler of the primeval forests of Abiezer.

Drumah spoke with the confidence that only those who were facing certain death can muster. "Gideon, son of Joash . . . the keeper of the grove!" She smiled in disbelief at the prospect of this good omen. "This stand has brought the Amorite people together in our honoring of the ancient ways. It has made your house of Manasseh as one with all our Amorite people. The gods must have ordained our meeting this day, for my eyes have sought you out, Gideon, these many years. The mere sight of you sets my heart aflutter with sincere desire." She lowered her head shyly now, her voice a whisper. "I must confess, I have dreamed of you these many years, and I have often fantasized about kissing your lips."

She kept her eyes on the ground, unwilling to raise her tearful gaze to his face because seeing him robust and vital before her might weaken her resolve. She had gone too far to turn back now. She attempted to justify the impossibility of her love for him: "It is a foolish dream, a childish fantasy, for I must be a virgin when I lie upon the altar of Baal to be sacrificed. This is my destiny so that Baal might find me worthy and with his favor bless all the Amorites."

Gideon's heart sank. Thoughts tumbled through his mind, but he found no words fitting to his feelings. Drumah seemed to see in him what others failed to see, and Gideon felt the first stirrings of confidence in his own ability. He drew back his shoulders, stretching to his full height, and with his ax nonchalantly slung over one shoulder, he offered Drumah his free hand. "Let us not talk about anything other than this moment, and let us walk away from here so that I might enjoy your beauty in the fullness of sunlight. Who can tell when another moment such as this will be given to us?"

They spoke of their dreams, but the essence of Drumah's hopes was forged in the furnace of desperation. They walked and talked, the warm blanket of their conversation unfolding gradually to expose the naked truth of their desire for one another. They wandered deeper and deeper into the primeval forest. It was as if each stride ensured a temporary reprieve from the unfortunate tragedy set to occur at the rising moon. As they rapidly forged a bond in the speaking of sweet nothings, the awakening of sensual desire began to blossom. Their fingers fumbled and found rest in the caress of fingers and palms. The velvet green of the valley floor far below was a majestic backdrop to the bruised indigo of the sky above. The base of an ancient oak afforded ample shade, offering them the lush splendor of soft grass. Gideon was swept up in a whirlwind of conflicting emotions. His heart was breaking at the thought of her life being wasted to appease the terrible greed of some dark god. Gideon could not fathom the depth of his loss since this was his first and only love. His heartstrings quivering and his voice taut with emotion, he sounded out an unlikely scheme that had taken root in his mind that may just hold the promise of her salvation.

"By the law of Moses, we cannot marry, for you are not of the house of Israel. I am forbidden to marry Canaanite women." Tears welled up in her eyes at his words, but he wiped them away and took her hands in his own. "Be that as it may," he continued, "if you agree to be with me, forsaking all others, I will take you to be my concubine." This time, he was unable to stem the tide of her tears as she released a flood of emotions, crying with profound happiness at finding love and for being spared the fate of certain death. Having no time to spare on traditional formalities, they exchanged tokens of their bond to seal the arrangement. "I have a ring," said Gideon. "With this ring, I give you my bond. I pledge to love you and care for you while I still have breath in my lungs." Gideon placed the ring in Drumah's palm, it being too large to put on a delicate finger.

"I will cherish this ring all the days of my life," Drumah promised, breathless and overcome with emotion. Lifting a necklace of fine silver from her neck, Drumah whispered, "I have this pendant of green stone. It is all I possess. I give it to you as a promise to love you and care for you and to forsake all others. I will be yours alone!" Gideon took the pendant, slipping it over his bull-like neck, the green stone resting out of sight beneath a flap of his rough-spun shirt. "I will wear it always around my neck and over my heart, where you shall always reside! This I promise."

Gideon caressed Drumah as delicately as he dared fearful of the power of his massive arms. In this carnal hunger of lovers, he harvested the flower of her passion, joyfully becoming one flesh. Their souls united in an attempt to escape the bonds of fate and death. The precious hours they spent together could bring severe punishment upon them both . . . unless some method of appeasement could be discovered that would stave off the inevitable. Gideon took Drumah to a nearby cave, far from prying eyes, where she would be safe during the time it took him to ensure her protection. Gideon's mind was already racing ahead, looking for a way to outwit destiny. He despaired of ever standing up to Joash, uncertain about how his father would respond to his deception. He also knew that the entire village would apply their minds to uncovering the truth about the missing girl destined for the altar of sacrifice. How could he keep Joash's reputation intact if he tarnished his own in the sight of all his tribesmen? Gideon took Drumah's hand, and they prayed feverishly to the God of Israel, imploring Him to find a way to save them both.

Gideon lamented the fact that he was a married man. To be constrained by a loveless marriage, arranged by his father, seemed a grievous burden to bear, especially now that he had fallen in desperate love with Drumah. Gideon had always conceded to his father's wishes. His wife, Ariel, had brought a dowry of additional land to the family clan. Ariel treated Gideon with contempt for his seeming weakness and endless apologies. He could not withstand her unnecessary onslaughts and constant demands. The union had produced a son, Jether, but the boy lacked confidence, much like his father. Ariel was also from the tribe of Manasseh. Their union was sealed by the authority of the priesthood and by covenant in the house of Israel.

CHAPTER 9

An Angel in Ophrah

The Midianites, the Ishmaelites, and all the children of the East, the horde, had descended upon Israel. They were wild men, nomads, living in tents, unable to tolerate the limits of towns or walled cities; they were cursed with the lust to wander. They migrated to wherever food and water were plentiful. Like locusts, they arrived in great numbers, with their cattle and their camels in tow. They entered into Israel to forage and to feast, devouring the harvest of tillers. Fields that once overflowed with plenty were left desolate and empty. If left unchecked, they would destroy their old enemy Israel with the desperate want of famine.

Israel was made barren, for there was no food for the sheep or the asses. The children had empty, swollen bellies. Cries went up to the Lord of Hosts, asking for relief from their oppressors. A prophet was summoned to Israel. He proclaimed the great day of the Lord, saying, "The Lord your God freed you from the Egyptians and the house of bondage. Fear not the gods of the Amorites in whose land you now dwell. But you have not obeyed my voice and have put false gods before me, and your harvest of inheritance has been put asunder."

Joash and Gideon were at the winepress, though they were threshing wheat to hide it from the Midianites and all who hungered in Ophrah. Gideon stammered, trying to put into words an explanation concerning the girl who was meant to be sacrificed, the missing Drumah. Instead, he shrank from his father's scornful glare. One false word could mean discovery. Joash left with two sacks of ground wheat, and Gideon was left, as usual, to clean up the chaff.

Gideon left the winepress, and at that moment, an angel, full of grace and truth, was dispatched to put right that which had gone wrong. Gideon made his way past an ancient oak in that it gave shade to the roof of the winepress, and it was in his usual path to a home where he was going to consider his next move. Suddenly, an angel of the Lord appeared to Gideon and spoke with the sound of rushing waters, "The Lord is with thee. Your prayers have been heard, thou mighty man of valor." Gideon, questioning his own senses, took several moments to gather his wits about him before answering. "Oh, my Lord, how can this be? If the Lord of hosts is with us, why has this curse befallen us? And where are all the miracles that our fathers have told us about—the parting of the sea, the plagues of Egypt, the manna in the desert? Are they but fables said to children? Why has the Lord forsaken us and delivered us into the hands of the Midianites?"

The Lord looked upon Gideon with favor and said, "Go, do what I command you, and do it with all your heart, all your mind, and all your strength. You will save Israel from the hand of the Midianite horde and from all the children of the East. You have been foreordained for this work. I had known you before you were in the womb. You heard the voice of the Lord, saying, 'Whom shall we send, and who will go for us?' Then you said, 'Here am I; send me.' Have I not sent you from the beginning?"

Gideon recoiled as if from a hot flame and drew back from the command of righteousness. He asked, "How am I, a lone man, to save Israel? Please forgive me, Lord, as you must mean another. My family is poor in Manasseh, as we have lived on the borders of Issachar and did not receive the inheritance of Abraham, and I am the least regarded in my father's house." The Lord said to him, "It is assured that I will be with you. If you are strong in me, you will have the power of my might, and you will smite the Midianites as if but one man." Gideon was uncertain as to whether this was but a dream—a phantom born from a troubled mind, or if it was, in fact, real. Gideon spoke out to the angel of the Lord, saying, "Lord, I need a divine sign that I, the least of men, have found grace in your sight and that we have truly been talking, as one man talks with another. Please do not leave this place, for I have an offering and a gift I would give to you." The Lord said, "I will wait for your offering."

Gideon was now heartened, and without permission or leave from his father, Joash, he slaughtered a young goat. He went to prepare the ritual offering of unleavened cakes, which was a remembrance that there was no time to delay in the day of repentance, for the deliverance of Israel was nigh unto salvation. Gideon put the flesh in a basket and the broth in a pot. Having prepared the offering, Gideon hurried back to the oak tree anxiously, hoping to find the angel of the Lord waiting for him. As always, the Lord was patient, for his fruits were sweet and many. The angel was waiting for Gideon. He sat leaning against the trunk of the ancient oak, at peace. There Gideon presented his offering to the angel of the Lord.

The angel spoke to Gideon, saying, "Take the flesh you have presented and the unleavened cakes, and place them upon this rock." The angel pointed to a boulder beneath the tree. "Upon this rock of salvation, pour out the broth for a sweet savor unto the Lord."

Gideon did so. Then the angel of the Lord, with an outstretched arm, holding the mighty scepter of his authority, put forth the end of it and touched the flesh and the unleavened cakes. There rose up a fire, and the flame of all righteousness came up from out of the rock and consumed the flesh and the unleavened cakes. As quickly as he had appeared, the angel vanished in the pillar of the rising smoke. Gideon realized that that he had seen an angel of the Lord, as Jacob had many generations ago. He was in fear for his life, for no sinful man sees the face of God and lives. Gideon cried out aloud, "Alas, O Lord God! I saw an angel of the Lord face to face."

The Lord replied, "Peace be unto you. Peace I leave with you. My peace I give unto you. Let not your heart be troubled nor afraid. Fear not, Gideon, for you will not die." Now Gideon knew the voice of the Lord, and the voice of the Lord he would hear that very evening, once again. Then Gideon praised the Lord of Lords and acknowledged Him as the King of Kings. What he had received was a miraculous answer to his prayer, but he had yet to find a way to save Drumah from her sacrifice to Baal, the Amorite god. Gideon knew now that he was to be sent on a mission, and that he had been foreordained to accomplish God's will from the beginning. His confidence waxed strong, like as a mustard seed that grows into a tree. Gideon built an altar on that very spot under the ancient oak on the rock, in honor of the Lord of peace, Jehovah Shalom.

CHAPTER 10

The Demise of the Lord of the Flies

That night, Gideon lay in his bed, tortured and tossed like a fish washed up on dry land. How was he to save Drumah? The Lord spoke again to Gideon, charging him to act. The Lord said, "Gideon, take your father's young bullock of seven years. There are two. Take the second one, for it is without blemish. Using the strength of this bullock, I command you to throw down the altar of Baal, for it is an outrage in my sight. This place of betrayal belongs to your father's house, so it has been given to you to act on my behalf. With your mighty ax, hew down the entire grove. Leave nothing standing. Once completed, build an altar unto the Lord your God on the heights of the stronghold, so it will be far above the place of Baal, for I order it so. Take this same second bullock, and make a burnt offering. Use the wood of the grove that is cut down to fuel the fire and to appease my indignation, and to repent of the evil that Israel has enacted by worshiping strange gods before me."

The Lord instructed Gideon to be wary of his father's household. "All the men of the city will seek after your head. The work cannot be done by the greater light of the day, only by stealth and by the lesser light of night."

Gideon went straightaway to the servants' quarters of his father's household and roused ten men, as this number was counted for righteousness by the Lord. It would be a rough night's work—the grove was great. The flickering sparks of fiery torches grew long shadows on the march through the forest, a trudge that set into motion the doom of Baal, the god of the Amorites.

Gideon had spent his entire youth enlarging the grove's boundaries. The altar of Baal was hewn of large, dark, and tightly fitted stones that would not easily give up their places in the hearts of men or in this powerful and formidable altar. The sounds of furious chopping, amid cracking, and then mighty crashing, broke the silence of the forest as massive primeval trees fell hard to the ground. No one spoke. Gideon, the ever faithful Phurah, and the other nine chosen men, worked as one, each man to his task as if this scene were rehearsed in a time before the earth was molten. Long poles were affixed to the altar of Baal. It took vigorous, repeated efforts to eventually topple the ancient monument; not one stone was left standing upon another. As it had been commanded, an altar to the most high God, Adonai, was erected on the outcropping at the very peak of the stronghold. Rough rocks were gathered; stones that had never known a mason's tool were piled together. The desperate braying of the bullock, as its throat was cut, echoed through the thick darkness just before the breaking dawn.

The bullock was hastily prepared. Fire from the wood of the sacred grove hungrily consumed the bullock's moist, blood-soaked flesh. The fire sputtered and then roared as the fat took hold, challenging the sun, now breaking through and flooding the grove.

The men of the city were not yet awakened by the cock's first crow. The blazing bullock was brightly visible in the near distance, where the sacred grove had once stood. From the city's overlook, the flames gave mute witness to the night's deadly and daring adventure. The grove had fallen. It had disappeared, as if wiped clean by an unseen hand. The altar of Baal had been thrown down, leaving a blank and empty space upon the hill. The second bullock of Joash had been sacrificed on the altar, built to honor the one true God of all creation. Gideon, Phurah, and the nine chosen servants, faint from the night's strenuous and continuous labor, found their way back to the servants' quarters in the house of Joash. Gideon woke his father, still in the twilight of a half-sleep of dreams. Joash woke with a start and asked, "What would you have of me? Is there an emergency?"

Gideon recounted the night's work to his father, describing how every blow of his ax had added to the strength of his resolve. He told Joash about the angel under the oak and how he was commanded to tear down the altar of Baal, using the trees of the grove to sacrifice the unblemished bullock. Gideon described how they had built an altar of rough stone to the Lord of Lords, set in the high place. He told Joash that this last night's labor had been commanded from heaven. A prophet was not often recognized in his own home, but Joash was touched by the hand of God, and he believed his son; besides, Gideon never lied. His word was known to be as immovable as the solid coarse stone newly quarried from the modest dust and dirt of the earth.

Meanwhile, the men of the city had gathered together in a committee of jackals, demanding to know who had committed this sacrilege, bringing Baal's anger upon them and the whole town. Inquiries quickly swept to every corner. Gossip stoked the rage of the frenzied mob. Gideon, son of Joash, was named as the guilty party! It was he who had devised this unforgivable and terrible act that would affect the entire populace. He had cut down the grove and defiled the altar of Baal. All the men of the city were quickly assembled. The unsettling din of their voices growled for justice. The baying pack stood before the house of Joash. Seeking blood, a spokesman for the crowd demanded, "Give us your son, Gideon, that he might be sacrificed to appease the god, Baal, for this act of sacrilege. For only then may we be spared retribution from the wrath of Baal." Joash feared for the life of his son. He put away his anger for the loss of his grove and the altar of Baal that was his fortunate bread and butter. He stood firm in his opposition squarely between the murderous crowd and his son Gideon.

Joash raised his already commanding voice, addressing the men who stood against him on the doorstep of his home: "Will you, mere men, save Baal, a god, from this outrage? Yes, he has brought upon our city this mockery and desecration, for which I am ashamed! Let Gideon be put to death while it is still morning before the sun rises in the sky. I call on Baal to plead for his own needs, to do the necessary deed that will avenge this insult of blasphemy. If Baal is the mighty god of the most high that we have adored for so long, for whom we have passed our children through the fire, then let him take heed against Gideon. Let Baal avenge himself upon the man who threw down his altar to the forest floor, who completely and utterly destroyed the sacred grove, where embers and sparks still light the last hour before dawn."

The rabble, now restless and confused, were murmuring about betrayal. Finally, the throng went silent, except for the roar of their crackling torches. In a state of tense expectation, they looked from one man to the next, eagerly anticipating and half expecting a miracle. They believed that the hand of their deity, Baal, would smite Gideon to oblivion. But the stillness was broken only by the shrill morning call of the laughing dove. To a man, the town knew that no judgment was coming. The growling of their empty bellies signaled hunger's relentless demand. They needed to be fed, and so, the multitude disbanded. On that day, Gideon was also called by a new name—"Jerubbaal," meaning, "Let Baal plead against him because he has thrown down his altar." Gideon, for the first time in his memory, had prevailed. It was the beginning of his march to valor.

CHAPTER 11

Drumah, My Queen

Gideon's prayer to rescue Drumah had been answered in a manner he could never have conceived or imagined. The punishment he had expected on both his and Drumah's behalf had been lifted by divine intervention. The cult of Baal was broken, the grove disowned, and the altar that now stood on high no longer served a foreign idol, but the one true God, Adonai. With his new-found courage, he related to his father how he had met Drumah while dutifully clearing the grove and how he had immediately fallen in love with her. Gideon had seen her before that day and always longed for her. "When I heard of her impending doom," he explained, "I decided to rescue Drumah, even though I knew full well it could have turned disastrously ill for both of us. I spirited her away, deep into that forest cave where you and I would seek shelter from storms when you took me hunting as a boy. I will now claim her as my concubine, for I have found the one true love of my life."

Joash, the patriarch of the tribe, listened to his son as he spoke, displaying a sincere intent to let Gideon speak all that was in his heart and mind without any prejudice. When Gideon paused, silence hung heavy. All that could be heard was the rhythm of his father's breath and his own doubting heartbeat. When Gideon had finished speaking, Joash spoke, his words in keeping with the law of Israel. "Drumah is not of the house of Israel. She is from the Canaanite city of Shechem, where in times past, Dinah, Jacobs's daughter, was raped, and where vengeance was taken. By our law, a woman of Shechem can be accepted in Israel only as a concubine." Joash was, however, not without compassion for his son's plight. "You have known the woman, and you have taken her as your concubine. The tokens of promise you have exchanged would satisfy the law and the prophets. No blessing is required of me, but freely do I give you my blessing, for it befits a man of your station to acquire a concubine."

Gideon thanked Joash for his loving approval. Just a few hours before, sweet Drumah's fate had hung in the east wind of oblivion. Her grim fate would have been sealed once she was wedded through her sacrificial death to Baal. Gideon would have been punished for his carnal liberties with her virginity. Instead, Drumah and Gideon had been spared on both counts—he from the men of the city, and she from Ba'al zebub or the Lord of the Flies. Gideon's challenge to an Amorite god had gone unanswered. He had vanquished all that stood before him.

The mob had dispersed for want of a leader and a brave-enough spokesman. The inaction of a powerless god sent each man back to his bowl of morning breakfast. Every man to his place, for daylight hours were burning, and a farmer's chores never wait on milking cows for the politics of vengeance.

94

Gideon made all haste to reach the cave in which he had hidden Drumah. He wanted to tell her about the night's incredible adventures, including his encounter with an angel, who said: "He would rescue all of the Israel." Gideon wondered about how one man could possibly accomplish all that had been spoken. His pace quickened in anticipation of the angel's prophecy and the sight of Drumah.

"Drumah! Drumah!" he cried. Her name rang out, echoing back at him from the entrance to the dark cave. She was not there; she was nowhere to be found. Gideon combed the hillside for any sign of her, but the forest would not yield her secret hiding place. He thought that a pack of ravenous wolves had perhaps carried her off. The more he thought along these lines, the more a paralyzing fear began to nip at his heels like a dark-mouthed cur. Perhaps she had despaired, lost all hope, and thrown herself over the waterfall, down to the bottom of the gorge. Gideon paused to pray, for God had spoken to him before. He heard these words, spoken in a small, still voice: "She is well. Take no concern for this day."

Gideon descended the narrow track leading down to the base of the waterfall, half-expecting to see Drumah along the way. His fear had subsided, replaced with hope and the expectation of seeing his beloved Drumah once more.

Gideon's eyes widened in excitement: there she was, safe and unharmed. Gratitude escaped from his puckered lips as he whispered: "Praise be to God in the highest."

Drumah was bathed in a cascade of shimmering light. Falling water wrapped her body in the hues of a pastel rainbow. Her perfect form, raw in its splendid beauty, held him breathlessly. His footsteps were lost in the rushing roar of the waterfall. Drumah looked up when she felt eyes on her body, first startled and then relieved to see that it was Gideon, her rescuer, the man of her dreams. She covered herself with a shy cloak, wild with excitement as Gideon approached. Her breathing was short and shallow, and though she whispered, Gideon managed to hear her over the sound of the rumbling waters. "Today, I felt comforted by some unseen force. I knew everything was going to be all right once I saw you again."

Gideon caressed her. He kissed her and vowed that they would never be parted. He spoke of last night's dangerous work, the overturning of the altar of Baal, and the destruction of the grove that was to be her place of bloody sacrifice. Now, it had been blessed and sanctified by the one true God, Adonai. He spoke of the angel in Ophrah, how he had been called "a mighty man of valor," and how he, as one man, was to save all of Israel from the Midianites.

Gideon confided to Drumah that she was now his concubine by law and that this had been agreed to by Joash. The law and the prophets were satisfied, and she would always be his one true love for all time. "We will always be together," he promised. "I solemnly swear this to you by all that is holy. This very day you will be with me. I want the whole city to know that you belong to me. My father has given us his consent and his blessing. As my concubine, even though a daughter of Shechem, this city will have to accept you. You will be considered a protected resident of my father's house." Drumah clung to him, tears of joy welling up in her eyes. "And to think," reminded Gideon, "you were almost sacrificed, but now we face together a new life of joy and loving bliss."

CHAPTER 12

A Pack of Wolves and a Murder of Crows

The Midianites, Amalekites, Ishmaelites, and all the children of the East lived as wild men in tents, migrating in the fashion of nomads, for they could not endure the confines of walled cities. The Bedouin thrived on the seasonal feast of the vagabond. Moving in countless numbers like locusts, they traveled where they would, seeking safe refuge for a day or a week in the fashion of fugitives. They would stop over for a feast of plenty when all had been made ready at the hour of harvest. Israel, arch-rival and an old enemy of these nomadic tribes, had become abundant in the production of wheat and barley, for they tilled, sowed, and planted from sunup to eventide. Like ants, they prepared for the coming of winter.

The Midianites, and all the children of the East, bringing herds of camels without number, came to lay waste the fertile valley of Jezreel, having timed their arrival for the season of reaping. With hungry mouths they filled their empty bellies, gorging themselves on the fruits of Israel's back-breaking labor. Famine was their greatest weapon; they reduced the fields of Israel, both wheat and barley. Israel could reckon on no increase. They were stripped of their bounty and left wanting though it was their time of plenty. The children of the East had no fear. As of yet, they had not been opposed in any way as they moved swiftly from valley to plain. Israel was desperate for the loss of their farming success and could not mount or sustain an adequate defense. There was no agreement or leadership due to the petty squabbling, spite, and mistrust among the competing tribes. There was no man able to gather them into a cause to form a much-needed alliance. Israel was doomed to stand idly by as its produce was stolen and its people ravaged by starvation.

The Spirit of the Lord had become a familiar and welcome guest to Gideon, communing directly with him through the channels of vivid dreams and inspiration . . . and sometimes an audible, still, small voice with the economy of words that would tingle his ears. At times, Gideon knew straightaway exactly what the Lord expected of him; at this moment, he was to call forth all the people of Abiezer. Gideon picked up the shofar of warning. The horn's mighty blast was known to carry a potential life-threatening alarm: the well-timed understanding of what was at stake could determine Israel's fate and the very survival of all of its people.

The city gathered in great haste to the meeting place. The shofar echoed through the mountain passes. The sound echoed, seeming to increase in volume until it reached the dens, caves, and deep into forest glades and thickets. Some took the course of a full day's travel to get to the gathering place. The city of Ophrah hurriedly flocked together in uneasy anticipation, only

98

to see Gideon holding the shofar of destiny. The crowd murmured in disbelief. Was this not the Gideon that threw down the altar of Baal and destroyed the sacred grove?

"Why have we been summoned? What is the news of danger?" a voice from the crowd anxiously demanded. Gideon replied, "It has come to me by Adonai, the most high God, to save Israel from the ravages of the Midian horde." A mocking voice called out from the gathered crowd, "God talks to him? It comes from spending too much time at the winepress." Some turned away, jeering and ridiculing the son of Joash, but most believed . . . for the Spirit had impressed upon them that this shy man, the least regarded in his father's house, had been set apart to gather together all the northern tribes into a righteous army of the most high God.

Ophrah and all of the Abiezrites agreed to Gideon's call and rallied to him, as if the hand of God had quickened them. Gideon sent the swiftest runners to the tribes of Israel to let them know about the large numbers of Abiezrites already assembled. Messengers were dispatched throughout all of the Manasseh, who also gathered to him. The tribes of Asher, Zebulun, and Naphtali received a summons to rally. Gideon, an ordinary farmer and the least regarded of men, was now appointed by God to be Israel's supreme commander.

The rumor of war spread to all the towns of Israel. It was swiftly carried to every nook and cranny by messengers, merchant caravans, and the gossip of washwomen. The word of war raced ahead more speedily than the swiftest horses, and as far south as the tribe of Ephraim. Ephraim questioned the leadership of an amateur farmer and his army of reapers and tillers . . . how would they attempt to break the yoke of the Midianite horde? Ephraim had not been asked or officially invited to participate in the work of war. All of the Ephraim agreed that this was an insult to their pride that would be dealt with in kind. Ephraim should be an obvious choice for their cunning in combat, and for their proven ability to win in the arena of conflict. This apparent snub further fueled tribal hostility. Ephraim had evidently been denied the spoil—as well as the glory—of battle.

Ephraim gathered her army with the greatest sense of urgency, as a hen gathers her brood at the approach of a storm. Their destination, the Jezreel Valley, was many leagues away, far to the north. Schooled in, and armed with, the tools of war, Ephraim was quick to march. They would see that the other tribes paid them the homage and respect their heritage deserved . . . the lion's share of glory and spoil would yet be theirs to secure.

CHAPTER 13

A Fleece, Once of Gold and Twice of Might

Gideon could see clouds of dust spread out as far off as the horizon. The roads, trails, and even the winding mountain passes were choked by the approach of warriors, armed and fearsome, and farmers, simply in search of high adventure. They came by daylight and by torchlight in an ongoing parade in a mutual bond of tribal pride. Gideon was overwhelmed by the response. His army grew by the day, and by the hour, in swelling numbers of dedicated followers. They looked to him, and only to him, for leadership, generalship, and spiritual inspiration.

Thoughts ran through Gideon's mind: Was there truly an angel in Ophrah? Or was it the plotting of a troubled mind? Did I, in fact, hear an angel call me "a mighty man of valor"? How quickly memory fades. Was the toppling of the altar of Baal, as well as the toppling of the sacred grove, all done just to save Drumah from certain destruction? Was this not done by my own will and by my own hand? Why would the Lord of Hosts, the

God of all creation, commune with me? I am now and I always have been a foolish, weak creature of this world . . .

Gideon struggled with the lifelong phantoms that had plagued him—self-doubt and a terrible lack of confidence. His self-esteem were the dregs of an empty barrel. These had been his constant companions, living in the shadows of humiliation and fear. Gideon wrestled endlessly with his hesitation, allowing it to grow into the ghost of second guessing that, time and again, led to frozen indecision. Gideon questioned, in equal part, the dire mistrust he felt concerning his own grip on what was true, as well as the charge he had been given to save Israel. The mantle he had accepted to be Israel's hero had become the weight of a mountain on his thinning shoulders. Gideon grappled with the agony of uncertainty and reeled from the burden of crushing disbelief. His desperation was fed by his unsure footing from the shifting sands of reality and the questioning of his own sanity.

Gideon called upon God, passionately petitioning Him for an answer to his grave doubts. "If Thou wilt save Israel by my hand, as Thou hast said, I need a sign—one I can feel with my hands, see with my eyes, and know in my heart—that I may acquire an unshakable faith. I would be strong in You, my Lord, and have the power of Your might. I would know with confidence that Thou hast chosen me as thine instrument to vanquish the enemies of Israel."

Gideon summoned his son, Jether, bidding him to fetch from the house of Joash the ram's fleece of prosperity. It was prominently displayed above the hearth in the great hall and was the very instrument Joash had used to sift for gold in the streams of the Eilat Mountains while making his way north to settle in the mountains of Ophrah. The bounty had been of sufficient value for him to build a large home, to buy fertile fields, and to secure the purchase of the grove. It was mainly through his gold that he had been accepted into the land of the Amorites.

The sun was about to set. The campfires of the gathered army were lit, for long shadows reached down from the mountain peaks to cover Ophrah in the dim glint of twilight. Gideon knelt upon the rocky ground, using the fleece for a cushion. He prayed: "If thou wilt save Israel by my hand, as Thou hast said—behold, I will put this fleece of wool on the stones of this landscape. By morning's first light, if the mountain dew is on the fleece alone, and all the earth beside it is dry, then shall I know that Thou would save Israel by my hand."

Gideon's prayer had been answered by the time the overriding rooster had crowed his challenge to the glory of the sun. Gideon rose early in anticipation of the confirmation he sought. He was half hoping that this weighty new mantle of responsibility would not be thrust upon him but be reserved for someone greater. Gideon did not feel up to the challenge or the task set before him. It was distressing for Gideon to compete with men because he had lived so long in defeat. He was unable to imagine being stretched so significantly as to take command of the army of the living God. Gideon woke Jether, his beloved son, and invited him to be a witness, to confirm or deny a hoped-for sign from God. Gideon did not want to depend on his own eyes—he was struggling to keep his wits about him. The fleece was thick with sweet morning dew, heavy with the weight of water. Taking a firm grip, Gideon and Jether between them wrung the covering, filling a bowl to the rim with the liquid evidence of God's acknowledgment. All around the fleece, the ground was carpeted with fine, dry powdered dust. In spite of the clarity he had asked for, Gideon's self-doubt still lingered. He remained unconvinced and would require a second sign of confirmation.

"My son," Gideon sighed, "it looks like Adonai has made his wishes known. The fleece is wet, and the ground remains dry—it is as I asked."

Jether, sensing his father's lingering uncertainty with the result, offered consolation: "Father, consider perhaps that because the fleece has many fine woolen hairs, the morning dew would more quickly settle upon it while the ground surrounding it is dry. The dew would not cling so stubbornly to the ground; it would more readily evaporate into the dry mountain air."

Gideon reflected on Jether's argument and said, "I will call again upon my Lord, our God, one last time on this matter. I will ask for grace and beg for His indulgence. I will ask once more that He confirms or denies that my name is upon His lips, that His hand is my guide. All of Israel hangs with the confidence of a worldly creature who is lacking, the lowliest of his servants. I must in my own mind be secure in the knowledge that I do his bidding."

Then, Gideon said unto God, "Let not Thy anger be hot against me. I will speak but this once. Let me prove Your will for me, I pray thee, but this once with the fleece. Let it now be dry only upon the fleece, and upon all the ground, let there be an abundance of dew."

And God did that night as Gideon had asked. Unsettled in his bed, Gideon could not wait for first light. He woke Jether from his deep slumber, for both his company and for confirmation of the result. Together, they reached the place where the fleece lay by the light of a torch. The wool was dry, and the ground was drenched with dew. When the sun broke through, warm and bright, Gideon's faith that God would use him as an instrument of Israel's salvation had been replaced by the knowledge that it was confirmed and made true. He stood ready to lead the army of Israel—to defeat the Midianite horde and all the children of the East, who counted themselves enemies of God's people. All doubt had been cast out, and Gideon's confidence waxed strong . . . for if the Lord God of Israel was with him, who could stand against him?

CHAPTER 14

Clean Hands, Fearless Hearts,
and Eyes Fixed Upon the Horizon

G ideon was given a new name, Jerubbaal, meaning "Let
Baal plead against him because he hath thrown down
his altar," giving him the acclaim of his brethren, as well as being
a great boost to his confidence. He had become the undisputed
leader of Israel's army; his honor became the standard the army
respectfully followed. Israel's army of volunteers needed a leader
who could charge them with the courage to act with one mind
and in one accord. Gideon sent sentries to the highest vantage
points to observe the surrounding area, where they could sound
an alarm to warn Israel's army when the enemy gathered. The
Midianite horde and all the children of the East had, as if by
design, appeared in Israel when the harvest was due. They settled
in with their wives, concubines, and livestock. They pitched their
tents as far as the eye could see; they filled the Jezreel on the
north side of the Hill Moreh. On the south shore of Moreh lay
Gideon, gathering the army of Israel.

The assembled clans of armed men totaled thirty-two thousand. Gathered together from a range of different tribes, many were young and eager but, as yet, untried as warriors. All sought after adventure and to prove that each of them were fearless and heroic. These were the green dreams of innocent youth. They rose up at dawn and pitched their tents beside the well of Harod. Rumor had it that their Midianite enemy was on the north side of the Hill Moreh—in the numbers of locusts filling the valley of Jezreel. Gideon believed this was where God had placed them. The army of Israel was outnumbered by more than four men to one. Panic and fear arose within a few; contending with such a vast mass of hostile alien invaders seemed futile. Surely they would accomplish only the loss of limb or certain death.

The Lord said unto Gideon, "The people who are with thee are too many for Me to give the Midianites into their hands, lest Israel boast themselves against Me. They will contend that it was by their own valor and by their own force. They will say, 'My own hand has saved me and not the Lord of Hosts.' Now, therefore, go to proclaim in the ears of the people, saying, 'Whosoever is fearful, afraid, and faint of heart, let him return from whence he came, and depart unashamed.'"

Twenty-two thousand turned away and prepared to retrace their steps back from whence they came, and there remained ten thousand who were fearless and unafraid.

Again, the Lord spoke to Gideon, "The people are yet too many, for there is no restraint concerning the Lord, whether to save by many or by a few. Bring them to the water, and I will try them, for your sake, there at the water's edge. It shall be that whom I say unto you, these shall go with you, the same shall go with you. Whomever I say shall not go with you, shall not go with you."

Gideon brought down the ten thousand to the water's edge. The mountain stream was fresh and pure. Those who had no fear stood bravely upon the near and far banks. Gideon, from the heights and overseeing the throng, in a loud and booming voice, commanded the potential army, "Drink your fill of these living waters, for the Lord God has commanded it so! In this, you might know God's strong hand and outstretched arm, His love for you, and His will for Israel!"

The Lord said unto Gideon, "Everyone that lapped the water with his tongue as a dog lapped, he shalt thou set by himself; likewise, everyone that boweth down upon his knees to drink. For the dog is impulsive and undisciplined, and the knees that had bowed down to foreign gods are not sanctified."

The Lord made a declaration to Gideon and gave him a final instruction: "By the three hundred men that lapped from their hands will I save you. I will deliver the Midianites into your hands. Let all the other people go, every man unto his place of abode."

The number of them that lapped by putting their hand to their mouth was three hundred men. Their hands were now cleaned in the stream. So, too, their hearts were cleansed of fear. Their vision was fixed upon the horizon and sharply focused on the task at hand. For in their clean hands, Israel would be redeemed from the Midianite horde and from all the sons of the East.

Perched high upon the steep boulder walls, with his young son, Jether, at his side, holding the double-bladed sword of authority, Gideon addressed the thousands of men before they took their leave. Some murmured with discontent. They had willingly heeded the call and had made the grueling journey in response to the strength of their faith in God. Gideon said to them, "Be not dismayed, but rejoice that only three hundred were chosen by God's mighty hand. There will be no mistaking by whose power and authority Israel will be reclaimed."

Before dismissing the ten thousand, Gideon put a request to them for provisions, saying, "This army of three hundred will need supplies. They will need barley bread, dried meats, and three hundred shofar trumpets. They will also need six hundred clay pots, and three hundred lamps full of oil, along with tinder and flints to ignite their fires." The ten thousand provided generously, supplying the three hundred with all they needed. The ninety-seven hundred were then dismissed by Gideon.

The host of Midian was spread out directly beneath Gideon's army on the floor of the Jezreel Valley. This setting had been pre-ordained to proclaim the glory of God and to reveal His might to Israel yet again. Gideon addressed the three hundred as one body, with the aim of assigning the captains over each division of one hundred men. A visual sweep of the group produced two faces that radiated a spiritual glow. "You! And you!" Gideon pointed to the two men, commanding them to step forward. "What are your names?" he inquired.

They replied in turn. "Elyon," said the first. Gideon nodded, knowing the name to mean "Father."

He looked at the second man. "My name is Ben," the soldier told him. Gideon smiled. The name meant "Son." It fitted that his captains bore the names "father" and "son." He put a hand on each of their shoulders: "You two will be my captains. Each of you will be responsible for one hundred men." Gideon lowered his hands. "Elyon, your division of one hundred will be called by the name 'Father.' And you, Ben, your one hundred will be called by the name of 'Son.' I will be the center mark. I will be wholly out front and centered . . . as a ghost in the darkness! My one hundred will be called 'Ghost.'"

Gideon presented the placement of his troops going into battle as it was given to him by the Lord God of Israel. "Ben, thirty paces to the right of center, and Elyon thirty paces to the left of center. Form one line and count off by threes." It was so. "Those who drew the number 'one,' to the left; the 'twos' will proceed to the center, and all that counted out 'three,' stand to the right. Shortest men to the front rank; those who stand at mid-height to the second row, and the very tallest to the back of the formation. Your captains of hundreds should be on the end of the flanks."

Gideon began explaining his strategy: "Men, I have been given a view of what we are about to do. I do this by the will and by the direction of the Lord God. It is given to us to act in one accord. The full assembly will move as if we were but one man." The men raised their clenched fists and outstretched arms in a salute of agreement and approval. "Gather you every man a trumpet," Gideon commanded. "Of the clay pots, take two. Take up a lamp, each of you, filled with oil, and with their wicks cut, trimmed, and made ready for the spark."

Every man did so and returned to his station. Gideon said, "From here on out, follow my every move as in my rhythm and timed perfectly to my pace." Again, a raised trumpet salute in response and in agreement. "The ranks will be set at thirty-three men in three rows with the captains of one hundred on the outer row. Present each company two arm's lengths apart, and two arm's lengths front to rear." They made it so.

Gideon gave detailed instructions regarding their approach to the horde. "The lamps will be lit and secured in these clay pitchers so that no flame will be visible—from near or from afar—to give away our position in the dark. Surprise will be on our side. We will suddenly appear, fair as the moon, bright as the sun, and fearsome as an army with banners. In their hearts and in their mind's eye, they will perceive the specter of God's omnipotence as they face the darkness of the pit in a fearful eclipse at midnight."

Gideon continued, "We will separate, so that each company of one hundred comes from three different directions, advancing on the Midianite camp, or so they will imagine. We will descend from the heights of the hill Moreh and fan out in three companies along the valley floor. We will keep hill Moreh to our north and mount Gilboa to our south, and we will be facing east. When all three companies are in their place, I will trumpet the alarm and call on every man to blow the ram's horn of the mighty shofar. Then, on every side, a trumpet's blast will raise the camp of Midian. At my direction, break the clay pot in your hands with the ribbed knuckle from the shofar horn. This will serve as a symbol of God's might. It will be like a thunderclap that would wake the dead. Release the dim light of the burning lamp high over your heads. It will be supposed by our enemy as blazing torches far off into the distance. The depth of field created will appear to reveal the full army of Israel on the march, on every side of their camp, and still far off in the distance. The loud, confusing noise of crashing crockery will choke their breath and put the fear of God into their hearts. At this point, every man must shout: 'The sword of the Lord and of Gideon! *Kherev l'Adonai u-l'Gid'on!'* This must be shouted in the loudest, most passionate voice you possess. Bring it forth from the intent of your heart and from your burning breast."

They practiced the rhythm of their march until every man's step was smooth and on cue. It was done in a perfect collective tempo. The men stepped and stomped in a strange cadence of unbridled passion. That night, after Gideon had stretched out and was just about to cross the threshold of visions, when the Lord said unto Gideon, "Arise!" Gideon had just dropped off into a deep sleep. At first, he questioned what he heard . . . Was it just a dream? He quickly revived, but again, he heard the voice of the Lord. Now it was as distinctive as the roar of a lion and the deafening rush of falling waters. The Lord said unto him, "Arise, and go down unto the camp of the host of Midian, for I have delivered them into thine hands. The shadow of night shall be a cloak and a shield unto you. But if you fear to go down, take Phurah, your manservant, with you for comfort and courage. Go now to the camp where the Midian host is at rest."

Gideon was still unsure of his role as commander. When he was left alone, the phantoms of his previous life would conjure up his all-too-familiar insecurities. He Woke Phurah, his childhood protector and mentor. Phurah had aged but was still formidable in the art of personal combat. The Lord told Gideon, "Thou shall hear what they say. Your hands will be strengthened. The last of your doubts shall vanish again and forever, so go you down unto the host and listen that you might hear."

Gideon and Phurah carried no light, so there would be nothing to give away their secret hike. The full moon was on the horizon and gave a silver cast to the well-worn goat path. Down they trudged to the far south side of the Hill of Moreh, and to the outskirts of the camp. They were close enough to be within earshot of the well-armed sentries. The Midianites, the Amalekites, and the Ishmaelites, and all the children of the East lay along the valley floor like a multitude of grasshoppers. Their camels were without number, as the sand on the seashore.

Gideon and Phurah, by stealth and the cover of night, silently slipped behind a tumble of boulders, just as the changing of the guard took place only a few paces away. A man began to speak to his captain. "Sir, I have had the most vivid and disturbing dream, I would not concern you, but I am prompted—no, compelled—by some unseen hand to relay this vision to you."

"Speak on," said Lexol, the captain of the relief.

"Behold, I dreamed a dream. Lo, a cake of barley bread tumbled into the host of Midian and came unto a tent and smote it that it fell, and overturned it, that the tent lay along."

Lexol had a firm recollection of the prophetic words of Adam, Gideon's oldest brother, these many years before. Lexol had slaughtered him at the Battle of Mount Tabor. Lexol answered, "This is nothing else, save the sword of Gideon, the son of Joash, a man of Israel. For into his hand hath God delivered Midian and all the host."

CHAPTER 15
At the Beginning of the Middle Watch (Midnight)

Hearing the telling of this dream and its explanation gave Gideon a fresh understanding of God's plan. Gideon and Phurah slipped back through the night under the cloak of darkness and scurried with God's speed back to the south side of Moreh and the sleeping encampment. Phurah had held his peace until now, but after hearing Lexol interpret the Midianite soldier's dream, he informed Gideon of his brothers' betrayal by Lexol with the consent of a death sentence from the two reigning Midianite princes all those many long years past. Lexol had promised freedom to Adam, Hosea, and Joseph but had, in its stead, delivered death. Confirming all that had taken place on that fateful day, as seen and now repeated from the tight lips of the trusted Phurah, this second witness, the matter was established. All doubt had been dispelled. Gideon now knew that he had been chosen by God to free Drumah, rescue Israel, and set right the spilled blood of his brothers, who called to him from the dust.

Gideon's spirits soared—his doubts ceased to exist. His self-confidence climbed, spiraling up on the wings of destiny. He felt confident that the mantle of a young lion was now his cloak of authority. The dark night of doubt had been answered by the bright light of revelation, for, in his heart, the Lord had written his story. He worshiped and praised, for his faith was made perfect. He quickly returned up the hill to where the fearless hearts and clean hands of the three hundred were settled. Phurah walked at his side, a witness to his climb of righteousness. Gideon was lifted to new heights by the promise of God's unfolding arms.

The faint campfire embers bore witness to the three hundred men having put down their heads for a needed rest. The day-long drill had taken its toll; the coordinated effort to attain perfection had been exacting. Their slumber was deep, and most had slipped into the region of dreams.

"Arise!" Gideon's shout woke every man in an instant. "The Lord God of Israel hath delivered into your hands the host of Midian this very night. We will engage in our deadly game of confused noise, dim lights, and crashing of clay pots at the beginning of the middle watch." Gideon shouted out his final commands. "Rally to your captains! Gather your trumpets! One for each man, as we planned! Spark your lamps! Nestle them snugly in the hot pocket of your clay pot, but omit the lid, as the flame needs to breathe." Gideon watched as the men sparked their lamps and placed them in the pots before he continued speaking.

"Speak not a word. Not a cough or a whisper. Wrap your feet in rags if needed to lighten the footfalls as we make our descent. We will organize into the formation, just as we trained, once we reach the bottom of the hill. We will separate quietly until each man has found his proper place."

Gideon led his band of three hundred men down the very same goat path he had used only hours before. They picked their way carefully, in single file, to the valley floor below. He directed the three companies of one hundred, "I will be the center. Ben's one hundred will flank me to the right, and Elyon will flank me to the left. We will surround the camp on three sides—as if three armies were closing in on the Midianite center. Once in place, I will walk to the very front, so every man will have a view of me, like a ghost, but wholly in sight. Go quickly! Take your places. Wait for the trumpet blast, so we can execute the drills we have so carefully practiced. And remember, the Lord God of Israel goes before us . . . who then can stand against us?"

He divided the three hundred men into three companies and said, "Have your trumpets ready in your right hand and your pitchers filled with your lighted lamps in your left hand. Look at me, and do likewise. When I come to the outside of the camp, watch and do as I do. When I and all who are with me blow their trumpets, then blow your trumpets on every side of all the camp. Having blown your horn, bring your hands together. Break your pitcher on the hard knuckle of the ram's horn of shofar. Free the light, raising it far above your head with your left hand. In your right hand, blow your shofar with a mighty blast and shout, 'The sword of the Lord and of Gideon! *Kherev l'Adonai u-l'Gid'on!* Then as one man, raise your foot and stomp the ground with might and weight, and remain in place just as we practiced."

Gideon and the three hundred men who were with him came to the outside of the Midianite camp at the beginning of the middle watch, on or about midnight. The watchmen were newly set, so there was a fog of confusion, being fresh from their beds and not yet in tune with the silence of shadows. The stillness was suddenly shattered by a crashing uproar of sound. Gideon blew his mighty trumpet, and then all three hundred blew their shofars with one accord. The moon fell dark; eerie fingers snatched the silver light, dispelling the lunar halo. Pitchers smashed and crashed with the crack of thunder against the hard bony knuckle of the ram's horn. The sound echoed against the opposing sides of the Hill of Moreh and Mount Gilboa. The three hundred flickering lamps were raised high over their heads to produce the subtle visual effect of being far off in the distance.

The shout: "The sword of the Lord and of Gideon! (Hah makh'aheerah Vav Adonai Vav Gid'on!)" boomed and then echoed louder and louder, feeding off the valley walls. The stomping sounded as if the whole of humanity were converging for a blood-curdling massacre of the whole of the Midianite horde. Every man stood his ground round about the camp and moved smartly in perfect harmony, precisely as they had been well practiced. All the Midianite host ran helter-skelter, crying and fleeing, for their hearts were filled with fear and dread. A whirlwind of panic engulfed their emotions, and their minds screamed in trembling terror from the uproar and the crashing waves of commotion.

The three hundred blew, chanted, and stomped the ground in a crescendo of confused sounds which seemed to get louder and louder until the Lord set every man's sword against his fellows. In the darkness of the night, the enemy appeared everywhere and nowhere to the Midianites. The mysterious gloom seemed to have a life of its own. The torches of Midian were doused. Flint lost its spark, and all enemy fire went dark. Like blind men, they continued to fight in a blood-soaked frenzy of bewilderment. None of the Midian hosts remained, not one. The greater part of the host had fled, to stay ahead of the wrath of God. They abandoned their swollen dead, now a portion for vultures and foxes. The victory was made plain at dawn with a body count, rows of corpses running along the fertile valley floor. Gideon had become the mighty man of valor foretold by an angel of the Lord. He had been forged into an irresistible force, fueled by faith made perfect.

A well-situated escape route had presented itself; the horde was in the disorder of confusion. The Princes Oreb and Zeeb (Raven and Wolf, respectively) took the grand remainder of the host on the longer route to Beth-Shittah in Zererath. The survival instinct of the Bedouin forced them to divide their headlong path of retreat. The twin kings, Zebah and Zalmunna, took the most direct and southern course along the border of Abelmeholah unto Tabatha. They were rushing to the shallows of the Beth-barah, to the crossover waters of the River Jordan and to the safety of their secure stronghold at Karkor.

The news of Gideon's decisive battle of miracles was, to those who heard the story told, as if a stout oak had been felled by a flimsy reed. It left no doubt as to God's omnipotence. Gideon's role as God's chosen commander was confirmed in the baptism of combat. Word quickly spread to all the coasts, where rumor and gossip made bigger the scope and deeds of heroes. The men of Israel, who had recently departed, felt the longing for the glory of battle. Their fear had been replaced by faith and the need to be counted in and not to be seen as dead weight. They were inspired by the recent turn of events. They gathered out of Naphtali and out of Asher and out of all Manasseh into an army of warrior-farmers, streaming to the plain of the next battle with a fearsome determination.

CHAPTER 16

Gather All the Young Men

The twin princes who had now become kings, Zalmunna and Zebah, had made a speedy departure at the first sign of trouble; it ensured their survival. Protecting the heads of the twin vipers was crucial. A secretive escape route had long since been established, affording them cover and concealing them, a carefully laid plan to prevent their capture. The largest share of the horde set off in a different direction to the route, followed by Zalmunna and Zebah, hoping to keep their losses to a minimum. The two princes, Oreb (Raven) and Zeeb (Wolf), and commanders and generals led the main body of camel warriors and all those who could still ride. They followed the kings along the valley floor to Beth-Shittah, and then on to Beth Shan. They planned to proceed to the east bank of the River Jordan and then directly south, in an anxious attempt to avoid any further massacres. They took to the waters and the fording place of the Jordan, east of Nobah, and then followed the caravan route of Jogbehah to the stronghold of Karkor.

Gideon sent messengers south, throughout the mount of Ephraim and to every town, village, and hamlet, speaking of the victory of God, the three hundred, and the sword of Gideon in the valley of the Jezreel. He wanted to capture the fleeing Midianites at the waters of Beth Barah and the fording place before they attempted to cross over the Jordan. Gideon planned to drive them—as hounds to the hunters—into the waiting arms of the fierce tribe of Ephraim.

Gideon's attempt at catching the kings in the jaws of a claw by driving them southward was not to be so because the army of Ephraim had long since departed. Ephraim was now engaged in a fierce battle of their own in the valley of the Jezreel. They had moved out swiftly at breakneck speed, marching northward to make up for lost time. Ephraim was headed to the last known location of the Midian enemy. The message to block the Beth-barah passage was eventually delivered to Ephraim at Beth Shan, but Ephraim had much bigger concerns to deal with. A crucial battle was forming that had all the signs of being brutal. The two princes of Midian were headed in their direction with the entire remaining portion of the Midianite camel cavalry. The two opposing forces were poised for a head-on collision.

Gideon was now in full pursuit of the two kings, the assassins of his brothers, along the flats on the west side of the Jordan. This geography was perfect for the camels' rapid retreat, as they were able to reach maximum gait in the open country. Not knowing what lay ahead or what was about to unfold behind, Gideon relied wholly on faith, assured that he would receive the correct directions from God. He had become God's predator, a real and growing threat to those who opposed Israel. His prey was just out of sight, but the trail was fresh, as attested to by the still-moist camel-dung droppings.

Ephraim's military leader, General Zev, a ruthless man by nature, would rally all to fight in spite of any tribal bickering. He was a man who was known to get things done quickly, able to take command in any spur-of-the-moment armed struggle. The general organized all those who had previously been dismissed as unnecessary to Gideon's yet-unfinished victory. This rabble of excess baggage, deemed by God as fearful, unclean, and wholly dispensable, now formed the center corps of the army of Beth Shan. The total force was substantial, but the Midianites were still formidable, deadly, and as dangerous as any cornered and wounded beast. Straddling their camels with their slashing Bedouin blades at the ready, they were as yet unaware that they were about to face a second deadly encounter in their race to escape the judgment of fate.

General Zev was a man known for his creative skill and cunning. His cadre included a pack of wolves, which he had raised and hand-fed since they were newborn pups, fresh from the teats of their mother's love. The pack of a hundred or so looked to Zev as their alpha male. They had grown accustomed to battle-attack—their entire lives had been spent in the protection of Zev while he slept and on the march. Pitied was the man who crossed the general, for the pack had grown fond of the taste of human flesh.

Naphtali, Asher, and all of the Manasseh heeled quickly under the commanding demands of General Zev. With retribution for Gideon's supposed slight of Ephraim guiding his motives, General Zev, using his cunning, sought to redress Ephraim's lack of invitation to Gideon's first encounter with the Midian empire. Was Gideon not from Ophrah? Since Gideon was no longer to be found, then the men of Ophrah would take the brunt of the first sting of battle.

The general began by laying out his battle plan in well-crafted details. Particular rises and ridges would be well-manned along a seven-mile corridor by warriors of each tribe. The Midian horde would be riding their camels, which would have to stay on the paths, avoiding steep-sided ravines. The uneven ground would slow their desert ships down on the high and dry drifts. Once they were halfway through the valley floor, the one hundred hungry wolves would be set loose. Wolves and camels, being natural enemies, would send the camels into a panic of flight— turning, colliding, and unseating their riders, and making them easy prey for the waiting infantry poised on the high ground, ready to drop down to ambush the unseated rider.

《 《 《 》 》 》

The Midianite princes, Oreb and Zeeb, led what remained of the main body of the Midianites, the Amalekites, and all the children of the East. They skirted the town of Beth-Shittah in an attempt to reorganize. They were still feeling stunned by the slaughter that had resulted from Gideon's sounding maneuver a few nights before. Their jangled nerves attested to the shock of their unsuspected defeat. Their need to scavenge provisions for themselves and fodder for their multitude of camels was critical. It was a long trek south to the fording place of the Jordan, and then on to the caravan route of Jogbehah and the security afforded by their stronghold of Karkor.

CHAPTER 17
Camels and Carnivores

The ingenious scheme of General Zev was to assign his troops to their stations before the first burn of daylight. This would shock the enemy, who would be rising out of the gloom and facing into the morning glare. The lights of torches were employed for the men to find their places. Every man found his mark and stood his ground. As each man took a stand, his flame was extinguished. Although hastily thrown together, the general's military tactic appeared sound. General Zev's wolves were separated into smaller packs so that every escape route could be guarded by these ferocious sentinels.

The outlook scout, stationed at the highest peak, gulped when he first saw the Midian horde. They were more numerous than expected and looked fearsome. His mouth was dry, and he had to spit twice before he was able to pucker his lips to sound the shofar. The bellowing boom of the ram's horn sent the alarm, signaling to the waiting army that death and destruction were galloping straight for them.

The casual trot of the Midianites' camels quickly turned their caravan into a driving wall of deadly, speeding hooves as they turned the corner into the Beth Shan Valley. They were going to make a run for it. The galloping throng soon met with the horrible sound of yells and growls. The strange sounds filled their hearts with fear and dread. Panic and momentum drove them to their final destruction. Their only course was to forge ahead. The princes, Zeeb and Oreb, had not prepared for battle, and turning around was no longer an option. In this tight space, with so many camels in a full-stretched gallop, it would be impossible. They would have to pass through a crucible of fire in their attempt to weave past the entrenched enemy at full pace. Their only option was breakneck speed. They would have to bully their way through scores of fixed infantry.

A makeshift weapon was craftily employed, courtesy of the skill and cunning of General Zev. A four-cubit length of pole with a loop of jute would be used to encircle the head of the rider and then over the head and around the neck. The forward momentum of the camel, then, would tighten the loop into a stranglehold and, in a snap, pull the riders down off the height of humps and onto the ground, where either the fall to the ground or the infantry sword could make short work of the stunned, dismounted rider.

The clamor of battle raged. Swirling dust clumped into black flakes of hot red blood. Camels screamed as they tumbled to their knees in a chorus of snapping bones and spitting teeth. Death rattles gurgled from men who were mortally wounded. The horde was now halfway through a boiling caldron of slaughter. The Midianites fought as only the damned can do, managing to open the road through the jaws of the closing trap. Then General Zev raised his hand, and at his command, the wolves were let loose to do their worst. The camels turned back on each other when the charging fangs of death triggered ancient instincts. In a frenzy of panic, some collided, and some were broadsided with a thump to the ground. The camels—once an impenetrable wall—had stalled! The Midianite advance had been ground to a crawl. Their prayers for deliverance went unanswered.

Prince Oreb's camel was a victim of the first wolf-pack attack. Prince Oreb was barely able to beat the ferocious pack back with his razor-sharp scimitar. He was hobbled by a vicious bite to the upper right thigh before hacking the animal to pieces. Dripping blood from the deep puncture wounds, Oreb was now forced to set out on foot. He began his climb to the highest ridge. For the moment, he was out of the fray and out of the fight. He made his way by the sheer force of will, keeping to the long shadows and out of the line of sight. He slid inside a yawning crag between two rocks at the very top of the peak. He waited for relief from the blanket of night, praying he would go undetected. The throbbing pain from his open wound kept him vigilant. His prospects of escape were looking as dim as the approaching twilight. The wolves picked up the scent of fresh blood on the trail—the hunt was on for the two princes, who were not among the dead. They were the prizes most sought after, the trophies of generals.

The wolves were first upon the wounded prince. They started to make short work of him. Prince Oreb stood his ground and killed several of the lesser beasts. They yelped out their final whimpers; Oreb's sword was quick and learned. He would have given a better account of himself but for his loss of blood. He was soon overwhelmed by a big gray with a thick coat and teeth like daggers. He was dragged to the ground, whipped around, and mauled like a child's toy doll. All the men stepped back and watched as the beast enjoyed its most savage work. With his neck exposed, it only took seconds before his throat was ripped out. A captain witnessing the brutal experience stepped up and said, "The Raven is dead, and we will call this place 'The Rock of Oreb' after the name of the prince, so none will forget the might of Ephraim."

General Zev was quickly alerted to this turn of events. Since he did not want to tax his men with the burden of Oreb's body, the standing order was that only the prince's head needed to be retrieved as a testament of victory. They placed it in a leather pouch, ready for transport and for ease of display. It represented Ephraim's decisive victory over the greater part of Midian's army. The horde had been ruthlessly dealt with and radically reduced, in some manner resembling Prince Oreb's headless body.

General Zev now turned his full attention to locating the remains or the whereabouts of Prince Zeeb, to make his victory over Midian complete and to increase his boasting to Gideon. He sought to insult Gideon for his failure to recognize Ephraim as the supreme military force in Israel and himself as their rightful commander.

Prince Zeeb, the younger of the two Midianite princes, found relief in the near-sundown. He managed to slip past the battle lines, due to his devoted bodyguards giving their all in securing their prince a path to safety. Zeeb escaped, reaching the open road, just ahead of the ever-thickening cloak of night. General Zev was keenly aware of the escape of Prince Zeeb and of his desperate flight to safety. The general's inner circle was told of the importance of his capture. Undoubtedly, and given enough time, the prince could organize revenge for the death of his brother, Oreb. He could without difficulty gather an army of mercenaries. Israel had many enemies, and this would ensure yet another brutal conflict that may lead to more war whose outcome would remain uncertain.

The general ordered his trusted inner circle, his fiercest and most loyal warriors, bodyguards, and captains, to accompany his second-in-command, the ruthless Captain Omar. Zev offered his best tracking wolves to ensure the capture of the errant prince, Zeeb. With a half-jest, the general quipped, "It takes a wolf to catch a wolf."

The wolves had picked up Zeeb's scent, and the company was on his trail before dawn's first burn of daylight. Bent on having them bring back the prince's head in an expressly designed leather pouch, General Zev made it clear he wanted a head . . . if not the prince's, then one of theirs would make do to fill the empty sack! Once Prince Zeeb's head had been secured, his chosen band of men were to wait on the west bank of the Jordan for the main force. When there, they were told to prepare for any scattered gangs of Midianite stragglers in a desperate flight to the fording place of the Jordan.

Meanwhile, Prince Zeeb pushed and prodded his camel, wounded, and on the verge of collapse, up the steep rise of an abandoned hillside vineyard. The camel spitted and sputtered and dropped down to his knees from the loss of blood and sheer exhaustion. The huge bull camel, named Amir, was sturdy and determined. He had been raised by the prince from a suckling calf; there was a strong bond between beast and master. Prince

Zeeb was now on foot. Even his camel had left him, giving the prince its last breath in his service. And now he was all alone. He had managed to travel eighteen miles from the battlefield over uneven ground. The prince now searched for a place to hide. He knew he would have to evade an almost-certain Hebrew search party, and he desperately needed a lungful of rest. He had no place to ease his fatigue. He was well aware that the predator had become the prey. His instincts were overridden by exhaustion. He felt desperate; morbid reflection dogged his every step.

With the last gasp of his fading strength, Prince Zeeb found protection from the elements. Providence had unearthed the shelter of a free-standing winepress, and within, an empty wine vat that had not seen service for many long years. It was dark and dry and held the promise of a perfect, secret hideaway. Who would think to look inside a wine vat? This was a ready-made cocoon. It was of ample size, allowing the prince to stretch out his weary bones and rest his head.

The tracking wolves made short work of scouting out Zeeb's hiding place. His snuffed-out camel still had the gold emblem of royalty around its neck. This clue assured Captain Omar of Zeeb's whereabouts. The captain could taste the sweet elixir of capture. His quarry was within reach. The wolves would have sniffed him out in a cavern or a crevice, no matter how dark or forsaken, and so they had! It was in the dim twilight that the prince lay down and tried to put to rest his exhaustion. The winepress appeared deserted at first, for the dust looked undisturbed as the wolves circled the water-tight wine vat containing the vintage of Zeeb. The years of fat-filled grapes had stained the wood red and masked the stench of human sweat. The deepening dark could serve up only the old ghosts of vanishing outlines.

"There is nothing here!" Omar shouted. He was the last one to leave when he was met with a sneeze uncaught. A speck of dust, the tickle of a seed grape allergy, amplified in the hollow of the wine vat, sealing Prince Zeeb's death warrant. The prince was quickly uncovered. Just as suddenly as he had given vent to his sneeze, so had the safety of his cocoon become his shrouded coffin. Zeeb was hoisted abruptly up and over the rim. He was forced to his knees, a position of humiliation for a general and a prince of Midian. Prince Zeeb was still groggy from his sleep of exhaustion. Two fierce warriors held his arms straight out on either side, to the right and to the left. The stout-armed executioner held high a single-edged blade, holding it ready for the head of Zeeb as he waited patiently. The executioner remained alert, watching for the nod of follow-through from Captain Omar.

Prince Zeeb, reckoning that his doom would be quick, almost felt relief. He was tired of running in purposeless circles. Torches were lit. Naked sparks cast ominous shadows, challenging the gloom of Zeeb's soon-to-be-permanent crypt. Captain Omar spoke into the silence. "Prince Zeeb, it appears the fangs of the wolf have permanently been blunted. Before we dispatch you to the netherworld, do you have anything you need to get off your chest? Apart from your head, of course?" he added with an upturned smirk in a feeble attempt at a grim jest at the prince's expense. Prince Zeeb opened his mouth in a shaky bid at redemption. At that moment, Omar nodded, and the executioner's blade arced down heavily, finding its mark. Zeeb's words forever caught in his throat, and his look of shock and disbelief became permanently etched on his face and mouth of his once remarkably elegant profile. As soon as the prince's severed head stopped rolling around, Omar snatched it up by his thick black hair, still dripping with blood and gore, and callously announced, "To commemorate this heady victory," with a smirk and a wink, "I will name this place, the Wine Vat of Zeeb."

Just as Gideon had hidden in a winepress to secure food and life for Ophrah from the theft of the marauding Midianite horde, so had Zeeb concealed himself in a winepress to shelter his own life from Israel. Zeeb's head was placed into the leather pouch specially designed for this trophy of war. General Zev considered it a confirmation of proof that Ephraim was Israel's absolute military scourge. Ephraim would not long endure Gideon's insult to their pride for excluding them from an invitation to war.

This slight, Zev brooded, was compounded by an unlearned farmer taking liberty with the birthright of Manasseh to assume command of Israel's army. Gideon would be held to account for this intolerable insult. General Zev was well-pleased with the trophy of Zeeb's severed head. He was greatly amused to hear of the indignity with which the prince was dispatched so unceremoniously—hiding in a wine vat. General Zev continued to pursue the remnants of the Midianite horde.

The remaining fragment of the once-mighty Midianite horde was as flimsy as a reed striking at the cedars of Lebanon. The yoke of Israel's burden had been broken. The staff of Midian's might was shattered, and the rod of their oppression had been lifted. Israel had found relief once more, through the Lord God's patient and tender mercies and to the ill-conceived slight to the pride of Ephraim.

CHAPTER 18

Bitter Is the Crust of Scorn

The vegetation in the wilderness was stripped, for the Midianites had lain the fields bare. Now the lack of supplies caused stomachs to grumble and mouths to gripe. Ephraim could easily resupply, especially with the fording place only a few days' trudge back west to their tribe's borders and bounty. But for now, General Zev felt the tribe of Ephraim's primary need was to restore their honor. The conquering tribe was now intent on testing Gideon, taunting him with ridicule that he might do or say something foolish, causing a grave or even a bloody retaliation. Gideon would be made sorely acquainted with Ephraim's great victory as witnessed by the display of ghastly trophies at the crossover shallows.

Gideon was in hot pursuit of the twin kings of Midian, Zebah and Zalmunna, but in spite of Gideon's best efforts, his three hundred warriors were not able to match the swift gait of Midian's camels. The kings' train of fifteen thousand men-at-arms was but a remnant of the once-mighty horde, yet they remained fearsome and formidable.

The Ishmaelites provided the inner circle of protection to the kings. They had sworn an oath to defend and to protect the Midianite royalty. A shekel's weight of pure Egyptian gold adorned each Ishmaelite bodyguard's ear in an unbroken circle, a token symbolizing their undying devotion and their pledge of faithfulness, even to the extent of sacrificing their own lives. These were the inner guard, the most fierce and loyal of all the kings' bodyguards.

The Midianite kings were the sworn enemies of Israel and had been ever since their first encounter at the Battle of Mount Tabor. They witnessed firsthand the ever-growing might of the wandering vagabonds who had escaped Egyptian rule. Israel was, after all, an uninvited and unwelcome visitor who, by force or by stealth, insisted on making a place for themselves. Now they had become an ever-increasing problem on the ancestral lands of the Midianites, Amalekites, Canaanites, and all the children of the East. The land of their birthright from the beginning of time was being stolen by the fertile increase and multiplication of the children called "Israel."

The two prince generals, Oreb, and Zeeb, were dead; the next generation of Midian royalty had been "crushed." At that point, Midian had agreed upon a standing tactic. If ever there was a threat to the entire body, the horde would split up into corps and companies. Separating and following different directions would ensure the ultimate survival of the Midian Empire—permitting them to meet again at the impregnable stronghold of Karkor by following the wilderness caravan trail of the Jogbehah. There they would be refreshed from their exhaustion, taking the opportunity to revive their war-torn bodies with much-needed rest and recuperation. It would also allow them to regroup and replace their recent dead. They would have time to plan for their future, working out how to guard against any further setbacks, attacks, and surprises.

Gideon's three hundred fearless warriors were steadfast in their resolve. Phurah, his faithful manservant, was determined to balance old accounts. Gideon's young son, Jether, stayed close to his father's side to learn the responsibility a firstborn son is obliged to acquire. The weighty mantle of leadership would one day be his prize. Jether was present at all the training. He had also participated in that fateful night of battle in which sound and terror had vanquished Israel's foe, yet his blade remained untested.

Gideon's three hundred gave their all, marching at a double-quick pace to overtake the kings before they reached the shallow river crossing. Gideon's plan was to hound his Midian prey to Beth Barah, where the army of Ephraim, only a few leagues west of the fording place, would be lying in wait. Gideon had counted on his message being delivered. He was unaware that the Battle of Beth Shan had taken place. Neither was Gideon aware that his failure to invite Ephraim to fight Midian had produced in them an imagined slight. Ephraim's forced march to settle the score over this dreamt-up insult was unknown to Gideon as he marched his three hundred chosen men in pursuit of the twin kings of Midian, Zebah and Zalmunna.

Gideon's small force, using all the speed they could muster, had reached Beth-barah. Their pursuit of Midian was intense. They marched without pause, refusing to slacken their pace. Their now-distant quarry was many days away, confirmed with the hard and dry camel droppings that Gideon's men began to use for fuel to ward off the desert chill. The warmth of the flames reflected the fiery zeal that burned within their hunters' hearts.

The twin kings and their entire company had easily forded the shallows and now paced leisurely east to the far side of the Jordan. The kings were headed into a desolate wilderness. A difficult route lay before them, a merchant's trail, used only by well-provisioned caravans of camels. The kings' saddles became thrones, for there was an open road to Karkor, which promised security and the safety afforded by the stronghold of home.

Gideon now had to admit that his message to Ephraim had not been received and that he, his son Jether, and the three hundred were left on their own and unaided campaign. Gideon had counted on the sorely needed provision of life-sustaining rations. Belts were tightened to quiet the growls of empty bellies. Perhaps this was a right time and place to catch a breath, as well as some fish. This momentary pause from war gave them the opportunity to gather their strength and think about how to continue pursuing their quarry without losing themselves to starvation.

Just then, as Gideon grew cold from a momentary shiver, induced by an empty belly and a short-lived depression, a blast from a distant shofar alerted the company to an approaching army. The army of Ephraim had been sighted and would soon be upon them. Ephraim's army had marched south along the west side of the Jordan. They would confront Gideon and the three hundred in less than an hour.

General Zev and his cadre of wolves led the battle-weary, hungry, but victorious host of heroes. They carried the disembodied heads of the princes of Midian, Zeeb, and Oreb, in their specially prepared fur-trimmed pouches. These trophies of war both confirmed and announced Ephraim's overwhelming and decisive defeat of the Midianite horde at Beth Shan. Ephraim's arrival smacked of divine intervention, for the timing could have been sooner, but not any later.

General Zev and the men of Ephraim had traveled several leagues out of their course to confront Gideon with a stern tongue lashing against his over-blown offense to the pride of Ephraim. They, too, were in need of a resupply of barley bread, meat, and some needed rest. The army of Ephraim, with General Zev at its head, had tracked the fleeing remnants of the once-countless horde. The west bank had been scoured until every surviving Midianite had been broken, had fled, or had been left for dead. They found only small bands of token resistance. They mopped up the last bites and snarls from the Battle of Beth Shan, but the pressure of men engaged in the conflict had driven all the available game to ground. Ephraim, like Gideon, was faint from hunger.

The men of Ephraim were now close enough to make their anger known. They had the advantage of being able to quickly depart, heading for their nearby home and much-needed provisions. Their stocks, too, had been used up. For days, they had been marching solely on vengeance and were unable to render aid or assistance to Gideon. They were only there to voice their displeasure and to express to Gideon how his scornful neglect to invite them to war had caused their loss of face. The lack of an invitation to the first encounter—readily afforded to the small tribes—required a pay-back. They would let Gideon know in no uncertain terms about what consequence he could expect from his tactless blunder.

The men of Ephraim approached Gideon, and a subordinate named Sheeran addressed him: "Why have you served us thus, that you called us not when you went to fight with the Midianites?" The man's tone was clipped and insistent.

General Zev picked up from where his captain trailed off. "When word came to my ears that a lowly, unlearned plowman from the tribe of Manasseh was going to lead an army of farmers, we made all necessary haste to join the fray," the general explained. "I, Zev, an experienced expert, schooled in the military arts, with my cadre of wolves and an army of combat-hardened veterans, made haste, so I could oversee the strategy outlining our victory. I made all due speed to ensure that Ephraim would partake in our share of the spoil and the glory in the service of Israel. Ephraim journeyed with all possible dispatch. We flew to the valley of Jezreel," he continued, "when word arrived to gather the tribes of Naphtali, Manasseh, Zebulun, Asher, and the thirty-one thousand and seven hundred men at arms who you, Gideon, dismissed. This was made known by gossip, later confirmed by a messenger."

Warming to his speech, General Zev curled his lip. "Our haste to Jezreel has rubbed us raw and taken us in a heated rush of anger. With every step, we chafed to outwit and outrun your insult of rejection. Ephraim would have stood fixed and firm, from the very first trumpet call to the last tumble of Midianite camels. Our delay came at the cost of your neglect, for you did not send us a timely invitation to battle. We arrived just in time to organize and deploy those tribes of Israel that were gathered to finish what you had started, but that you had left behind in your dogged pursuit of kings."

Gideon: The Sound and the Glory

General Zev now recounted his victory at Beth Shan to enlighten Gideon concerning Ephraim's role in the war. He included in his recounting the attack of his wolves, the long sticks of jute and loops, the tracking down of the princes, Oreb and Zeeb, and their headless torsos rotting in far-flung places.

The general took singular pride and pleasure in retelling the story of Zeeb—his hiding in the winepress, his fateful sneeze, and the unspoken words forever to be caught on the lips of his gaping mouth. Then, with an expression of glee, he summarily produced both heads from the shielding of their respective pouches for Gideon's immediate inspection. "Here, see for yourself," Zev offered, lifting the heads for Gideon's inspection. "Confirm that these are what remains of Midian's royal dead. Confirm this now for all of the Israel." Swollen with pride, Zev finished his bluster with one final sentence. "This capture leaves no doubt as to the military prowess and genius of Ephraim! Meaning, of course, myself."

Gideon, faint from his forced fast, enlarged by his genuine spirit of humility, allowed himself to respond with a show of modesty. His voice gentle, he spoke his reply. "What have I done now in comparison with you? Is not the charity gleaning of the grapes of Ephraim superior to the best vintage produced by Abiezer?" The message evident in Gideon's words was that even Ephraim's smallest victory is greater than Manasseh's and all the best efforts of the Abiezrite attempts at combat success.

Gideon needed to pacify and bolster the esteem of Ephraim. He played down his role at Jezreel and continued speaking. "I had but frightened the Midianite horde with childish ploys, using deafening sounds of war, the camouflage of flickering lamps, and a loud chant. God led us to victory! It was God Who directed me to all things righteous. I was to keep our numbers to but a few, so there would be no uncertainty that God had the leading role. My blade, as of yet, has never known the taste of flesh, nor has it been stained red by our enemy's blood. We are simple farmers, unskilled in war, but now we fight as soldiers. We cannot compare ourselves to you, with your great and brilliant strategy and your resounding victory at Beth Shan. You demonstrated this by gathering the heads of the Midianite princes, Oreb and Zeeb."

Gideon's humility had found its mark. It softened General Zev's heart and cooled the heated emotion of Ephraim's soldiers. It doused the hot flames of their fury and soothed the dagger wounds to their pride. As he talked, their anger toward him lessened, at least for the present. Gideon struck a peaceable accord to ensure a final victory—he knew he would have to charm Ephraim to join forces. Gideon made his offer of alliance in a sincere plea for Ephraim's assistance.

"Come, and join with me now, for we are brothers in Israel, bent on destroying our common enemy, the twin kings of Midian, Zebah and Zalmunna. Together, they have the resolve of their combined will and enough gold to cause us further hardship. You must concede that the head of the viper has two deadly fangs, placed now at a distance, but waiting and plotting to strike at our very heart. They could easily reemerge to take their revenge upon us for the beheading of their two princes. They require only enough time to reorganize, so they may, once again, become a deadly threat. They have enough gold in Midian to purchase an army of trained and vicious mercenaries to do their dirty work. If we allow this pause in the action and forego the chase, our advantage will be vented in a release of pressure that will give the kings time to rearm. All that we have achieved will be a hill of winding-sheets and a yard of burial mounds. General Zev, your army of Ephraim and my three hundred will make short work of the remaining horde. We will finish with glory and know a greater spoil!"

General Zev listened with real interest to Gideon's petition. Gideon expressed a daring passion for the undertaking, and General Zev saw merit in the enterprise. Ephraim established among themselves all that they had heard before General Zev gave his reply. "We have exhausted our supplies. We have not a morsel of food, neither for you nor ourselves. Our stomachs echo in growls of discontent. These many days there has been no game because of the heavy traffic of Midian's flight and our pursuit. Our army grows weary, and our warriors grow faint from hunger. We are, however, close to Ephraim's border, our home. Join us," the general offered, an awkward attempt at friendliness, "for we can give you a breather from war and a place of safety to recuperate before you pursue the kings into the barren desert. Without food, you will suffer hunger and death."

The general, seeing the steely resolve of refusal in Gideon's eyes, suddenly hardened his tone, and his words took on a menacing ring of warning. "We have nothing to give you, not even a crust of barley bread to sustain you. If you insist on this reckless adventure, continuing into the wilderness unaided, you, Gideon, your son, your manservant, and your three hundred men will die with absolute certainty and without a shadow of a doubt! You will fail. You will be a feast for worms and a portion for vultures; we will march over your bleached bones in the wasteland of the Jogbehah."

Gideon stood toe to toe with General Zev, and, with all of the Ephraim listening, gave his reply. "I will continue on, even if it means going it alone, for the God of Israel goes before me. And so, for righteousness's sake, I will put it to a vote because it is given to every man the choice of bread or faith." The three hundred, Jether, and Phurah, were gathered there and overheard all that had been thrashed out between Gideon and Zev.

Ben, a captain of one hundred, was familiar with the territory about to be explored. He whispered in Gideon's ear that the trek along the Jabbok River had two way-stations, where they would find aid: at Succoth and Penuel, both towns of Israel, they would be sure to find help and the relief of bread. The placement of these two cities along the Jabbok River suggested a grand design and seemed to Gideon righteous confirmation that his path was preordained. Gideon had heard of both cities, spoken of in the legends of Israel; he had heard these names in the songs sung to him as a little child.

Succoth was the place that Jacob, who had become Israel, had once called home. And Penuel was the very place Jacob had wrestled an angel of God, prevailing against man and finding favor with God. It resonated strongly with Gideon that Jacob had seen the face of God and lived, and that Gideon had had the same experience when he saw the face of an angel, and he, too, had survived. Jacob had built a monument there and called the place Penuel. Gideon grasped that he was retracing the footsteps of Jacob, and in the silence of his thoughts, his faith was made perfect. He knew he was on a mission ordained by God, and God always makes a way for those who seek after Him.

Gideon turned to the three hundred and asked, "What is your agreement, you mighty men of Israel? Do you go with me into the uncertain wilderness of faith or the promise of ease and comfort from the vintage of Ephraim?" To a man, each raised his right hand to the square, and as if with one voice chanted, "The sword of the Lord and of Gideon!" *Kherev l'Adonai u-l'Gid'on!*

CHAPTER 19

A Pursuit by Faith and Not by Bread (Succoth)

Gideon and the three hundred came to the Jordan and passed over. Although they were faint, they pursued. Once the decision was made to proceed on faith alone, the pangs of hunger seemed to fade. Hunger no longer had the power to dominate every waking thought. The three hundred were now all of one mind, one goal, and with one absolute leader. As God's chosen soldiers, they had accepted what they had perceived to be God's eternal purpose and confirmed that they would endure whatever their mission demanded. Now was the time to participate in a divine fast, focused solely on the task at hand. The esprit de corps and morale of the three hundred was of the highest caliber—their loving God had provided them with fire, water, and the strength of endurance—due to the conviction that they had been foreordained to be his avenging warriors.

The nights were frigid, and the cold sent chills to the bone, but the days were sweltering hot. They sweated continually, and their toes blistered as they chafed inside their gritty sandals. They wrestled with the ravages of the physical only to be sustained by the spiritual. Their only relief came from the babbling sounds of the fast-moving Jordan River; they went against its flow in a northerly direction to the southern branch of the Jabbok tributary. Gideon and his men turned east to the oasis town of Succoth. There they hoped to find relief from the menace of famine. They had not a moment to waste or a drop of energy to spare. Silence gave rhythm to the swiftness of their stride; no strength was squandered on the idle chat of complaint.

Suddenly, a haven of salvation appeared as if from out of the ground. Around a blind curve—a bend in the River Jabbok—was the town of Succoth, set against a blazing red horizon. Succoth was viewed just over the top of a hill, packed tight with massive boulders.

Gideon taught his son, Jether, a stripling youth of fourteen years, the history and the significance of the town named Succoth: "It commemorates the temporary palm-thatched shelters used by the children of Israel in their endless trek across the desert. It restores to our remembrance that we are all short-lived guests of God here in the wilderness of life. There was a commandment to always entertain strangers, for some have entertained angels unawares. Our ancient father, Jacob, also settled there. He received the new name of 'Israel,' made manifest to him by an angel of God."

The town's generosity was all but assured! Spirits soared as mouths salivated with anticipation, and empty bellies rubbed up against the stern backbone of a just cause. The siren's beckoning call to duty and loyalty kept their character tightly bound to their honor, but the specter of famine would strain the strongest resolve. Eyes widened in the eagerness of breaking the forced fast. They made haste to the main gate. There was not a moment to lose to gain the manna of grace, the sweet taste of that first bite, and the savor of a long-awaited morsel followed by a course of larger helpings.

Gideon, with an ashen-faced Jether at his side, was seen by the princes and elders as a desperate plea to sustain life and limb. Gideon, in his hour of greatest need, asked to speak to the Council of Elders. He said unto the men of Succoth, "Give, I pray you, loaves of bread unto the people that follow me, for they are faint. I am pursuing after Zebah and Zalmunna, kings of Midian."

The princes of Succoth conferred together about this uninvited guest's request. He had boldly placed himself and his band of soldiers to lean upon Succoth's generosity for a beggar's feast—only enough bread to keep body and soul together, for without food and drink, these uninvited vagabonds would certainly perish.

The princes' deliberations were short lived; their agreement to a man was harsh and self-serving. What they peddled was the same as a death sentence. "The kings have always dealt with us fairly, and they have not trampled upon our sovereignty, as we both have benefited as trading partners," the princes and elders of Succoth reasoned among themselves. "Gideon's enemies are our friends, who might very well call down the fury of their wrath upon us; we could suffer a bloodbath if they were given to revenge. And what is the likelihood that this small handful of Israelite men, who, by their own admission, are led by a farmer, could possibly prevail against the might of the Midianites? No, brethren, if we concede to their demands, we will certainly be played for the fool on the day of reckoning." Addressing Gideon, a prince of

Succoth asked, "Are Zebah and Zalmunna now in your hand?"
Gideon's heart tripped into a double rhythm as he realized what
the prince actually meant. The young prince continued. "For if
you had overcome and been victorious and had the twin kings
in hand, we would be glad to empty our storehouse in a feast of
plenty." Gideon's jaw clenched tight, but he had the presence of
mind to let the prince finish speaking. "You are a small band of
weary and faint soldiers. Even by a great stretch of the imagination, you cannot overpower the horde and all the children of the
East. We see this as a wild fantasy and a high-flying dream." Now
the prince curled his lip, presenting to Gideon the scorn behind
his words. "Because your small band will not, in all likelihood,
capture the kings, we dare not offer you even a crust of bread,
and we say, to one and all, depart!"

Gideon's reply was unflappable and measured. "I dare not,
and will not, with a hostile force of arms, insist on taking that
which is not mine. My army's strength cannot be squandered
or used up.

"It is a must that our hands remain clean and not be soiled
with the blood of the unjust. We choose to endure without fault
or sin; we will not be stained with your blood until we have run
down our quarry, who has dealt cruelly with Israel. Our hands are
to be used only in the service of our God, who is our Lord and
our King. We are in His service and will bring to conclusion His
pursuit, for He has promised us complete and total victory. Of
this, you will be made painfully aware, as you gasp in agony for
the breath of life, and as plainly as I now stand before your eyes."

Gideon took a step forward, his eyes now only two inches
from the young prince's, who had to tilt his head back and raise

his face to keep holding Gideon's eyes. "Therefore," growled Gideon in a menacing rumble, "when the Lord has delivered Zebah and Zalmunna into my hand, then I will tear your flesh with the thorns of the wilderness and with sharp briers." These words hung in the air long after the company had vanished, leaving only the prophecy of a menacing curse in the castoff dirt from dust and sandals.

CHAPTER 20

The Face of God and Angels (Penuel)

A dark cloud settled over Gideon's army of three hundred. Wrath filled the void of empty bellies. The poisonous dregs of expectations were regretfully digested; their much-needed relief from a meager meal of bread had vanished into a slow death sentence. Jether took the forced fast the hardest. The hostility of his dashed hopes spilled into brooding bitterness—he was still a youth, and he had not yet mastered the discipline of patience. The black curtain of night unfurled the chill of empty and shrunken Stomachs, in keeping with the vast and barren wasteland that lay before them.

To comfort Jether's hunger-pangs and to soothe his band of three hundred starving men, as they lay down their weary heads and shrinking vests, Gideon spoke of Israel's ancient legends. He was talking about Jacob, son of Isaac, now called Israel. Gideon told them about the personal experience Jacob had that led to his name being changed to Israel—an involvement with which Gideon was partially familiar. He had looked upon an angel of the Lord face to face and had lived, and thankfully he had also been spared the wrestling match that Jacob had been forced to endure. Jether's eyes shone with admiration. Gideon told how Jacob's experience related to Penuel—the next oasis and their last hope of reprieve from starvation before they reached the horde on Karkor. For Jacob said, "I have seen the face of God and lived." And he called the place Penuel, and he explained the history behind the city's high tower—the pride of its citizens. The Tower was a monument to the exact spot where Jacob had prevailed against man and found favor with God—and where he had received his new name, Israel. Gideon and the three hundred waxed solid in their confidence that the relief they sought would be forthcoming in that holy place. The anticipated savor of breaking bread gave them faith in the hope of tomorrow's bounty.

Gideon recounted Jacob's story in detail for the benefit of Jether and for all of his men, to bring them relief from the gnawing desperation of their circumstances. Gideon sat at the fire, adding camel patties to the small flame as he spoke. Jether and the soldiers lay back, looking at the bright stars, warm and comfortable. Listening to the voice of God's chosen leader, their hunger pangs lessened, and they felt safe, like children held in the embrace of bedtime stories. The fresh wood hissed and crackled as it took flame, and Gideon's deep baritone soothed the hearts of his anxious listeners.

"Jacob was in deadly fear because he, by deception and guile, had stolen his older brother Esau's birthright. With a winding train of camels in a caravan, all laden with precious gems and fine, handmade goods, Jacob was on a journey of reunion. Driving before him flocks and herds of livestock to add to the gifts borne on the caravan of reconciliation. Jacob hoped to soften his brother's fierce anger and ask for the salve of forgiveness." Jether loved this story. He felt himself smile; his hunger was forgotten. "Esau lived by the law of the sword," Gideon continued, pleased at seeing his son's smile. "Jacob wanted to avoid his brother's wrath and mend broken fences. Knowing that his brother, Esau, was advancing toward him with his own group of servants in tow, Jacob grew fearful as he drew closer to this uncertain reception. He feared his brother's wrath, convinced that Esau was seeking righteous vengeance, now long denied these many years.

"Jacob lagged ever further behind the caravan, finally catching up with his family and servants at the Jabbok River. He was paralyzed with fear and decided to rest his weary head on this side of the Jabbok before crossing over in the light of day. But in the dead of night, he rose up and helped his family and servants across the river before turning back to his camp, now desolate. Standing beneath the stars, all alone, a man approached Jacob, and they began to wrestle. They did not cease wrestling until the break of day. When the man saw that he prevailed not against Jacob, he touched the hollow of his thigh. The hollow of Jacob's thigh was put out of joint, yet they still wrestled together. The hollow of the thigh is where oaths are set apart and have the strength of a covenant. It is the place closest to your seed. Thus as a result, when you swear to a man with your hand under his thigh, you swear by your ancestors, and also by your future posterity. And so, with the powers of heaven, the man blessed the seed of Jacob. That blessing carries through to this very day—and to all the children of Israel, forever!

"The man said, 'Let me go, for the day breaks.'

Jacob said, 'I will not let you go, except you bless me.'

The man asked, 'What is your name?'

He answered, 'Jacob.'

The man said, 'Your name shall no longer be called Jacob, but Israel, for, as a prince, you have power with God and with men, and you have prevailed.'

Jacob asked him, 'Tell me, I pray, your name.'

Wherefore is it that you ask my name? For it is the new name, and I am forbidden to repeat it. It is set apart, and only to be uttered in a certain place and time.'

The man blessed Jacob there.

Jacob called the place Penuel and said, 'I have seen God face to face, and my life is preserved.' Jacob passed over Penuel. The sun rose upon him, and he forever halted upon his thigh. For he who limps is still walking. And so it was with Jacob,"

Gideon reached for another dried camel chip, stirring it into the dying embers of twigs and sticks. His men breathed peacefully as they lay beneath the broad black canopy of sky, studded with shooting stars. None slept, but neither did they think of their gnawing hunger. An old log had washed up on the river's bank and was gratefully accepted as a gift from God. It immediately ignited and started spitting sparks into a now roaring-fire. Gideon rolled on with a colorful tale, this time relating to them his own failings as a man.

《 《 《 》 》 》

"I had lived my entire life as a slave with doubt and fear. I was also the least regarded in my father's house . . . until I, too, had an encounter with an angel at the winepress; prearranged by the God of our forefathers—Abraham, Isaac, and Jacob. The Lord said unto me, 'Surely I will be with you, and you shall smite the Midianites as one man.' When I, Gideon, perceived that he was an angel of the Lord, I said, 'Alas, O Lord God! I have seen an angel of the Lord face to face!' And the Lord said unto me, 'Peace be unto thee. Fear not. Thou shall not die.'"

Gideon sat for a short while, looking to the heavens. He thanked God for saving him from the worship of a foreign god; one who had no substance or strength enough to challenge Gideon, who had become Jerubbaal. He who had contended with Baal and prevailed; for Baal had been unable to plead against him, even though he had thrown down his altar. Gideon, content, laid down his head and all had slipped away, satisfied, without bread, yet filled, having a clear conscience only known to the righteous.

«« «« «« »» »»

All slept well and deeply, for they were filled with the knowledge of God. They awoke refreshed and renewed. His powerful word had lessened their bedeviling hunger pangs because they all knew God would not let them die. "The Lord is our portion," said their souls, "therefore, we will hope in Him. We are renewed every morning. Great is thy faithfulness."

Restless discontent had been replaced with the vision of a lavish banquet. Within a few days' march, they would see the gleaming tower of hope, which was the city of Penuel. By all that was holy, how could the people of Penuel not assist the army of righteousness with sufficient bread to carry on the Lord's fight for the redemption of Israel? The Tower first came into view, a sinister structure, casting a dark shadow over the landscape. Gideon and the faint company crossed over the Jabbok to the exact spot where Jacob had wrestled the angel. The sun was rising to their right as they crossed the Jabbock. The dawn's first light was dimmed by the Tower's dark shadow. Gideon and the three hundred made their way to the locked town gate, met by armed guards offering a warning—as to the grim consequences meted out to unwelcome intruders.

"We do not take kindly to armed prowlers!" they warned.

Gideon calmly told the guards he wanted to speak to the elders and princes of the town. In turn, he explained to them there would be grave consequences for those who turned him down in his hour of greatest need. The guards summoned the princes and elders of Penuel. They stood at the locked gate, frowning at Gideon and his men with open hostility. Calling up strength from a well deep within, Gideon spoke politely and with patience.

"We are the army of God. We are searching out the remainder of the horde of Midian for their destruction. We seek to take the heads of the serpent—those twin Midian kings, Zebah and Zalmunna. But first, we have an urgent request for bread. The last time we ate a morsel escapes my memory, but it has been many days. We seek your generosity since we fight a common foe. Lacking bread, we may well perish in this barren wilderness. Succoth, your nearest neighbor to the west, summarily turned down our petition for provisions. For their lack of hospitality to my men, on a mission from our Almighty God, they will feel the sting of my anger upon the completion of our mission. The kings of Midian will be in our possession and under our control when we return. All we ask of you is bread, each man his portion, in the need to sustain body and soul."

The elders debated, conferred, and mulled over Gideon's petition, weighing all their options in the careful discussion. Finally, one respected elder bluntly stated what seemed painfully obvious to all. "How can this small force of little or no consequence, ill-equipped, and on the edge of starvation, possibly defeat the might of Midian's horde and capture the twin kings? It is a ridiculous quest and surely impossible! In their aid, we would proclaim our contempt for a neighbor with whom we have traded over these many years—very successfully, I might add. Not only would we put an end to our friendship with these desert neighbors, but we would be recognized as their enemy. We would surely have to endure their vengeful wrath, and it would put an end to our long-term and profitable association. It could very well spell doom for our town and the pride that is our Tower: Penuel."

The elders, showing a united front, addressed Gideon, their spokesman delivering their message in a brisk curt tone. "No aid will be given to you! Had you already these kings in your hand, we would gladly have opened the storehouse to offer you a feast of plenty. As it stands, all we see is a desperate man with no chance of success. Depart and leave us in our peace. May God go with you."

Beside himself with rage, Gideon clutched at the hilt of his sword. Driven instinctively to lash out at those who had denied a righteous cause, he fought down the urge; grateful for the locked gate between himself and his self-righteous, self-serving enemy. His cause seemed hopeless to the natural eye. He and his men were turned away from the city gate, to be a feast for vultures. Penuel was the last town before reaching the stronghold of Karkor. They would have to face their enemy without nourishment; they would have to be sustained only by God's grace. Gideon restrained himself. Using every ounce of his self-control, he said, "I will not obtain by force what is not mine. My men will not be wasted in such futility. We will save our strength for Midian. Rest assured that our hands will not be soiled by the stain of your blood. Our might is directed by God to better use in the destruction of the Midianite Empire."

Lifting his hand from the hilt of his sword, Gideon spoke a final word of warning to the elders and princes of Penuel. "When I return to this gate, I will break it open, and then I will pull down this Tower. No stone will rest upon another. Your prized and lofty Tower, symbolic of Jacob's encounter with an angel, will be wrestled to the ground. You speak of God with your lips, but your hearts are far from Him. The Lord God of Israel has no part in your edifice, for He would write a new message in the fleshy parts of your heart. You have turned this sacred place into a place to raise your vanity to the sky. You and your Tower of Babel will be a table for jackals and foxes."

Once again, and now for the third time, Gideon and the three hundred departed empty-handed, faint, and starving. As they left the gate of Penuel behind them, there could be no doubt that they were held tightly by the mighty hand of the Lord God of Israel. They went forth solely by faith—having not been given the needed bread of physical nourishment—for no food from man's hand had been forthcoming.

CHAPTER 21

Secure Holds with Back Doors

The journey to Karkor was a climb to higher ground; drier, and rougher. They were reluctant to leave the ready supply of sweet water. The only comfort they had known was the swift-moving River Jabbok. Gideon turned his men north and east to the mountain stronghold of Karkor. Gideon instructed, "Secure your oil-filled lamps in your hip pouch. Remove them from your pitchers, and fill these clay pots to the rim with water. Drink up; fill your bellies to the top like a camel's hump. Where we go, there will be none. The self-control of an occasional sip will be just as important as the cooling relief from the scarcity of shadows, for there will be no pardon in the noonday sun in this high and dry desert country. The dust will choke your throats, and the parchedness will blister lips."

Gideon and the three hundred were sustained only by the grace of faith. The army of God acted as if it were impossible to fail. Their morale remained supernatural. They even joked about the glory of spoil and the reckoning of Succoth and Penuel, as if the scales of justice had already been weighed in the balance. Jether was now made of sterner stuff, having been through this experience, but the lad halted at times and struggled with the extreme hardship. It was not seemly for the son of Gideon to falter, and he managed by his frail force of will to keep up his spirits and remain steadfast.

Gideon went up by the way of them that dwelt in tents on the east of Nobah and Jogbehah. It was a desolate route, frequented mainly by camel caravans and bandits. An exhausting trek under the best of conditions—even when stocked with provisions of bread, meat, and water. For a band of starving soldiers, it would be approaching the impossible, except for the favor of God and the sheer determination of courageous men.

Zebah and Zalmunna and their host of about fifteen thousand men were all that were left of the children of the East. A hundred and twenty thousand who drew the sword had fallen or had fled.

Gideon and the three hundred approached Karkor from the blind side at the foot of the desert floor, because the stronghold was secure. A kettle of vultures, circling in flight, marked the spot where a bronze-skinned youth had been stripped half-naked. He was staked out on the ground with his hands and legs tightly bound. He would surely have died had Gideon not happened along. He would have been ravaged by the sun, stung by poisonous scorpions, or eaten by wild beasts on the prowl. Left to the mercy of the desert, the young lad was as good as dead. Skeletons were piled high, bleached from the heat and picked clean of meat. Skulls with empty eye sockets littered the landscape. This was a place of execution.

"Cut the cords that bind the lad," Gideon commanded.

"I have only a mouthful of water. Dampen your lips, and sip it slowly before speaking," Gideon suggested gently to the young lad. "Who are you?" he asked. "Why have you been condemned to death?"

"My name is Abdul," the youngster whispered in a scratchy, feeble croak.

"Take another sip to wet your lips and soothe your parched throat." The boy did as he was told. Gideon asked again, "Why have you been sentenced to death?"

"The kings, upon their return, were cross and ill-tempered, as if something had gone terribly wrong. They noticed, at once, that I had left the locker to the meats and bread unprotected and the door wide open. I was about the camp, watering the camels, and I fell asleep in the noonday heat—so their wrath was twofold. Public execution, the usual punishment for any rebellion—no matter how small—is to be cast off that peak high above our heads," he told Gideon; pointing up to the sheer cliff precipice. "Since I was caught asleep," he continued, "I was not to enjoy a swift and merciful end. The kings commanded that I lie out in the dust to endure a longer punishment. Knowing the strength of my youth would allow me to survive a considerable length of time, I would suffer long before I would succumb to the stinging and gnawing of desert creatures . . . or from the relentless heat of the day or by the numbing cold of the night. My suffering would be a warning to all those who would put sleep ahead of their duty to serve the kings and the horde of Midian." Regaining his strength, Abdul asked Gideon, "How did you find me here in this wasteland? You are not of the horde or any of the sons of the East."

"We were attracted by the sight of circling vultures," Gideon explained. "They have flown off now, for they see there is no dying creature here; only a young man restored to the living." The lad smiled up at his savior. "My name is Gideon," he told the young man. "We are from Israel," he added, "here to kill the kings and destroy what remains of the horde."

"But, sir," Abdul questioned, "they are about fifteen thousand men with swords, scimitars, axes, and spears. You are but a few. How will you accomplish this miracle?"

Gideon, with the confidence and boldness of faith made perfect, said, "The Lord God of Israel goes before us. He shall find a way or make one."

"You have saved my life, and now you own it. Command me!" A fire lit Abdul's eyes, kindled by the chilling possibility in the settling of scores. "Your enemy is now my enemy. I can show you a secret passage to the very top. No guards are ever posted there, for it is an abyss, and is, in actual fact, impossible to gain access. Come with me!" Abdul beckoned.

He had been half-dead from the heat, but now he was alive; revived at the chilling prospect of sweet revenge. "Gideon, I will show you the secret passage that I recently became aware of. It was by accident that I had stumbled upon it. I will show you how to climb to the very top and gain entrance to the stronghold without anyone's knowledge. No challenge will meet us. We will not be observed or even noticed. The only ones who come out to the edge are forsaken lovers, the condemned, and philosophers to contemplate the empty vastness."

Gideon nodded, smiling at Abdul. "Show me this undis-covered route of secrecy." With ease and minimal effort, they hurriedly climbed to the place of vantage spoken of by Abdul. Cautiously, Gideon edged around a giant boulder, emerging on the other side with a full view of the stronghold. He was amazed, once more, at the finest details of God's plan. The entire layout of the compound had been made available to him by the grateful Abdul. Gideon was now able to construct his own perfect battle plan, down to the smallest detail. The two quickly descended, and Gideon gathered up his soon-to-be-invisible army of ghosts, marching out of the heavens. Jether was valiant, but starvation had brought a pall of gray death to his face. The three hundred did not complain—without bread, all would soon perish. The famished company traveled to a hiding place several furlongs from Karkor, to avoid detection. Gideon paced the perimeter of his encampment—his mind racing. He turned to face his men. "We have no time to waste!" Gideon's confidence was fueled by his faith, a faith that had helped the three hundred so far. Once more, they caught the flame of his purpose: his desire to overcome the hounds of famine that were snapping at their empty bellies. He erased their doubt with the resolve of faith and determination.

"Rally on me, so you may hear choice words made clear. Men, brothers, comrades, and soldiers of the Lord God of Israel—we have prevailed against the might of the Midianite horde before. We have endured distress and the lack of provision. Now is the time of our trial in the furnace of affliction! We have been valiant, and our hands have remained clean. We have esteemed the Lord God, Adonai—holding Him in the highest regard. We have pursued our adversary by faith and have hungered for the bread of human kindness. We have struggled longer than I would have thought it possible, but now is our time to shine—in our duty to God, to ourselves, and to Israel. The barley bread needed to sustain our lives is within reach, and it lies in the hands of the Horde—secure on the very top of Mount Karkor. We must prevail or perish in our attempt. Our need for food will lead us to a beggar's death if we are not committed, mind, body, and will of soul!" Gideon surveyed his men, recognizing the spark of hope in the light of their eyes.

"We can give our last breath in praise of the Lord God in battle, or we can sound a coward's whimper—allowing starvation and death to prevail over us here in the Jogbehah." Gideon stretched out his arm and cupped his hand. "We have been kept alive because we reside in the shadow of His strong hand and outstretched arm." Gideon modeled the shooting of an imaginary arrow from an imaginary bow, saying, "We are like a polished shaft that is hidden in God's quiver. Let us make ready for the launch!" He let his arms drop to his sides. "I heard the voice of the Lord when he asked: 'Whom will I send? Who will go for us?' And I answered, saying, 'Here am I! Send me!' Men, this is a righteous act that was foreordained before the matter of the world was organized into its rotation; before the sun first burst into fire."

Throwing back his head, Gideon raised both arms skyward, proclaiming, "Trust in our God, who makes all things possible, and we shall overcome. We shall prosper in our attempt at scouring the land clean of all Israel's enemies! The Lord God of Israel and the bread of life is the prize. We will survive and conquer by the will of God this very night."

They agreed with a hand to the square—as if by one man rehearsed before the Earth had formed. They shouted with one voice, "The sword of the Lord and of Gideon!" *Kherev l'Adonai u-l'Gid'on!* The sound carried to the mountain wall. From a distance, it could easily have been mistaken for an errant clap of thunder.

CHAPTER 22

Blood and Fire

Every battle of the warrior is with confused noise and garments rolled in blood—but this one would be fought with burning and fuel of fire. Gideon pressed his men to stand ready. "We will repeat our success—yet again deceiving our enemy with an uproar of sound. We will rely on a wave of noise that will pierce their ears, and our flickering lamps will blind the mind's eye of our opposition. They will perceive of great numbers and blazing torches. Even the bravest heart will faint—and dread will be the dagger of their imagination. We will visit them with a terror worse than death itself. You have been disciplined and have skimped on drink. Take your last swallow. Make your water pitchers hollow. We will trim the wicks, light the lamps, and secure them in the clay pots. Have your shofars ready in your hands. Remember to spit, to moisten your lips, and wait for the hint of my horn's first blast. We will emerge from behind that boulder at the top, and fall upon our enemy at the beginning of the middle watch."

Gideon stepped boldly to and fro before them as he spoke. "As before," he directed, "we will separate into three groups of one hundred. Each group will have thirty-three men in each row of three. Again, this will give our enemy the illusion of facing a deadly strength in numbers, and the expanse over which we are spread will be perceived as limitless. Since our backs will be to the void, our flickering lamps will be seen as blazing torches in the distance as if we were an army of phantoms slipping out from behind the dark blind of night. They will see three separate armies coming directly at them from three different directions—all from another dimension. Once we are organized on the ground, I will be up front and center. Follow my lead, men, as we had initially agreed. But this time, and after the third loud shout, we will advance. Wait for my signal. When I swing my arm over my head, the first rank will hurl their lamps. The spilling oil will create a curtain of fire. We will strike out, smartly punching through the smoke and the burning, and then the second rank will do the same as we advance through the flames. The third corps will finish the job with a heave of their lamps and a loud shout. We will be in the midst of them; they will part in advance of us in a sea of red blood. We have nothing left to give, our strength is all but spent, and we will be either quick or dead in the attempt of would-be heroes. As before, each company in unison of movement and purpose will act as if but one man—for the Lord God of Israel goes before us. Spark your lamps!"

Gideon had now become the mighty man of valor decreed by the angel at the winepress in Ophrah. Nothing would undermine his faith; nothing would stand in the way of his success. The three hundred, along with Gideon, Phurah, and Jether, followed

Abdul through the winding passageway to the high plateau of the once-secure Karkor. Elyon and Ben, Gideon's two captains, set apart the distance of their companies without the utterance of a word. They walked with muffled footfalls. If they were detected, the advantage of their surprise would be wasted. A wayward lip, a cough, or a sneeze, would bring upon them a rain of death. They waited in the shadows, their breathing short and shallow, in anticipation of this spiritual battle for life and bread.

Gideon blew his mighty trumpet of righteousness, and every man followed suit, blowing their shofars loudly. As before, the moon fell dark . . . as if dark fingers had clutched out the light. The heavens dropped, sweeping over the Midianite stronghold in an eerie, low-lying fog at the height of a man's knees. The outline of borders and edges disappeared into the mist. The pitchers crashed like thunder when strong hands came together in a symbol of might, as each man smashed his clay pot against the ram's horn knuckle. The sound echoed against the walls of the valley floor below. The three hundred flickering lamps were raised high over their heads to produce the deceptive effect of being far off in the distance. The shout from three hundred Battle-fired voices chanting—"The sword of the Lord and of Gideon Kherev l'Adonai u-l'Gid'on!—reverberated off the ancient stone. The footfalls of Gideon's advancing army sounded as if the world were massing together to attack—bent on the violent slaughter of what remained of the Midianite horde. They stood, every man in his place round about the plateau of fate. The Midianites ran, cried, or lashed out wildly. Their hearts were filled with fear. It seemed as if an army of ghosts had appeared out of the thin desert air.

And then the three hundred blew, chanted, and stomped the ground—building to a crescendo of sound. It increased until it was maddening. The Lord set every man's sword against his fellow. In the dark and in the terror, the enemy of Midian seemed everywhere and nowhere, due to the lack of light. They continued to fight like blind men, in a blood-soaked frenzy of slaughter. The three hundred slowly half-stepped forward—this time advancing into the maelstrom of fire. The Midianites were in the chaos of confusion. The ground under their feet seemed to have vanished. By droves, many enemy companies tumbled over the rocky crescent—their moans and shrieks spiraling downward into the black abyss of the bottomless pit.

The twin kings, as was their custom, at the first sign of danger or possible capture, made haste—quickly departing in search of safety. The Midian Empire would quickly unravel without the kings to guide them; especially now that the two princes, Oreb and Zeeb, who had been trained as generals, were now presumed dead. The kings, their fiercest personal bodyguards in attendance, astride their camels, were now above the fog bank. Their torches blazed, revealing their present position, and the direction of their flight was made evident. Gideon, sensing an opportunity, commanded his company to advance on the torch-lit route of the kings' headlong flight. Gideon's men hurled their lamps by rank to create fireballs of spilled oil. As each line of one hundred men advanced into to the fire-break, the next line heaved their lamps—extending the path to the next curtain of fire. It was so overwhelming that the mob of remaining Midianites parted on both sides. Some ran, some were pushed off the invisible edge, flying down below to the sleep of oblivion. The kings were the only silhouettes visible on the landscape during their futile attempt at fleeing Gideon's wrath.

This ploy had so unnerved the remaining Midianites that they either ran off the dark chasm in confusion or waited for the relief of death from the sharp swords of Gideon's men—welcoming destruction for their unending, blood-curdling nightmare. Stricken with fear, their very breath caught short in their throats. They killed each other with murderous blows—believing that the enemy was now upon them. Gideon's advance was like a charging elephant through bulrush reeds. The host parted in a sea of red blood, just as Gideon had predicted. The three hundred made short work of all who came within arm's reach of their swords of justice. The host was finally and utterly embarrassed, scattered, or knocked off from the cliffs of the abyss.

The kings attempted to flee, but Gideon pursued with the strength of ten. The three hundred were drunk with enemy blood and fresh from the fight. Only the punch of combat stress kept them quick and alive—allowing them to rise above and meet the challenge until first light. The kings rode with the fear of fleeing prey, straight into the gaping jaws of mix-up and delay. Their last mistake, prompted by their haste, ensured no escape. They had run into a steep, walled canyon. They were boxed in. The only way out was up and over the canyon cliff, which wasn't an option. Or, they could double back, into the waiting arms of Gideon, the three hundred, and the judgment of God.

The three hundred only followed the torch light that marked the kings' trail. They pursued them in the midst of fog and through a deeper dark. Gideon had them by the hip and quickly closed in for the kill. He made sure they would not slip away in the dark and in the haze of fog. He could now finish what had been so long in coming. The kings' bodyguards were sworn to give their own lives, if necessary, to defend and protect the two kings. The guards were the strongest and fiercest of all the Ishmaelite warriors, but their efforts were to no avail. In an instant, they were overpowered and overwhelmed. They were quickly dispatched into the afterlife and sent to rest with their freshly departed brethren . . . though rest for them was not altogether certain.

The kings gave up, handing themselves over to Gideon's men with little or no struggle. Their age had worn them down; they no longer had the vigor of youth. Many years of lavish meals in too much abundance, and being pampered by servants, had wasted away their strength, and their fortitude—leaving slack sinew and flabby muscle. This night's work had left them panting and in a state of near exhaustion. They were led away, strapped to their camels' saddles and pulled along like children's toys, without complaint or murmur. The kings were taken back to the scene of this night's slaughter; returned to the secure Midianite tomb of Karkor.

And Gideon, the son of Joash, returned from the battle before the sun was up! The morning was eerily dark, and filled with the last gasps of the dying, the death rattles, and moans of those who had been mortally wounded. Thousands of bodies were strewn all about, near, above, and far below the high-walled cliff. The only horde now in view were the legions of hooked-billed raptors, intent on their portion before the worms and swarms of black flies finished feasting.

Abdul opened the storehouse. "It's time that we break our fast. Look, we have rolls of barley bread, meat, and the plenty of kings."

Gideon warned his men, "Do not stuff your belly in a feast of excess. It will swell your bellies dangerously, having been empty these many days. Eating on an empty stomach to excess has been known to kill."

Before the first crust of bread or mouthful of wine was taken, a prayer of thanksgiving was offered in dutiful acknowledgment of all the Lord God of Israel had done. Gideon knelt upon the ground. His three hundred and Jether followed after him. Gideon prayed, "Hallelujah! I give thanks unto Adonai with my whole heart, in the council of the upright and in the congregation of the righteous; the works of Adonai are great, sought by all those who delight in Him. His work is glory and majesty. His righteousness endures forever. He has made us an eternal memory for His great works and causes. Adonai is gracious and abounds in tender mercies. He has given food unto them who fear Him. He will ever be mindful of His covenant. As it was in the beginning, so shall it be in the end, everlasting to everlasting. In the name of Adonai, we claim victory."

The three hundred were weary. Having their fill, they rested only a little while. The stench of so many dead was becoming unbearable. Every man took the spoil of Ishmaelite gold earrings. It was an Ishmaelite custom to be so adorned. Gideon's three hundred took all things gold and silver, and all things precious, packing the camels with all they could carry. They emptied the storehouse, taking with them every kind of foodstuff on offer. At last, Gideon proclaimed, "With the kings of Midian in our custody, we will go to visit Penuel and Succoth—and they will know the vengeance of our wrath—for the last shall be first, and the first shall be last."

CHAPTER 23

Wrath Is Cruel and Anger Is Outrageous

Rested, and strong in the Lord and in the power of His might, Gideon and the three hundred set about to put right, an injustice committed at the lofty tower of Penuel. They came with victory on their lips, not as a vagabond band of beggars praying for a handout of bread to sustain body and soul. Gideon and the three hundred had now fed upon the sweet barley bread that was made from the labor of their own hands, and had partaken of a sumptuous spiritual feast—delighting in every word that proceeds out of the mouth of God. They were champions and victors! They now had the upper hand, having the twin kings of Midian, Zebah and Zalmunna, in their grasp.

As Gideon had promised, he returned to keep his word and wreak a righteous vengeance. He and the three hundred entered the city walls with swords drawn. With a turn of faultless fortune, Gideon's timing was perfect—all the princes and elders were seated together at a wedding banquet. All their men-at-arms were feasting on a river of wine, a table of delicacies set before them. Merriment and laughter soon turned to shrieks of disaster. The joyful music was abruptly interrupted by the sight of three hundred armed men seeking an audience—intent on the settling of scores.

"I have returned, as promised," Gideon growled. "The kings of Midian are in my capture, and their host has been destroyed. For want of bread, my men and I could all have died out in the wilderness. Only by our faith and the grace of God have we survived. You were a friend to our enemy, and so now you remain an enemy of God, to Israel, and to me." Gideon's eyes flashed with passion, kindled by the imminent fulfillment of moral reckoning. "Gather all the men," he ordered his captains. "Herd them into their greatly treasured and highly esteemed Tower of pride. There they will add fuel to my wrath with their own blistering fat. When they are gathered together in their Tower, bolt the door from the outside. Gather wood, furniture, and anything else that will burn. Heap it at the base and all around the Tower to the height of the gate, and then fetch me a barrel of oil. Together, we will fill pails and pitchers to the brim with oil, and douse it all —wood, stone, and porch."

Gideon pronounced the sentence of death. With an overarm stretch, he cast the first torch at the ready-made crematorium. The torch did cartwheels in the air, coming to rest in an exploding burst of revenge. Dozens of firebrands quickly followed until the blaze licked skyward, encircling the roof of the doomed Tower. Their screams could be heard for a long time until finally, all had succumbed to the smoke and the heat. The men of Penuel were being cooked alive, their bodies fueling the fury of justice upheld. The inferno lasted the better part of the day. The fire had weakened all of the Tower's mortar joints until it finally buckled and crumbled into a pile of rubble. Gideon, in a solemn tone of prophecy, related again how Jacob had wrestled an angel of the Lord in the very same spot as he now stood, wrestling the Tower of Penuel down into the dust.

The women of Penuel were in the throes of mourning; the wedding feast had turned into a funeral pyre. All their grown sons, husbands, fathers, and uncles had succumbed. The women quickly put away their sackcloth and ashes to attend to more pressing and practical matters. Survival for themselves and their small children was vital. The women presented a petition to Gideon, pleading for their own lives and for the needs of their offspring. One aged woman spoke for the rest: "We cannot survive for very long without our men to provide for our needs. We will go wanting. We, as well as our innocent children, will surely die. Our deaths will surely torment you if you have a conscience. Our blood will be on your hands, and you will have shed innocent blood, for we have done you no wrong."

Gideon prayerfully considered their plea and said, "Very well, you shall not bear the burden of infidelity committed by your men toward God and Israel. Gather up your herds and flocks. Fill your carts with all that you hold as precious, and accompany us up to the Jezreel."

And so Gideon, the three hundred, the kings of Midian, the widows, unmarried virgins, and the children of Penuel, all in tow, continued their journey back up to the Jezreel Valley. A day of reckoning was yet at hand, though, for the hostile reception suffered at Succoth. The townsmen who had turned down Gideon and his men, denying them a kind word and a crust of bread, would be dealt with next. Gideon headed due west to the settlement of Succoth. He would make his victory known in no uncertain terms. Gideon and his company of heroes crossed south over the river Jabbok in the footsteps of Jacob. From there, he would head for Beth-barah, the fording place of the Jordan, before turning north onto the broad highway, along the west side of the river, that would take him to Drumah, and home.

Gideon came upon a young man of Succoth and inquired of him about the leaders of the town. The young man described the princes of Succoth and the elders, even threescore and seventeen men.

Then, Gideon came unto the men of Succoth and said, "Behold, Zebah and Zalmunna, with whom you did chide me. You said, 'Are the hands of Zebah and Zalmunna now in thine hand, that we should give bread unto thy men that are weary?' And here they are, locked in my custody!"

Gideon took the elders of the city and cuffed them in turn to pillar and post, scourged their flesh with the sharp thorns and wilderness prickly briers. With them, he taught the men of Succoth the price of betrayal. Gideon and his captains of hundreds and lieutenants of tens beat the men of Succoth, some to the bone until they bled black blood, but there were none left for dead. They taught these men with welts and with stripes the penalty for causing the Lord's anointed to be cast out to the wild beasts as a banquet for the lesser creatures.

Gideon would not deprive the innocent for the reckless decision of the elders and the princes of Penuel. He refused to deprive the women and children of the substance that ensured their survival, but he was not prepared to take on the surplus baggage of any additional human cargo. Instead, Gideon demanded as a ransom for his mercy, in granting them the breath of life, the spoil of gold, precious gems, and surplus foodstuff. Gideon would need food and wealth now that there were many mouths to feed, with many leagues still to travel to the Jezreel. Extra carts of cargo were loaded. Gideon left the men of Succoth more learned and much wiser, yet only half-alive when balanced against his first arrival.

CHAPTER 24

A Vengeance of Sons and Brothers

The presence of the twin kings was no longer essential to prove or confirm Gideon's victory at Karkor to the towns of Succoth and Penuel. The kings had fulfilled their role in Gideon's vengeance and now began to outweigh their usefulness—feeding them had become a waste of resources. Guards, food, and servants were needed to keep the captives alive and in check. They had become a liability. They presented a potential threat to Israel's future—able to gather another army of mercenaries to retaliate against Gideon's people if left alive.

Zebah and Zalmunna were quite likable and pleasant to be around. Of course, they were high-born and skilled in all the social graces—extremely polite, excellent conversationalists, and charming to a fault. They were used to holding court with educated intellectuals. Their servants, generals, and underlings did all the heavy lifting because the kings' highest concern was the appearance of their regal bearing and their majesty. Gideon had another consideration, secretive and personal—a motivation he had kept hidden—waiting its turn as it brewed in the deep, dark, chilled vaults of bitter memory. Gideon was now presented with both the opportunity and the means to accomplish a vengeful justice. The blood of his brothers called out to Gideon from the dust, for their untimely execution by Zebah and Zalmunna was about to be addressed. It was time to balance the scales and put the cries of his dead brothers to rest. Gideon had been biding his time, but wondered now if he would relish the act with the same satisfaction his imagination had savored.

Gideon said unto Zebah and Zalmunna, "What manner of men were they whom you slew at Tabor?"

They answered, "As you are, so were they. Each one resembled the children of you, the king."

Gideon responded, "They were my brothers, even the sons of my mother. As the Lord lives, if you had saved them alive, I would not slay you." Gideon shook his head. "You see me as a king because your vanity will not allow you to admit that you were bested by a simple farmer. You see me as a prince, so you give me the title of equal. You do this only to pacify your well-cultivated egos."

Gideon stood before them. He began telling them about a haunting memory he harbored.

"This story was told to me as a child. My three brothers took part in Deborah and Barak's war against Sisera, the Jabin's mercenary general. Their mission was to scout and report back as to the enemy's position far below Mount Tabor. Our servant, Phurah, who had accompanied them, managed to escape his bonds, fleeing Sisera's captivity. He is now a living witness to your command to slaughter my brothers. Phurah also relayed the prophetic words of my oldest brother, Adam. Phurah bravely recovered their headless bodies that now lie enshrined in Ophrah in the Abiezrite. They will not find peace or rest until their assassins are similarly broken and have become a portion for foxes."

Gideon commanded his firstborn, Jether, "Up and slay them!" But Jether did not draw his sword. He feared, for he was yet a youth. He had been brave in the rhythm of battle, but his blade had never tasted the cut and rush of blood. He had been kept in the center company, protected by the three hundred, and he was never far from the protection of his father's right arm. The kings knew that this was a blood feud and that no reprieve, no mercy, would be forthcoming. Justice was needed as much for the living as it was a promise of peace for the dearly departed. It has been known from the beginning that mercy cannot rob justice. Zebah and Zalmunna braced themselves for the inevitable, preparing to die with the dignity and grace befitting the station of kings.

The call to this youth, with his unsure and untested blade, would surely mean a slow and painful death. They would be hacked slowly to pieces—neck, body, and limb—in a bloodbath of mutilation. With conviction, did not their rank demand, if not require, the hand of a suitable equal? One who had acquired the standing of King? In this manner, they were prepared to be dispatched. It would mean the least amount of agony and no amount of shame, compared to being disgraced from a painfully prolonged mutilation in death by cuts and slices. Zebah and Zalmunna exchanged a glance. Then Zalmunna said to Gideon: "Rise and fall upon us, for as the man is, so is his strength."

Gideon arose and made quick work of the twin kings. They were bowed at the waist, on their knees in the posture of the penitent, as they awaited their release from life and the ridicule of capture. With one mighty blow, Gideon severed heads from torsos. They were both dead and without breath before they crumpled, lifeless, to the floor.

So, slew Gideon the kings of Midian, Zebah and Zalmunna. He took away the ornaments that were on their camels' necks. The ornaments of gold that bedecked the camels were the seal of the kings' grandeur and the imposing nature of their office. Securing the ornaments ensured that the camels were saved from the burden of riders, just as Israel was now saved from the affliction of the Midianites, the Ishmaelites, and all the children of the East. All the tribes had been made free from the Midianites' ravenous gluttony. They could no longer steal the backbreaking labor and toil of Israel.

CHAPTER 25

For the Want of a King
and an Ephod of Golden Rings

Beth-barah and the fording place were but victory laps on the other side of the Jordan—two points west, and then south to the Beth-barah before turning due north, back to the house of Joash in Ophrah. It was a long haul back to the border town of Issachar. The trek was a pleasant, blue-sky journey without incident or accident. All but a few of the women of Penuel were in the spirit of grief and mourning, but they soon came to accept their plight. Acceptance spoke of hope and survival for both them and their offspring. Some among the three hundred took wives and sweethearts from among the female refugees of Penuel.

As they approached their differing paths back to tribe and home, a council was called to elect a future king. The night before the men of the tribes of Asher, Zebulun, Naphtali, and Manasseh would separate and each to go his own way, they hastily convened to announce their selection. The men of Israel said to Gideon, "Rule over us, both you and your son, and your son's son also, for you delivered us from the hands of the Midianites."

And Gideon said unto them, "I will not rule over you, neither shall my son rule over you. The Lord shall rule over you, and He shall be your king, but I would request that you give me the earrings of His prey." He referred to the golden earrings of the Ishmaelites. They answered, "We will willingly give them."

They spread a garment, and every man cast the earrings of his prey onto the garment. The weight of the golden earrings was one thousand and seven hundred shekels of gold (forty-three pounds). They also put on the garment the ornaments and gold collars, the purple raiment that was on the kings of Midian, and the gold chains that were about the necks of their camels. Each man saluted Gideon before he departed and carried with him glory, spoil, and the treasured memories of high adventure in the satisfaction that comes from doing the will of God. Gideon was welcomed home and hailed as a hero, savior, and Israel's deliverer from the Midian horde. Ophrah paid homage to him, in gratitude. They held a feast for he who had become their favorite son. With the spoils, Gideon made an ephod of gold, the likes of which had never been seen, imagined, or even conceived. Past ephods were made of linen with the intermittent gold thread. The ephod was a richly embroidered, apron-like vestment with two shoulder straps and ornamental attachments for securing the Breastplate of Judgment. The breastplate was adorned with twelve gems engraved with the names of the Twelve Tribes of Israel, and a pocket or pouch that contained the Urim (lights) and Thummin (perfection), the two seer stones. The Urim and Thummim were placed inside the breastplate and over the heart as a reminder that Israel was always over God's heart. But Gideon's Ephod of Gold had no Urim and Thummim, for the seer stones were wanting. Gideon could only reproduce a glittering likeness of the sacred original. This was done with pure intent in a heartfelt thanks to honor God.

Gideon planned to make the ephod unique, and this was his attempt to acknowledge God in the highest regard, demonstrating his love, awe, and respect. He was poor in Manasseh, partly because he was poorly schooled in the knowledge of the word of God. He did not know the graven images of the foreigners' gods as the Lord God had commanded, "Thou shalt not desire the silver or gold that is on them, nor take it unto thee, lest thou be snared therein: for it is an abomination to the Lord thy God." Unknown to Gideon, the gold earrings worn by the Ishmaelites were the sign of a covenant—a promise to serve idols and demi-gods—and that in the wearing of this heathen jewelry, they had agreed to be servants unto those strange gods and be bound to them forever.

Exodus
And all the people brake off the golden earrings which were in their ears, and brought them unto Aaron.

And he received them at their hand, and fashioned it with a graving tool, after he had made it a molten calf: and they said, "These be thy gods, O Israel, which brought thee up out of the land of Egypt."

The gratitude and reverence shown to the Lord God of Israel were made hollow. It became a generational curse for the house of

181

Gideon: The Sound and the Glory

Gideon, and to all who came to possess the Baal-berith. Gideon, in his innocence, believed that this grand gesture in creating the ephod, the Baal-berith or Lord of the Covenant, was an acknowledgment of the greatness of God, and praise to Him for the success of his remarkable adventures. Gideon had used only as much gold as was required for the ephod and again as much for the breastplate. The remaining spoils of gold were sold, and the proceeds were gathered for the construction of a great home of his own. And Jerubbaal, the son of Joash, went and dwelt in his own house in his city, even in Ophrah.

His father Joash inquired about the long train of single females with their flocks, households, and carts full of little ones. Gideon related the story of Penuel and the necessity for charity, so as not to punish the innocent for the crimes of their husbands, fathers, and brothers. Joash had a report of his own, saying, "During the Battle of Beth Shan, many of the young men from Ophrah never returned from the conflict. My son, it is good that you have brought back spoil in abundance. Many women will look at you, so they can attain the position of wife. You are a hero in Israel and will be sought out as a much-needed provider." Joash raised his right hand, placing it on Gideon's left shoulder.

"Gideon, my courageous son," Joash added, "I would ask a favor of you. After the destruction of my grove, my income has been reduced to poverty. I would ask that you allow me to be the keeper of that place where the Baal-berith will be displayed."

Gideon readily agreed, saying, "You saved me from the townspeople attempting to settle the score for Baal; you, therefore, will be the head warden, and your income will be greater than before."

Meanwhile, Drumah, Gideon's concubine, and his only true love, was painfully absent. She was nowhere to be seen at the festive homecoming of Ophrah's first and only local hero during the back slapping, speech making, and non-stop flattering. Gideon inquired and searched but to no avail. No one had seen her since Gideon had marched triumphantly into town. He thought about where they had first met and fallen in love. With all the speed he could muster, he made his way to the rocky outcrop at the top of the hill, where the grove of Joash once stood. And there she was! His hero's heart fluttered, his breath became shallow, and his emotions whirled out of control. She was even more beautiful than the vivid fantasies of his carnal desires.

Drumah, like an angel of light, glided down and into Gideon's waiting arms. Their first kiss was bliss, and they spent hours locked in passion. Gideon began telling her of his victories, speaking at length, but Drumah, gently swaying, said, "There will be time enough at the fireside for these tales of a hero's achievements. I prefer to look into the bottomless wells of your eyes, knowing you are still alive and that we will never be parted again in this lifetime."

Gideon bowed his head. A thoughtful expression crossed his face as he looked up and said, "There is a tale that must be told . . . for the consequence of my decision has followed me home and will continue to press on me." Drumah put a hand to his cheek and then rubbed the crease from his brow.

Gideon told her about the women of Penuel. "As you might already know, the women in Ophrah are without men from the losses at Beth Shan. I have much wealth from the spoils and will build us a great house to accommodate the need for many wives.

This I do only as a duty, as charity, to see to their welfare. This is what the God of Israel would have of me."

Drumah placed her hand over his heart. "I know your heart, Gideon, son of Joash, and I will be at your side in good weather and foul. My love for you knows no bounds."

Gideon had threescore and ten sons of his body begotten, and of daughters one score and ten, for he had the spoil of gold and was the prize among a small handful of men. He saw to the well-being of many wives. His concubine, Drumah, who was from Shechem, a town of Canaan, bore him a son and named him Abimelech, which means "my father is king." Gideon doted on Abimelech, being the son of his only true love. This made Drumah content. She was happy to see Gideon favor her Canaanite blood over all of his other sons, born to him in the covenant of Israel.

Gideon, having the acclaim of his brethren, was raised to the privileged position of a judge in Israel—a natural consequence of being both a hero and the son of Joash. Gideon had become known for his wisdom and his vast store of knowledge. His mind was renewed, having been touched by the hand of God; his verdicts were always merciful, genuine, and just. Gideon had given unto his spoiled son Abimelech, the care of the Golden Ephod. He lorded over his brothers with the rights of an undue favor and boasted of being their father's favorite. When it came to the usual teasing and bullying among brothers, Gideon was quick to protest and protect Abimelech against his other sons. He would always turn a blind eye to Abimelech's wildly mistaken belief in his own superiority. Abimelech seemed always to have his father's permission, in whatever scheme he attempted. This was due to their noble father's unwavering love for Drumah, Abimelech's mother.

Gideon lay dying, and with his last ebb of life, he summoned all his sons and daughters to bless them and direct their ways. Gideon's massive bed was removed to the great hall where all his brood could be assembled. With his ebbing strength, he addressed the one hundred lives he claimed to have begotten; of whom he was the paterfamilias, the patriarch, dad, and father. Drumah held his hand, refusing to leave his side. She helped to raise him up into a sitting position. In spite of his age, he had retained a spiritual glow, a characteristic stamped into his person from living a life of righteousness.

Gideon raised his arms to heaven and said, "Praise the name of the Lord, my children, with all of your heart, might, and strength, with every word, and in every deed. Lord God, bless my children, I pray. Bless my daughters to be Your handmaidens, Adonai. Bless them with fertility and with the patience to withstand the evil day. Give them faith to endure to the end, which is the beginning of life everlasting." He laid hands on each daughter and pronounced their names. He then turned to his sons and proclaimed, "My sons, you are the branch and root of my posterity. You are like the Cedars of Lebanon, tall and proud. Don't ever shrink from your duty to God. Swell not with vanity or ambition, and seek not the acclaim of men but of the Lord your God. Always remain humble as the dust, and leave behind the lust of the flesh, the lust of the eyes, and the pride of life that warps the mind and bends the soul beyond its proper place in the world. Put on the full armor of God to protect against the day of pestilence. Look to the renewing of your mind by seeking the word of God so you might avoid the rot and decay of conceit and contempt. I would caution you all to crush any and every desire to be king, for the Lord alone is King. Trust in Him and live. And now, to all of my sons, I declare that you shall be a congress of judges to rule and reign. Some will agree and some will abstain, but seventy is the number of righteousness that you shall maintain—no more and no less. And so, to my son, Abimelech, I bequeath the Baal-berith, to do with as he sees fit." And with his blessings bestowed, Gideon, the son of Joash, died at a ripe old age. He was buried in the sepulcher of Joash, his father, in Ophrah of the Abiezrite.

Isaiah 9:4-6

For thou hast broken the yoke of his burden, and the staff of his shoulder, the rod of his oppressor, as in the day of Midian. (The rock of Oreb and so, in the day of Gideon)

And it shall come to pass in that day, that his burden shall be taken up from off thy shoulder, and his yoke from off thy neck and the yoke shall be destroyed because of the resurrection of souls. The Lord has broken the staff of the wicked, the scepters of the rulers of dominions and principalities. The rod of him that smote thee is broken; (the burden of sin, the staff of the wicked, and the yoke of the grave).

For every battle of the warrior is with confused noise, and garments rolled in blood, but this shall be with burning and fuel of fire.

The Messiah, "Therefore, I speak to them in parables: because seeing, they see not; and hearing, they hear not; neither do they understand. And they discern it all as confused noise." And He was clothed with a vesture dipped in blood (garments wrapped in his blood) and his name is called the Word of God. And the light of Israel shall be for a fire, and His Holy One for a flame, and shall burn and shall devour. The fuel is the thorns and the briars, which is the world—and all consumed in one day.

For unto us a child is born, unto us a son is given: and the government (the sardonyx stones that anchor the breastplate of judgement on the high priest's ephod) shall be upon his shoulder: and his name shall be called Wonderful, Counselor, The mighty God, The everlasting Father, and The Prince of Peace. Selah.

Part Three

CHAPTER 26

Evil for Good and Good for Evil

Gideon's legacy of greatness was short-lived. As soon as Gideon was put to rest, the children of Israel turned again and went whoring after Baalim. They made the Baal-berith, or the Lord of the Covenant, an idol of worship. A holy covenant with the God of Israel had, once again, reverted to an agreement with Baalim. The children of Israel did not remember the Lord their God, who had delivered them out of the hands of all their enemies on every side. Neither did they show kindness to the house of Jerubbaal, namely Gideon, according to all the goodness which he had shown unto Israel.

All Israel went a-whoring after the Golden Ephod, and it became a snare unto Gideon and his house. The Ephod of Gold was glorious and brilliant; it sparkled with the glint of jewels, displaying the masterful work of great craftsmanship. Rumors of miracles milled about, spreading to all the coasts of Israel and beyond; many made pilgrimages of piety, just for the chance to plead their wishes, wants, and desires to the Baal-berith. Israel,

Gideon: The Sound and the Glory

Canaan, and the Amorites were greedy for the promised blessings of wealth, health, and prosperity. They gave freely of tithes and offerings in an abundance of pledges. Travelers from foreign lands spoke about meaningful changes and of good fortune. Marvelous stories of healing and total restoration resounded in the gossip of the day. It was also believed that women who were barren would become fertile just by being in the idol's presence. The legs of the lame were said to be strengthened, the blind to find a new view, and the dumb were reported to have their tongues loosed.

The Ephod could stand upright as its structure was stiffly fashioned; it became a majestic centerpiece, placed onto a finely chiseled pedestal carved from imported marble. Elevated to the height of man's eyes, it presented an image of grandeur. Seen through a lens that seemed to confer upon it an essence of deity, it had become an icon that people associated with God, even though it was a mere artifact. People treated it as a famous religious relic as if preserved from the Tabernacle built in the day of Moses. They invested it with their own idolatrous mysticism, filling it with the dark magic and wicked imaginings.

The mysterious ephod referred to as the Baal-berith or Lord of the Covenant, was well attended by a flock of false priests and prophets. The invisible snare attached to the Ephod of Gold had become an affliction to the House of Gideon. The seventy sons of Gideon had formed an assembly where all laws and judgments were debated—and they were not adverse to exchanging blows when they disagreed, or when their egos were frayed to the point of violence from the ruthless aggression of prideful siblings.

Abimelech had acquired a vile mixture of ambition and arrogance. He considered putting to use the wealth-making potential of the Baal-berith. Realizing it could easily be delivered to the Canaanite city of Shechem, he planned to put it under the control of his cousins in the tower House of Milo. The transfer would curry the favor of followers in a scheme he was hatching to be the king in all of Israel. This plan was completely at odds with his father's wishes. Gideon had consistently refused all pleas for worldly dominion, recognizing the danger of succumbing to man's authority. Gideon had been faithful in acknowledging God alone as the only true king.

Abimelech had nursed a great hurt as a boy growing up in Ophrah. He was often mocked; teased by his brothers for being a half-breed. Vicious fistfights were all too familiar. Violence would spread in defense of his mother's honor and his suspect Canaanite heritage. Abimelech would sometimes make a good show of defending himself, and every now and again, Gideon would take the stick of submission to punish the self-righteous bullies. Abimelech would occasionally limp home, bloodied and beaten. These painful memories gnawed and festered in the young boy's mind. The time had finally arrived to gorge on the tasty savor of his long-awaited and sweet revenge.

Abimelech called a great council, to the irritation of all his half-brothers, for he had the right to do so. The brothers settled down from the gripe of being roused; each found his place. Jether, the eldest, found his seat at the head of the table. He gaveled the congress to order, for all agreed that he was the chief referee. The great hall was filled to the brim with hostile feelings; the novice young leaned against the cold stone walls of experience. Jether opened the proceedings, saying, "Abimelech, state your petition."

Abimelech spoke, saying, "The ephod is mine. It is my inheritance. It was granted unto me with Abba's or Daddy's dying wish," he argued, pausing slightly before he continued. "I don't doubt that we all shall pay homage and honor to our deceased father's last request." He allowed his eyes to roam the room, daring anyone to challenge this sentiment. "I would take what is rightfully mine and move Baal-berith to the House of Milo in Shechem. I tell you this out of respect for our father's wishes, because what I do with my lawful property is none of your concern and none of your business."

Abimelech's demand was met with a dumbstruck silence that hung from the hook of uneasiness. Jether brokered the debate with the calm of common sense and addressed the group in the presence of Abimelech. "We require some time to deliberate your outrageous demand; you have caught us by surprise. If you would be so kind as to step outside and partake of some wine, we will summon you in due course once we have thrashed out our differences." Abimelech stepped outside, eager to down the suggested goblet of homegrown vintage. Brother Avner, a gifted orator, spoke next. Being a practical man, he recognized the value of utility, arguing to refute Abimelech's suggestion: "The Baal-berith brings us much-needed revenue. It has carried its acclaim to far-reaching territories and has provided us a rich bounty of wealth. I say we deny Abimelech's claim."

Calev, speaking from his heart, addressed his brothers next. "Brethren, the Baal-berith has become an obsession of our people and promotes the worship of Baalim, the Canaanite god that our father was mightily celebrated for destroying. This idolatrous practice has once again found favor with our people. I believe, therefore, it would be a blessing if Abimelech were to possess it and rid us of its danger. Besides, it would suit Shechem better, where the worship of Baalim is popular among the Canaanites. I say we grant Abimelech's petition. And good riddance to the golden idol!"

The debate swung to and fro, filled at times with fury and then with the bitterness of venom. Each brother had an opinion, generally split into two camps: the value of wealth versus the onset of a creeping and subtle idolatry. The verdict's hinge was thin, the decision divided, dependent now upon the tie-breaking wisdom of Jether. Jether took his leave, choosing to sit quietly under the ancient oak, where his father Gideon had boasted an encounter with an angel face to face. He sat on top of the rock next to the winepress. After fervent prayer and meditation, Jether returned. Inspired with fresh confidence, he made his announcement to his not-so-kind commune of brothers.

"Abimelech will have his way. I was with our father from the beginning of his adventures, and the Baal-berith was conceived with the highest of noble intentions. It was meant to acknowledge the glory of God, especially for all the miracles He so liberally granted: our father's unmatched battle success and his covenant with the Almighty God, Adonai. Yet now, all that good is turning to evil, so we shall put it far from us! As Calev made plain, this is an opportunity for us to be rid of this wicked thing before it consumes us all. You have my decision." And so it was passed, by the narrowest of margins. Abimelech had gained more than the possession of the Baal-berith. He had greased a political cog, boosting his confidence in a scheme of intrigue. Using the Baal-berith, he meant to nail down his quest to hold the scepter of absolute monarchy, and to wield the sword of both life and death.

In time, Abimelech made his home in Shechem and was well received as a cousin to his mother's brethren. The placement of the Ephod under their control made his welcome possible, allowing him to be absorbed graciously into his new society.

Abimelech, allied with patience and time, permitted the Ephod to reap its harvest of offerings from the halt and afflicted, and the wishful thinking of pilgrims—those who sought the fulfillment of dreams—whether their restoration to health or in the coin of unearned wealth. The merchants were delighted at being given the opportunity to fulfill the many needs of travelers. Meals, bedding, and a lively trade in souvenirs proved to be a hefty windfall of silver and gold. Shechem prospered.

A feast of red wine and the fatted calf of subtle diplomacy were prepared in a shrewd appeal for assistance in Abimelech's quest for dominion. Abimelech gathered together his brethren in the house of his mother's flesh and reminded them of the importance of blood, saying, "I need you to fill the ears of Shechem. Tell the citizens it is better for them that I rule. Having me rule will be particularly useful to you, my dear cousins, as you will, on all accounts, receive the greatest advantage of my generosity and bounty. Explain to them that I, Abimelech, will personally rule without malice and without the distractions born from the slow process of debate and consensus currently practiced by the council of seventy. I will dismiss with the edge of my blade the council of the seventy sons of Jerubbaal, who are hard pressed to make the simplest decisions, always inclined to the benefit of Israel, never the cause of Canaan."

The minds of Abimelech's cousins were flush with strong wine, their bellies bulged with meat, and their pockets overflowed, jingling with coins and offerings freshly reaped from the Baal-berith. With one accord, they gathered to parley, their purpose firmly fixed on upholding their new patron in support of his generosity. Zebul sat on the top step, speaking for the clan. "Abimelech, we have heard your plea, and we agree to your scheme. It has excellent merit! After the dispatch of the congress of seventy in Ophrah, you will have our support. There is wisdom in your proposition of a coup. We will enforce your claim to Shechem and support your royal aspirations. We can and we will sway the hearts of Shechem. The sons of Canaan will agree—you are one of us; you are also a child of Israel, as was your father, Gideon, before you. Israel will, therefore, also honor and support your rise to majesty, Brother Abimelech. To a man, you have our word; we will support your ambition to the throne."

Shechem affirmed that having a king, one who is both a Canaanite and an Israelite, would bring unto both nations stature and glory. Abimelech requested wealth from the house of the Baal-berith, secured from the treasury of gifts and offerings. With seventy pieces of silver—one for each brother—he was confident to negotiate a bargain with assassins, liars, and henchmen. Seventy pieces of silver—this was the price of Abimelech's rise to glory in the commerce of betrayal and murder.

CHAPTER 27

Details, Devils, and Mayhem

Abimelech gathered his gang of henchmen—villainous scoundrels to the last man! They would slit a throat for a purse of gold or stab a liver for two bits of silver. The plot had to be fleshed out. The murder of Abimelech's kin—brothers from a different mother—was a deadly and dangerous affair, and could not be entered into with half a heart or half a mind. With subtle cunning and the disarming surprise of perfect timing, Abimelech's plan was ready to be set into motion.

Zebul was the patriarch of the House of Milo and the mayor of Shechem. All plans and designs carried out in Shechem had to be sounded out before him. Abimelech lobbied Zebul for more men, saying, "I have recruited a crew of liars, vain scoundrels, and void of honor, whose only allegiance is to him that pays the greatest bounty at any given moment. I need the peace of mind that comes from trust placed in a family and the force of weight carried by the Canaanite men of Shechem."

Zebul responded straightaway, "This venture cannot be undermanned or ill-conceived if it is to succeed. Restraint in any form is for the weak and the cowardly! I have considered your plan long into the night, and now that it is hard afoot, I have begun to recognize an opportunity for a long-awaited retribution. I seek to balance out an ancient grievance. The sons of Jacob, namely Levi and Simeon, murdered Prince Shechem, whose name is enshrined in the name of our city. Also did they kill Hamor, Shechem's father, the king. He and all his men were slaughtered when they were at their weakest. This ruthless betrayal by the sons of Israel was followed by the sacking of our city. The children of Israel took for themselves all the spoils of our wealth and all our little ones. The wives of those they slaughtered were taken captive. Nothing of value was left behind, neither nail nor piss pot. You will receive your allotment of the shield, sword, and spear. Speak to me of your scheme, Abimelech. I have an eager ear. Bare me your strategy."

Abimelech was beside himself with relief. He exhaled audibly, bowing his head in a prickly posture of gratitude, but quickly recovered his natural arrogance, speaking as if the wicked act had already been accomplished. "You honor me, Zebul, as well as all within the House of Milo. Every man of Shechem will have his part to play, and when every man has dulled his sword on the chopping rock with the blood of my brothers, the anointing of a new king will be upheld in Israel."

Zebul looked Abimelech in the eye with the hint of a smirk curling his lip. "That was a stirring and fanciful delivery, Your Majesty, spoken with a hint of jest. Yet consider this—covert raids depend solely on the exactness of timing, and with the utmost attention given to the smallest detail . . . so tell me all, and I will know far better than most whether or not you have the ghost of a chance."

After collecting his thoughts, Abimelech began weaving the fine threads in his tapestry of treachery in a matter-of-fact monotone. Abimelech laid out his cunning scheme for the mass murder of his brothers. "A messenger carrying my signet seal will be sent to the house of Jerubbaal, demanding an interview at noon. Seven days hence, the entire congress of siblings will meet. It is my right to address any and all grievances, imagined or real. I will invent a dispute that must be addressed. Our bylaws stipulate a week's notice, giving enough time for all to gather. It will be a regular work day, and most will be hung over. The farmers will be down in the valley of Jezreel, planting, and hoeing, while some will be on the upper slopes dressing the vines for this season's new wine. The city will be empty, except women and children, the lame, the blind, and a few harmless winebibbers. There will be no immediate threat to our invasion."

Zebul focused on Abimelech, his piercing eyes boring into him. He leaned forward to comment on Abimelech's sinister tapestry of conspiracy, sensing looseness in the details of the intricate stitching. "I see weakness in your approach."

This jolting note took Abimelech up short, and he inquired, "Pray tell, I am most interested in your advice. How do you suggest I tighten this noose?"

Zebul replied. "Your seventy brothers will be tightly packed, practically in a circle around you. They will be armed and ready for a fight, presenting a formidable hurdle. Once the mask of your deception is dropped, the very ground on which you stand will attempt to swallow you up! They are burly and vigorous, and lest you forget, they are the sons of Jerubbaal, your father, and they will fight like cornered lions. You will be the main course on their menu, cousin!"

Abimelech responded politely, his manner reasonable and controlled. His need for diplomacy far outstripped the thin peel of insult just experienced. Tamping down his ire at having to bear the brunt of these sarcastic comments, Abimelech responded. "You know, you are quite correct. Their attempt at vengeance will be ferocious . . . this I expect. My brothers are an unruly lot, and in the heat of an argument, their passions are boldly unbridled. It is not uncommon for fists to fly, with bruised egos becoming impossible to rein in. However, cuts and stabs are less forgiving. We agreed that weapons were not to be permitted in the big house or in the great hall. Even daggers are surrendered. They are securely stashed away in the arms locker before admission is allowed. Only one sergeant-at-arms may perform the official duty of arms-bearer. He keeps a long spear to keep at bay any bitter debate between warring vanities and injured pride. I will enter the gate with a small train, so as to quell any suspicion. One man will steal away the shofar that is permanently available in the town center, preventing the sounding of a warning alarm. Meanwhile, a crew of assassins will see to the armory attendant, hurriedly removing all the weapons to a prearranged hiding place."

Zebul was visibly impressed with Abimelech's attention to detail, but he was still not convinced. "Abimelech, how will you overcome the guards at the thresholds of both the main gate and the great hall?"

Gideon: The Sound and the Glory

Abimelech responded with bravado and a show of confidence. "I have calculated all the scheduled events. The timing must be exact! We will need to coordinate this with absolute accuracy. The House of Milo and all the men of Shechem, along with my troop, will form two companies. My covert crew of cutthroats will separate from the main body two miles from the approach to the main gate. The rest of you will hide in the fields of boulders and trees, and in hollows, so as not to be detected by the Ophrah lookouts. Once we have secured the gate and all the guards have been disabled, we will signal you from the parapets with a fiery crimson banner attached to an arrow. You will all rise up and charge the unprotected stronghold. I will be at the speaking platform of the great hall, and there you will find me. You, Zebul, with seventy men, will rush in. You will be unopposed, and will enter with your swords already drawn. Circle quickly around the judgment table and behind every chair, with your weapons tickling my brothers' throats. The master of arms will lose his spear immediately, and behind every brother, a sword or dagger will quell their defiance and their ability to retaliate. I will announce that the women and children have been taken hostage, explaining that, if there is the slightest attempt to resist, these will be the first Israelites slaughtered. I will offer my proposal to each of my brothers. If they individually swear to acknowledge me as their king and sovereign, they will live. They must swear fealty to me on the rock of fire where Jerubbaal, our shared father, claimed to have encountered an angel. On that rock, considered by the sons of my bone and my blood to be a holy place, all will go well with them and their families if they agree to comply—that will be the lie to gain Shechem's complicity in the coming mayhem."

Abimelech divulged all that was on his mind. He kept nothing to himself and relished the premeditated carnage. His brothers would be butchered! He would kill them all! Not one would be spared. His real plan was so dreadful that it might repulse his hard-won partners, causing him to caution Zebul to maintain a tight lip, so none would have cause to reconsider their part in such a wholly wicked and willful enterprise.

Zebul's admiration was rekindled. He slapped Abimelech on the back. "Well done! It will be a master stroke in deception. Cold, devious, and cunning. Well done, cousin. You favor your mother's Canaanite blood. Send the dispatch informing them of your alleged dispute. I will prepare the men for their twenty-eight-mile march to Ophrah in the days ahead. I will also brace them for the celebration of the dynasty of Abimelech."

CHAPTER 28:
The High Crimes of Plans and Designs

The greatest risk was from uncorked lips and the tipping over of red wineskins that could easily spill, staining the cloth of strategy. Everything pivoted on the greased hinge of secrecy. The gates of Shechem were guarded and closed; none was permitted an outlet once the plan was set in motion. A scale model of Ophrah was measured in clay, increasing the understanding of the layout and reducing the risk of their calculated gamble.

The messenger had made the round trip and had delivered the calculated invitation to the council. It was agreed that every brother would attend, allowing Abimelech his right to vent, a space to air his fabricated list of grievances.

Zebul, with Abimelech to his immediate left, gathered the combatants, both killers and townsfolk, for their final marching orders. "Men, cousins, and brothers in arms, we trek to Ophrah to seek justice for our blood and for our God, Baalim. Our God, whose altar was brought low, and his grove spilled, spoilt, and spurned— all this for the glory of Adonai, the God of Israel.

Abimelech is both of Canaan and of Israel, and he would be our king. He will find favor with Shechem and all of Canaan. We have suffered unfairness at the rulings of the congress held by the sons of Jerubbaal. Today, all our damages, these many ancient wrongs, will be set right." Zebul's name was cheered three times, all the while attempting to spur on the unruly mob in a warped sense of twisted justice.

Abimelech stepped up to instill in his henchmen the importance of surprise and to insist on the sharp tick of timing. "Men, we will start at the setting of the sun, so our movements are not chanced upon. The entrance of my arrival with my cadre and then assassins is critical, down to the very hour. Minutes cannot be misplaced or squandered. We have all rehearsed and know what part to play in our drama of conspiracy. Today we will overthrow this city. Our takeover will be complete! The city will be vacant, and the sons of Jerubbaal will be unarmed at the great table, waiting for my entrance. All guards and weapons will be under our control. All the women and children will be rounded up and locked away. These, our hostages, will give us the needed leverage of submission. Ten hours will put us at Ophrah's threshold. We will rest at sunrise and remain hidden. A small company of twelve assassins will arise at eleven. This tiny crew will not evoke suspicion. Meanwhile, the men of Shechem, the House of Milo, and the remaining fifty-eight mercenaries—under the command of Zebul—will hide in the grassy knoll four miles before the city walls. There you will remain, resting and undetected, until the sun makes its noonday zenith. A blood-red streamer will be fastened to an arrow and launched skyward when you are within view of the stronghold, to confirm that all is well with our scheme and all are in their place of concealment. One o'clock—an hour beyond the agreed time of our meeting—will give all the brothers who have lagged behind enough time to find their chairs at the table. Proceed with great haste, at a double-time pace, where you will storm the door of the great hall."

Abimelech turned to his future right-hand man. "Zebul, do remember to bring my scimitar to me, for I will be exposed to the naked hatred of my brothers, alone, and without the protection of arms." Zebul nodded, offering Abimelech a toothy grin. "Let us form up and depart."

The full moon was a gift of silver light, and it made their secretive passage less hazardous. The only creatures that ventured out in the dark of night were wild beasts and liars, waiting to snare those in need and unsuspecting travelers. An army of shadows, they spoke little, for there was nothing to say. Time was counted by the number of miles. Finally, the troop took refuge in the underbrush and hollows, to prevent detection. All slept soundly, except for the wary eyes of the outpost guards. The stirring came at the eleventh hour, when Abimelech and his band of slayers took their trek to the gates of Ophrah. The challenge from the gate had the menace of a growl: "Who approaches Ophrah? Intruders and trespassers will not be tolerated." Abimelech growled back, "I, Abimelech, the son of Jerubbaal, a judge of the ruling congress of brothers. My traveling companions and I are here to attend the gathering in the house of decrees and decisions."

The guard replied, "You are known here and are expected. Enter freely, you and all your company. Be quick about you, for the unruly gathering of brothers has lost all signs of dignity and order."

The High Crimes of Plans and Designs

Abimelech signaled his company of ruffians with a nod and a wink. They all dispersed into the shadows that seek to make blind the sight of law and order. Abimelech knew every rock and stone, for this was his boyhood ancestral home and where he grew to manhood. As he drew near to the house of Gideon, he was met with scowls of contempt for the removal of the celebrated Baal-berith. Many still considered its removal a slight to Ophrah, and a boon of wealth and prestige for their rival city of Shechem.

CHAPTER 29

A Harvest of Heads

Abimelech entered the porch and immediately surrendered his dagger and his sword—but not his vengeance—to the keeper of weapons, and only then was he granted access. He confidently strode onto the porch of the great hall, where he was met by Jether, the eldest member, the firstborn son of his father, brother, and umpire of the assembly. Jether, a little troubled by his spoiled half-brother's tardiness, still managed to address Abimelech with gracious politeness.

"Brother, we are pleased that you have finally appeared. I, for one, was concerned you might have been ambushed by bandits or beasts, but I see you are well. The late hour has ensured that all are in attendance. We have called the roll, and all are present. We are all anxious to hear your petition of grievance. Please take your place on the high step of requests. We will endure, for the hour grows late, and only a few have partaken of the midday meal." Jether shouted over the din, saying, "Let peace be among us. Let the cup of judgment be our portion, and all glory to

Adonai, our King, our Lord, and our Ruler forever! Let us start by giving Abimelech his right to be heard." Jether took his seat at the head of the table and directly under the fleece of abundance.

Abimelech launched into his stalling tactic, immediately diving into a rambling monologue. His only concern was to give his henchmen time enough to do their dirty work. They had to secure the guards, the gate, the shofar horn of warning, and the stacked weapons of the seventy brothers. Abimelech also had to give them sufficient time to usher in the men of Shechem and the House of Milo and to rush the great hall to subdue all his brothers and fellow judges. Abimelech, having waffled on for fifteen minutes about trivial social matters in Shechem, decided the time was right to start his real speech. He paused, waiting for absolute silence, and then began to speak again.

"Brothers, honored judges and sons of my father, we have come to a crossroads of conscience. Our father, Jerubbaal, refused to be king of Israel, which was his right and his privilege. However, for him to say neither us, his sons, nor our sons, should ever rule over our brethren as kings was a birthright denied to all of us and to the glory of our posterity. His words were spoken without our agreement." Abimelech paused to take the pulse of the room. All eyes were fastened on him, and every ear tuned in to listen to his brazen speech. So far, he was merely warming up to his claim to majesty. To the seventy, it seemed fairly typical from their spoiled and overindulged half-brother. Abimelech continued, "Brothers and judges, so much is debated, and there are always too many catches and snarls of indecision. Nothing is ever completed due to the bitterness that resonates from within this assembly. I propose we disband this congress of seventy to proclaim me king! Who is better suited than me? I am both an Israelite and a Canaanite. This move will unify the country." The collective growl of scorn was met with a burst from the door as the men of Shechem, with swords and scimitars drawn, flooded the great hall. In a crashing wave of motion, they circled the table. The spear held by the master-of-arms was quickly snapped in two. The sons of Gideon were defenseless against the onslaught of Zebul and the House of Milo.

Zebul handed Abimelech his scimitar, who began wielding it over his head in a menacing manner. "Your life or your death will depend on your cooperation and your pledge," he threatened. "Not as an assembly do I offer you this opportunity, but separately. Each individual must make his choice, unaided and alone. The safety of your wives and children will be bargained away if there is any attempt at an uprising. You will be taken to the rock of fire where our father, Jerubbaal, claimed to have seen an angel. If you will swear loyalty to me and give me your absolute allegiance, it will go well with you. Jether, the honor is yours, being the firstborn son. I offer you now first opportunity to take a pledge of loyalty to me." Some of the brothers tried to stand but were manhandled back into their seats. Those who attempted to speak were clubbed over the head, their mouths stuffed with gags.

Jether pleaded with his brothers not to struggle. "My brothers, it is our duty to our wives and children to ensure their safety. We must avoid the possibility that they may be wounded. I know Abimelech, and believe me when I say he will stop at nothing to accomplish his despicable designs. He will not harm the innocent unless we give him cause, but if we do not comply, he will slaughter every last one of them. I urge you all now to do what is necessary, so we might avoid unnecessary bloodshed." Jether turned to Abimelech. "I do agree to your demands, Abimelech, and I will accompany you to the sacred boulder." Zebul remained in the great hall to maintain order and control while Jether was escorted by Abimelech through death's door, which closed blindly behind him.

On Jether's way past the winepress and to the base of the ancient oak, Jether passed a building where he saw a heavily guarded doorway and a multitude of women and children. This was where Abimelech had restrained the innocent, along with with a smattering of ill and old men. As Jether walked, a pack of ruffians jeered and jibed at him as he was forced along to his certain death. Finally, he was forced face down on the cutting edge of the fire stone that had stood as a memorial to Gideon's encounter with an angel of the Lord. The memorial now became a flagstone to the evil deeds of Abimelech, witnessed by the dark shadows of an ancient oak. Jether's arms were pulled apart by two menacing thugs, allowing Abimelech complete control over his older brother. His strut of confidence was a dead giveaway concerning what was to come. He stepped up to the stone and addressed Jether.

"You, my oldest brother—you who accompanied Father on all his legendary adventures—I have harbored an envy of your relationship with him. I long to have shared those experiences with him. You, Jether, were always the kindest to me, so this act will be the most difficult for me to carry out. You always attempted to protect me from the ridicule, violence, and bigotry of our brothers. So, I start with you, to make certain there can be no turning back. With your blood, I will stain this rock. It will be my retribution too long denied! This final moment of your life, the next scene in this deadly act, will be sealed by my hatred of all of you, and will confirm my ultimate sovereignty." Jether looked up at his younger half-brother as best he could under the force of restraints. "Is this to be a holocaust? Am I the first in the line of seventy? Am I to be your first attempt at a legal massacre?"

Abimelech, looking down at the face of his older brother, replied with a smirk, "Think me unjust? I have three questions to put to you. Your answers will decide the outcome of your fate, and in this way, you captain your own destiny. Do you, Jether, endorse me as your king, ruler and sovereign?" Jether knew that, if he disagreed, he would forfeit his life. He also knew that once Abimelech had taken this step, he would be left with no choice—not one brother would be left alive. Either that or he, Jether, would be mixed up in the settling of Abimelech's old scores.

"I agree, and I will swear an oath of allegiance," Jether replied, mustering the humility of wisdom and common sense. Abimelech was prepared for such an agreement, and in some measure, he expected it, especially when life and death could be so easily tipped in the balance of meaningful words.

Jether pondered his situation, reasoning that payback for the humiliation Abimelech had suffered as a child would now be addressed with the revenge of genocide. Timing and finely detailed planning would be necessary for the slaughter of siblings. Abimelech chuckled as if reading his brother's mind. "Well said, Jether. I put the next question to you: Will you now and forever disavow Adonai and take back Baalim, the god of the Amorites, and all his minions?" Jether had not been expecting such a revealing question of faith, and could not speak an immediate answer. Abimelech, in an unexpected moment of compassion, added, "Jether, because of your kindness to me, I will reveal the last question, to quell your worry." Without further pause, and with no sign of regret, Abimelech asked his final question. "Will you give me your firstborn child to be put through the fire in a sacrifice to Baalim, that he might accept our petition for his forgiveness for the destruction of his grove and the toppling of his altar?"

Jether could not agree to Abimelech's criminal suggestion. He dares not! Both he and his father, Jerubbaal, had suffered terrible starvation and survived impossible odds, sustained only by the hand of God. Abimelech took the matter into his own hands. "Well, to answer one of your earlier questions, this will be a legal execution! Since you will not agree to the gods of my reign. Your silence is proof of your refusal. I regard it as treason, and so yes, this is to be a legal execution. My first decree as soon-to-be king is to pronounce upon you, Jether, the sentence of death!" Abimelech nodded to a hulk of a man with a battle-ax in his hand. Jether was firmly stretched across the rock, his bare neck exposed to assist the executioner. The slayer allowed his ax to hover over Jether's exposed neck, measuring the accuracy of his impending blow. In one vicious swipe, Jether's head was severed, covering the angel stone with innocent blood.

Jether's remains, both body and head, were dragged behind the winepress; a bucket of water was splashed to wash down the gore-covered stone. This gruesome scene was repeated with increasing speed. Sometimes Abimelech's questions were altogether dismissed. As the blood of each brother was poured out in a gush, it became increasingly evident that the entire charade was merely a deception. None would be left alive! The chance they would seek revenge or plan a revolt would always be looming. It was sunset when the field and vineyard laborers started winding their way home. From down below and up above, they were unaware of the ongoing carnage and the the steady stream of blood soaking the ground and covering the Angel Rock. The farmers and livestock drovers returning back home to Ophrah in small groups were set upon and subdued. All their weapons were taken away; even their pitchforks, hoes, and shearing knives were set aside and safeguarded. Torches were sparked to raise some light, giving the macabre scene an eerie relief of deadly dark shadows.

The youngest son of Jerubbaal was Jotham. He was slight but sturdy, requiring the least amount of care and protection. The room soon emptied of brothers; it had become plain that, once through the heavily guarded blue doors, there was no returning. The remaining few communicated through winks, nods, and words that would confuse any outsiders. Distracting their weary custodians by all suddenly suffering from a fit of coughing, they threw the men of Shechem into confusion. Using this distraction, they took a stand; everyone on cue began to grapple, hands about necks or struggling to free the men of Shechem's hands from about their exposed throats. In the resulting scuffle, Jotham slipped handily under the table, quickly disappearing under some thin, loose floor boards. Jotham was an accomplished prankster; he had played this trick before when younger and smaller of stature. This time, it was a tight fit, as he was nearly full grown, but desperation acted as a lubricant; he slid in, remaining still, for his life and breath depended on it.

The slaughter continued without pause. Behind the winepress lay a multitude of corpses stacked up like cord wood. First light focused on the next-to-last son of Jerubbaal enduring his execution. Abimelech's blood was up; the killing frenzy had sustained this most heartless of jackals. Zebul applauded his kinsman. "Abimelech, this night is the stuff of legend! I had known your intent but did not think you had the grist to wheel such butchery. You have the makings of a royal dynasty. My report, My Lord: the great hall stands empty, but there was one sparked rebellion, an ill-timed uprising quickly overwhelmed."

Abimelech, ill at ease, asked Zebul, "Where is Jotham, the youngest? I had undoubtedly laid eyes on his face when I first entered the chamber, yet he is not among the lifeless. I thought perhaps you were saving him for last. Go! Scour the hall. Check all avenues of exit and approach. He must be found. He is the only one who could challenge my right to ascend the throne or mount a rebellion to take revenge. We must ferret out his whereabouts, leaving nothing to the blind folly of negligence." Abimelech took charge and, being familiar with all the hiding places, was painstakingly thorough. Jotham could hear the footfalls directly overhead but knew his detection would mean certain death. He held his breath.

"Give it up," Zebul finally pleaded, feeling extremely frustrated. "Every hidden den has been searched, and some of these steps have even been repeated, the fine comb has lost its tooth. The sun is up, and we have been busy this long and gruesome night. We need to gather together and head back to Shechem to prepare for your coronation. You put too much fear into such as Jotham, the young one. He will disappear and never be seen or heard from again. I have had my fill of killing. Another headless corpse, and I will spew. Let us retire from here."

Abimelech was spent. The stress of mass murder had taken its toll, and he relented. "Yes, I wish to depart this graveyard that was once my home, but there is a week's work of organization before we can head back to Shechem. Gather together the townsfolk. I would address them to relieve their suspense and to warn them of the dire penalties of rebellion against the new order."

The city was in a state of a collective shock. Confusion swept through the town. The jarring horn of shofar broadcast a general assembly. Who would be next on the chopping block? Abimelech and Captain Zebul were flanked by a gang of blood-splattered ruffians. Abimelech strutted across the square, exhibiting what he supposed to be the poise of royalty. Abimelech stopped and stared out at the people with eyes as black as coals. He took note of the strange, cold silence that could be felt.

"My neighbors and friends," he began, "it is with a sad heart that I address you this day. I speak to you of the formidable combination of execution and obligation. Some may cry that this day's work is a crime against decency. The truth, however, is that I have done what needed to be done to ensure your safety and well-being. The congress of judges—Jerubbaal's legacy—was useless and unfeeling. It did not look to the needs of the greater community, and this has left you and me in peril, from without and from within. We have insulted Baal in the striking of his altar and in the destruction of his grove. I have the right to bind up what was torn apart and to make right many ancient wrongs. My heritage allows me this right. I am both Canaanite and Israelite, and as the one remaining son of Gideon, I will be the first king of this land and see to equal justice for all."

All the men of Shechem, the House of Milo, and all the hirelings growled a weary cheer, while Ophrah looked on, dreading to hear who, or what might be next on Abimelech's evil agenda. Abimelech continued after a brief silence. He had been expecting their acclaim and approval but received nothing from all those who had known him and his family as heroes and as pillars of the community. Feeling disappointed, he continued, "We will replant the grove my grandfather, Joash, owned—the place that was the center of our pleasure and leisure. We will return to the worship of Baalim, and connect back to the ancient roots of our Amorite heritage. We will prosper greatly and glut our natural desires. Our city will plead with Moloch for his favor when we pass our children through the fire." Jadzia, Jether's wife, now one of the many stunned and grieving widows yelled out, "Who are you, to tell us to pass our children through the inferno?" "If you truly believe this, then YOU now would be a heap of charred bone and decrepit flesh, less than carrion, not fit for worms, Abimelech." Abimelech, red-faced with rage addressed his former sister in law; "I will dismiss your outburst of rebellion because of your sudden sorrow, but hear me now Jadzia, if one more word passes your lips you and your children will be the first to embrace the sacrificial blaze. Do not charge me, woman, or you will join this night's blood-soaked holocaust." The hush had a weight for the lack of breath. Abimelech gamely returned to his speech making without the slightest twinge of conscience or regret. "We will also shun the punishing God of the Hebrews." I will assign a committee of governing elders to oversee the reconstruction of the Baalim altar. They will manage in my stead and will monitor the levy of taxes. These will be collected and sent forth by messenger to me in the harvest seasons of barley, wheat, and wine. Trust me as your king, and, together, we will have a new dawn of prosperity."

A week passed, busily spent in creating a faithful batch of newly appointed officers to oversee the civil affairs of the city. Abimelech personally directed the layout of a greater grove and the placement of the polished altar stones. He and his Canaanite cousins quartered in Gideon's home and the house of the recently slain Congress of Brothers. Yet the ghosts of betrayal unhinged his mind and unnerved his rest with menacing moans and visions of headless phantoms.

Townspeople were assigned to dress and prepare the bodies of the slain brothers, who were all laid to rest with their father in the sepulcher of Joash in Ophrah of the Abiezrites.

CHAPTER 30

In the Shadow of Fire and Brambles

The twenty-eight-mile return to Shechem was filled with stories of mayhem endured and schemes coming to execution. It was the stuff of legend. The wine was this crew's favorite spoil, and many barrels had been impounded. The first keg of payment was readily pressed into fees decreed by Abimelech, the pretender, to satisfy the future needs of royalty.

Jotham was all but forgotten, yet he would not go away so quickly. He was shrewd in the art of evasion! Having had years of practice, he was used to endlessly hiding and ducking from his many brothers, who had kept him busy with menial labor attending to their endless personal errands. Jotham hid in the underbrush and in the clefts of rocks, staying focused on the whereabouts of his adversary and half-breed brother, Abimelech, whom he hated above all others. It was the season of berries, roots, and vengeance. On this cold table, he would seek his fill in the banquet halls of justice. Jotham, with the stealth and cunning of a wounded animal, waited in the shadows. He lagged far enough behind Abimelech's staggering troop, who were drunk with wine and boasting of spilled blood, to render them unaware of his planned ambush. They all wound down to the valley of Shechem, oblivious to the assassin's dagger, poised to pierce the savage breast of a double-minded blood brother.

One night between towns, an opportunity seemed to present itself. Abimelech and his men retreated into the rocks and weeds. Jotham stood ready to seize his moment, thirsting to quench his hot parched soul with the cold elixir of vengeance. He fell in among the shadows, listening for the first sign of snoring. His ears picked up a light conversation; he sharpened his focus, homing in on Abimelech's thin, shrill voice: "Zebul, we need watchmen to guard against potential troubles. Wild beasts prowl this region, looking for an easy kill. There are also some thieves and liars who work these byways in the dead of night, seeking to plunder and murder the unwary traveler."

The guards were doubled, forming a protective wall around Abimelech's guilty conscience. There would be no retribution tonight! Jotham kept vigilant until the middle of the second watch, waiting for an opportunity, after which he departed to a safer distance for some much-needed rest and to plan his next attempt.

Zebul was elevated to captain and was second only to Abimelech, the ruler of Shechem. Zebul addressed his king: "You have made known your intention to claim the throne. There is no one to stand in your way. The stage is set. All possible contenders but one have gasped their last breath. That one is but a youth, hiding out either in a vacant cave or high atop a mountain range . . . all the rest you have handily, or should I say 'headlessly' dispatched. You have the right to the throne by birth, and you have applied the right of conquest. You have indeed proven yourself to possess in abundance the sterner stuff found in the unyielding backbones of sovereigns. Becoming the first king of both Israel and of Canaan, you have cast the mold of destiny and dynasty. There is, however, one element lacking in your rise to kingship. One ritual needed before you hold the crown and scepter."

Abimelech, looking confused, gestured for Zebul to continue. "Pray tell, what is required? What ritual do I lack?"

Zebul smiled. "The ritual of your coronation, of course. You have taken the throne by your own hand, but without the formal ceremony needed to proclaim you regent, along with the acclaim of gods and notables, you will remain vulnerable and will be ridiculed as a bloodthirsty tyrant."

Abimelech was visibly delighted at the prospect of a spectacle, especially one that granted him sacred rites and assured him the actual submission of subjects. Brimming with confidence and self-satisfaction, Abimelech hoisted himself up to his full height and stature. "By all means, let us make my coronation official."

Zebul bowed slightly, evidenced by a silly smile with an upturned lip and a tightly clenched fist.

"We will gather all the men of Shechem. And all the House of Milo—your cousins in conspiracy—they are, after all, your chief supporters. A few days will be needed for preparation. A crown and cloak need to be created, and the makings of a feast. There must be meat aplenty, with a score of tapped barrels of convincing wine to help ferment your rise to glory."

Abimelech's victorious entrance into Shechem was a troubled occasion. Rumors had traveled faster than the speed of feet, proclaiming the bloodcurdling adventure enacted by Jerubbaal's half-breed son and the men of Shechem. The days of preparation passed quickly. Calves were slaughtered, and a lusterless crown was forged from the sparks of irony, villainy, and deceit.

Jotham kept up, following cagily behind the murderous crew, close enough to choke on the grit and dust of his brother's cold and callous treachery. His quest to salve the viper's bite was fueled by the innocent blood of his three score and ten dead brothers. His luck held; he stumbled upon a hideout in a wooded stretch just outside the Shechem Gate, where he could slip in and out of the city. Jotham waited, somewhat impatiently, for a chance to close in on Abimelech's throat. Security had doubled and then doubled again. Abimelech remained untouchable and unreachable. Even an attempt at a suicide mission would be foolhardy. Jotham would have sacrificed his own life if it had not been so utterly and completely futile. Jotham acquired the hooded rags and beggar's bowl of a vagabond and so easily remained invisible in the middle of crowds.

« « « » » »

Shechem rested in the shadow of Mount Gerizim, the holy mountain. There stood, inset on a rocky plateau, a house of God peopled by hermits and priests, visited only, on the rarest of occasions, by the pious and the devout, seeking the pilgrimage of inner peace. Eli, the younger, and Uzzi, the chief high priest, were both aware of the Baal-berith, but Eli would possess it for himself, as a prize, to proclaim himself worthy in the eyes of Shiloh. Eli dismissed rumors that the Ephod of Gold had become an evil snare to the house of Gideon, instrumental in the death of seventy of his sons. He considered these tales as unreliable hearsay. Eli found Uzzi prayerfully working in the garden. With flattery and guile, Eli swayed Uzzi into granting him permission to journey down Mount Gerizim to Shechem. His excuse was that he would gather up herbs, medicines, and much-needed provisions. "I would like your permission to enter Shechem," he said to the old priest. "Are any of the storehouses in need of restocking? I will collect what is desirable. I will gather up herbs and buy medicines. While I am there, it would please me to have a closer look at the Baal-berith, to see if the rumors of its power to heal are true."

Uzzi replied, "Go if you must, but do not tarry—there is unrest in the air from the murder of brothers and the coronation of one who would be an evil emperor."

Eli had secretly longed to examine the Baal-berith since its recent arrival down below in Sachem. He coveted the ephod, wanting to take it into Israel's custody once again, so his people Israel would benefit from Gideon's treasured memory. Eli took his leave and made his journey to Shechem town, modestly mixing in with the crowd of newly arrived pious pilgrims. Eli eagerly paid the price of admission. Using the temple's money, he gave it up to the warden who governed the tower of Milo's prize attraction. The Golden Ephod was everything and more than Eli had hoped for. He had read accounts that gave detailed descriptions of the intricate workmanship of Aaron's ephod, but this ephod was different. It was made of pure gold, with fine gold spun as thin as gossamer; it was woven seamlessly, and it was artistically inspired. It had two shoulder straps with the brilliant black-red and white sardonyx stones engraved with the names of the sons of Israel, six names on each stone in the order of their birth. The stones anchored the breastplate of judgment with two golden cords. The breastplate had the twelve precious stones in the banner colours that represented each tribe. The bottom edge of the breastplate had two braided gold chains to restrain the breastplate from flapping. All the settings were in gold—it was a work and a wonder to behold.

Eli turned his examination to the mighty Breastplate of Judgment. He mused, "It is missing the Urim and Thummin. How grand would it be to possess this precious artifact? But how? It belongs to the House of Milo, a holy relic in the hands of infidels."

Lost in thought while exiting, a beggar's bowl was thrust upon him, just missing his face and halting any forward progress. Jotham, spurred on by the desperate need for food, said: "Kind priest, having just been in the presence of such glory, would you be so inclined to spare pence for some life-sustaining bread and wine for one who is starving for the milk of human kindness?"

Eli was moved by the young beggar's plea and said, "I can do better than that, and you can accompany me to the inn. We will feast together on the evening's meat, for I am impressed to hear the tale of your story. Consider this the price for your supper." Jotham readily agreed as good judgment and caution were freely cast asunder by the demands of a shrunken stomach.

The conversation was sparse, but the meal was sumptuous, for crumbs, to a beggar is, oftentimes, regarded as a feast. The second cup of wine is a lubricant that slips past the guards of mind and tongue. Eli took the initiative and introduced himself, "My Name is Eli, son of Ithamar. I am a Levite and the chancellor of temple treasure on Mount Gerizim. What is your name, lad?" Jotham hesitated in his response, for the mention of his name in the wrong ears would mean certain death at the hands of Abimelech. Jotham felt assured that a priest would not betray a confidence but whispered ever so slightly in the priest's pitched ear, "My name is Jotham, the last full-blood son of Jerubbaal and sole survivor of Abimelech's massacre."

Eli could not be sure he believed what he heard and almost asked the lad to repeat himself but thought better of the greater danger of its repetition. Eli collected his thoughts and moved closer so as not be overheard and, in a barely audible murmur, asked "What then, young Jotham, are you doing in these dangerous surroundings? You have put yourself in harm's way, have you not?"

Jotham, with a steely stare, grasped tight the handle of his dagger and, with a muffled growl, said, "I am here to pierce the heart of a black-hearted half-brother, or I will die in the attempt—but not for the lack of trying."

Eli considered Jotham's plight and, after a long pause, said, "The killing of a king is a delicate undertaking, even for one who is a pretender. "Jotham's eyes squinted with boiling rage, and in a raspy whisper he hissed: "Abimelech can never be king of Israel; his mother is a gentile, a Canaanite concubine," Eli nodded his head in agreement, and continued, "Remember Jotham, that Abimelech has an ever increasing number of bodyguards, and one anointed, even falsely, he will have an army at his disposal. Your best hope Jotham, once the crown is placed on his head, is to make quick tracks—for you carry your father's royal seed of lineage. It is up to you, and no other, to preserve his pureblood legacy. I must depart and get back to the temple. If you need a friend to talk to or if I can help in any way, take the narrow road up to the temple gate. May God be with you Jotham, son of Jerubbaal."

Gideon: The Sound and the Glory

The time had arrived, and so had Abimelech. He walked into the shade under the sacred terebinth tree—the tree where Joshua had Israel bury all their idols of worship and all their golden earrings that had been symbolic of their service to foreign gods. The shade of the tree at the ninth hour, created by the deep, cool canopy, displayed an aspect of royal protection. It seemed a shelter of the king, whose job it was to cover and shield his people. The men of Shechem stood shoulder to shoulder, and the full house of Milo was present—all there to support their cousin in his ultimate moment of triumph.

An ancient Canaanite tradition practiced in the ordaining of a king was being whispered among the crowd. Tradition proclaimed that a king could be ordained only with the understanding of an open challenge. In ancient times, a physical combat to the death was required. In more recent times, the challenge had been reduced to an ordeal of verbal combat, given to a thrust and parry of intellect—and it must be enacted before the crown could rest upon the contender's brow—proclaiming his wisdom and capacity for leadership. The king's coronation had to be forcefully upheld and defended by the sureness of his newly acquired subjects of having decided correctly.

This event was open to all the men of Shechem, of whom most were in attendance. Only the bedridden were absent. This process ensured there was no question or doubt down the line as to who the keeper of the scepter would be. Only once this verbal challenge and refusal (or acceptance) had been completed was the anointing ritual to be undertaken. This process assured the legality of the new king's coronation.

Zebul stood at the right hand of Abimelech. He had found his place of power and acclaim at Abimelech's side. He had become his cousin's most loyal follower; his support of Abimelech served his own selfish ends, the raw power in the setting of agendas and precedents. In his powerful and booming voice, he started the process. "Friends, brothers, and most notable citizens of Shechem, we have gathered here in the plain of the pillar to install the first king of Israel, who will also be a king in Canaan. As is our tradition, I must announce to all present that, if there is anyone among you who believes he would be better suited to fulfill our needs and that the citizens of Shechem would receive greater benefit from his leadership, let him make his challenge and stake his claim. Let him display his courage to enter into debate with Abimelech, who stands as the current choice." Zebul's challenge went unheeded, except for the rustle of leaves from the terebinth tree, a cough, and an errant sneeze. None was so inclined to shoulder such a responsible role, to accept the burden of state, or to chance the wrath of Abimelech.

Zebul, knowing some discussion was required to consummate the ceremony, called out to Zayith, saying: "Zayith, will you reign over us?"

And Zayith replied, "Should I abandon my groves of olives, and the presses that turn my fruit into oil? My current labor benefits both God and man, so I must decline. I agree that Abimelech is the chosen one."

Zebul, now anxious for the heft of consent, called out again, this time to Hemor. "Hemor! Come and reign over us!"

And Hemor replied, "I have many fields filled with sweet figs that require all my attention. My life is fruitful, and I am busy with my own deeds. I, too, am not the man for you. It is Abimelech to whom I give my allegiance."

Zebul was not yet content, as a minimum of three challenges and refusals was required to conclude the ritual.

Zebul looked around the crowd and focused in on Hirvi, saying, "Hirvi, you have a voice in this community. You are a leader among us. You are also the keeper of the vineyard that provides sweet fruit for the winepress. Come! Reign over us!"

And Hirvi replied, "Shall I leave the production of my beautiful wine that cheereth God and man for the press of government? No! To Abimelech that honor must go, he who is both Canaanite and Israelite. The hand of fate has already ordained his regency, and so I agree. It is he, not I, who must reign over all our people."

And then the congregation said unto Abimelech as if with one voice, "Come thou, Abimelech, and reign over us!"

And Abimelech said unto the men of Shechem, "If you anoint me king over you, then come and put your trust in my shadow." The oil of olives was spilled on his head, and the prayers of infidels were mouthed. A cheer went up as a torch was passed around to symbolize the fire of Moloch.

The festivities began as soon as the knees that had been bent in a ritual of homage could be straightened. The men stood to partake of sweet wine, wetting their parched lips with the spirits of the gods. The pressing of flesh commenced, and bellies were stretched in shameless gluttony that lasted deep into the night.

The rumor of Abimelech's crowning was well-received, the first ever to be regarded as valid in Israel. Gossip of this historical event acquired the speed with which bad news travels, spreading abroad to distant shores: to Tyre in the north, and to Beer, on the borders of Moab to the south. The rude insult of Abimelech's coronation pricked the ears of Jotham, causing further injury to his freshly hardened heart, leaving him feeling frustrated and drained of energy. The scales of justice would have to remain tipped in Abimelech's favor for now. His rise to king required the need for even more security, having been proclaimed the anointed sovereign. This made an already daunting assassin's task less likely and even impossible. Jotham decided that Shechem was not a safe place to hide. It was just a matter of time, he would be discovered, and his fate would be linked to that of his many dead brothers.

Jotham had made a fast friend in Shechem. He told Jotham of a house of God high atop Mount Gerizim, the mountain that looked down over the rooftops of Shechem—a place where he might find comfort, solace, and perhaps even sanctuary. The friend, Eli, son of Ithamar, had the honorary office of chancellor of the temple treasures. Jotham, being a fugitive, needed a safe refuge immediately, so he went to seek the counsel of Eli on Mount Gerizim. Jotham scaled the heights of Mount Gerizim, that sacred mount where God had stayed the hand of Abraham and where Abram had paid his tithe to the high priest, Melchizedek, king of Salem. Jotham shouted for entrance at the temple gate. It was a religious temple, snuggled in an alcove on a high plateau overlooking the shallow Shechem Valley. Eli came to the doorway. "Who is it calling upon this temple?"

Jotham replied, "It is I, Jotham, the youngest son of Jerubbaal from the city of Ophrah. I come seeking refuge from my murderous half-brother, Abimelech."

Eli answered, saying, "I have received word of Abimelech's coronation under the terebinth tree. Though it is an outrage that your half-brother has been crowned king, we regretfully cannot offer you sanctuary, Jotham, son of Jerubbaal. If Abimelech gets wind that you are over his head, he will undoubtedly scour the mountain. He will murder all of us for attempting to protect you. Alas, you must continue on your way, but before you depart, I will give you food and water to sustain you while you flee."

Jotham replied. "I am grateful, but I have nothing to give you in return."

Eli brightened, realizing there was one thing Jotham could do for him. "Can you tell me the history of the Baal-berith?"

Jotham answered Eli, saying, "It was a gift to God from my father, Jerubbaal. It symbolized a bond between him and the Lord God Adonai. Jerubbaal dedicated it to Adonai for seeing to his protection and for His grace in allowing my father to overcome impossible odds, so he could crush the enemies of Israel."

Eli pondered his friend's difficulty, and asked, "Where will you go?"

Jotham replied, looking defiantly down to the valley floor and the red and gray rooftops of Shechem. He answered, "I have a close friend who resides in Beer. I will make my way to him speedily, but first I have one last undertaking before I go into hiding. I will call to the heavens for vengeance."

Taking his leave of Eli, Jotham immediately climbed to the very peak of Mount Gerizim, overlooking the shallow gorge of Shechem, where the voice of a tormented soul would carry far and echo through the valley down below. It was Jotham's intention to curse those who had murdered his brothers, allowing Adonai—in whom all punishment and blessings reside—to judge their fate.

Jotham, with his natural eyes, saw men as vain and covetous creatures, with all but a few deemed as enemies of God. But with his spiritual eyes, Jotham saw men as trees, comprising both

root and branch. With this understanding, he cursed them with
a parable, after reaching an overhanging balcony high up on
Mount Gerizim's summit. Jotham lifted up his voice, projecting
it to echo down, banking off the valley walls and flooding every
ear in Shechem.

> *Hearken unto me, ye men of Shechem that God may
> hearken unto you. The trees went forth at one time to anoint
> a king over them, and they said unto the olive tree, "Reign
> thou over us."*
>
> *But the olive tree said unto them, "Should I leave my
> fatness, wherewith by me, they honor God and man, and
> go to be promoted over the trees?"*
>
> *And the trees said unto the fig tree, "Come thou and
> reign over us."*
>
> *But the fig tree said unto them, "Should I forsake my
> sweetness, and my good fruit, and go to be promoted over
> the trees?"*
>
> *Then said the trees unto the vine, "Come thou, and
> reign over us."*
>
> *And the vine said unto them, "Should I leave my wine,
> which cheereth God and man, and go to be promoted over
> the trees?"*
>
> *Then said all the trees unto the bramble, "Come thou,
> and reign over us."*
>
> *And the bramble said unto the trees, "If you anoint me
> king over you, then come and put your trust in my shadow;
> and if not, let fire come out of the bramble, and devour the
> cedars of Lebanon . . . or all righteousness. Now, therefore,*

if ye have done truly and sincerely, in that ye have made Abimelech king, and if ye have dealt well with Jerubbaal and his house, and have done unto him according to the deserving of his hands . . .

(For my father fought for you, and adventured his life far, and delivered you out of the hand of Midian. Yet ye are risen up against the House of Gideon this day, and have slain his sons, threescore and ten persons upon one stone, and have made Abimelech, the son of his maidservant, king over the men of Shechem because he is your brother) . . .

If ye then have dealt truly and sincerely with Jerubbaal and with his house this day, then rejoice ye in Abimelech, and let him also rejoice in you. But if not, let fire come out from Abimelech to devour the men of Shechem, and the House of Milo, and let fire come out from the men of Shechem, and from the dynasty of Milo to devour Abimelech.

The brambles were for burning and not for shelter. So, too, was the burning hatred of Jotham's curse. Jotham spewed forth his plague on the men of Shechem and, in so doing, had published his exact whereabouts. Abimelech would rally his forces, making all haste to extinguish the life of the only remaining challenger to his authority. Jotham slid rapidly down the far side of Mount Gerizim, making all haste and wasting not a step in his desperate flight to Beer on the border of Moab and resided there for fear of Abimelech, his brother.

CHAPTER 31

The Curse of Wine and a Conspiracy of Liars

Eleven hundred days into Abimelech's reign, God sent an evil spirit of fear and loathing between Abimelech and the men of Shechem. That spirit did stretch tight their well-being on the rack of guilt and shame. Dishonor had strained any possibility of repairing the growing rift between the men of Shechem and King Abimelech.

The king's murmurs of sorrow grew in proportion to the frequency of his terrifying nightmares; headless visions overruled waking dreams. Abimelech's cousins were his first supporters but now were the first to speak of the cruelty done to the seventy sons of Jerubbaal. They talked about how a river of blood had been spilled and how it would come back to claim damages in an attempt to balance out the scales of an horrific injustice. The cry from the wrongs done to the cedars of Lebanon was overcoming the men of Shechem. It was they who had participated in the massacre and were slowly being infected by the mounting burden of truth and their fear of divine retribution.

Gideon: The Sound and the Glory

The mere sight of Abimelech was a constant reminder, forever forcing them to relive that night of horror and mayhem. The men of Shechem, especially Abimelech's cousins, who were the Keepers of the citadel, stood guilty—willing volunteers in the butchery and the bedlam. Bitterness crooked every casual smile of every simple greeting, coloring Abimelech's legacy in Shechem, which was viewed with the distorted eye of dishonor.

Zebul, Abimelech's captain, friend, and on-the-ground deputy in Shechem, was known for giving timely advice and inspired counsel. "Abimelech, moving your residence to the lordly city of Arumah will reap many benefits. Firstly, your personage right here in Shechem will no longer be a constant reminder of our night of bloodshed and carnage. And then there is the issue of the taxes you have introduced; they have made you unpopular with the people. Even though the Baal-berith, the Ephod of Gold, kept in the high tower on display, does generate enough wealth to offset your tax rolls, it is yet a shallow attempt to dull the memory of your family's holocaust. More time is required to dull these recent remembrances. Arumah is only six miles southeast of Shechem, and you will be shielded by Mount Gerizim."

Abimelech thought carefully about his limited options before responding to Zebul's suggestion. "As usual, Zebul, your counsel is wise and timely. I will build a new palace on the lofty plateau of Arumah. But I will visit you, my old friend, and my family, here in Shechem, on festive occasions such as marriage. I will also visit during the gathering of taxes and will be present when corrective justice must be meted out, such as in the passing of death sentences."

And so Abimelech departed with his staff for the elevated plateau of Arumah. "This will be more to my liking," he thought

234

to himself, "as it agrees with my grand ambition to be a king of kings." He counted on this move to mask the stench of death from the nostrils of the ordinary people, relying on the fragrant scent of forgetfulness. The dark cloud of his mass murder had crept in, and its stench had been cemented into the cracks and crevices of Shechem's daily living.

A shadow council was held. The plan was to hatch a scheme to find a way out of these dark days that faced the elders and princes of Shechem, a plan to relieve the people from the ever-tightening grip of fear and misgiving. Hirvi, the master of the vineyard, had heard the curse of Jotham ring out from the heavens, and ever since, he had become unhinged by the threat of his own extinction. Hirvi spoke first to his brethren. "Men of Shechem, we have been convicted by a curse, a curse that resulted from the terrible deaths of many innocent people, in which we played a part. Abimelech convinced us to assist him, insisting his plan would benefit Shechem and Canaan. Not only were we involved in the butchery of Abimelech's brothers, but we also agreed to hoist him over us to be our lord and king. Our offense is thus twofold, compounding in equal measure our punishment to satisfy the demands of justice."

Hemor spoke next. "What are we to do? He is our anointed king and has at his command an army to carry out his bidding."

Hirvi, with a smirk and a wink, picked up on Hemor's comment. "Yes, Hemor. You are quite correct. If we do attempt to send Abimelech off to an early grave in the hopes of releasing ourselves from Jotham's curse—and to revoke our ever-increasing tax burden—we will have to employ cunning and trickery to make his elimination look like a random act, a chance accident of fate and bad luck." The room grew still. Each man looked around, trying to measure the group's reaction to Hirvi's suggestion of high treason.

Keret, speaking for the house of Milo, took his opportunity. "We, too, would like to see our cousin sent to the worm, but all care must be taken not to link us to this treason. Besides which, Zebul remains loyal. If he sniffs out the slightest sign of treachery, we will meet the same end as the sons of Jerubbaal." Fear for life and limb crept in; the jitters of insecurity froze the room in a cold shiver of confusion and uncertainty.

Hirvi broke the silence. "Hear me out. I have thought long and hard in the consideration of a plan. Even if it fails to kill Abimelech, it will not come back to haunt us. We will engage highway robbers, skilled in the arts of both waylay and murder. Their hire will come from the stretched pockets of all who are now present, and not from the telltale trail that would lead back to us from the Baal-berith treasury. I will be their only contact, limiting our risk of exposure. Abimelech travels frequently—but only when the whim strikes him—between Arumah, his mountain stronghold, and Shechem. He moves about with light and vain protectors when passing through Mount Gerizim, and that is where our henchmen will ambush this cursed usurper. The genius of the plot is that they will regularly rob all who pass by. This will lead everyone to consider their practice is nothing out of the ordinary. It certainly won't amount to being thought of as a conspiracy to assassinate the king. His death will be thought of as only an unfortunate accident, being at the wrong place at the wrong time."

The plan was put in place and could well have succeeded, except that Abimelech had become sick and had taken to his bed. Enough time passed during his mending for news of robbers on the king's highway to stir his sheriffs to marshal enough force to surround the criminals. Men were sent to ferret out the nest of vipers, thereby making safe the common passage between Shechem and Arumah. Rumors persisted that these robberies had been the stirring of treachery by the angry and disenchanted people of Shechem, but no proof was forthcoming, as all the hired liars were either killed or had shrunk back into the familiar refuge of caverns and shadows.

Gaal, the son of Ebed, from the house of Hamor—he who was the father of Shechem—lived on the other side of the Jordan with his clan of Canaanite ruffians. Gaal had drunk the bitter cup of envy and disgust. An Israelite had been anointed as king of Canaan, and Gaal took this as a personal affront. Gaal often did business with Hirvi, the master of Shechem's vineyard, ferrying wineskins across the river to sell to his clan of Canaanite hooligans. Many a wineskin had been sealed with the corkscrew of rumors with the added twist and turns of current events, providing Gaal with a ready supply of vintage wine, as well as all the juicy gossip from the far side of the Jordan.

Gaal had gathered together his brethren, instilling in them a sense of bravado by filling their minds with strong wine and stiffening their backbone with his warlike speechmaking. Gaal then traveled, fully armed, to start a quarrel he hoped would topple the lofty aims of Abimelech. Gaal assembled the men of Shechem at a time when open conflict and the discontent of unrest was the spit on everyone's lips. He put familiar words to their thoughts, for he was one of them. He was eagerly accepted, being local, and the men of Shechem put their confidence in him, in the hope that a new champion and savior had been recruited.

His band's fondness for the grape filled their eager mouths with strong wine, loosening already rowdy tongues with blunder and bluster. Gaal rallied his fellow winebibbers and those men of Shechem who supported him with a rousing speech. "We will make merry, given the prospect of our escape from Abimelech's tyranny." Gaal motioned to his wine merchant, Hirvi, bending his elbow and curling his fingers, and bringing his hand up to his gaping mouth in the fetching signal of a winebibber. "The skins are dry, and so am I. Let us go into the fields to gather in the harvest so we can crush down the grapes and become wet with bravado and merriment."

Overfilled skins were soon fermented, leading to a wild jubilee that burst forth in the hall of Baal-berith, their god. Flushed with the bravery of a rabid pack of wolves, they cursed Abimelech. One at a time they cursed him, and at times in unison; with song and with the dance, they cursed him. Gaal, the son of Ebed, stood tall on a makeshift platform in front of the Ephod of Gold. He shouted out in his drunken frenzy, his voice carrying over the din and the cursing: "Who is Abimelech? And who is Shechem? Who is Abimelech that we should serve him? Is he not the son of Jerubbaal? And Zebul, his captain? I say we serve the men of Hamor, who is the father of Shechem! His house, his decedents, and our family of heritage. Why should we serve Abimelech? He is a man of Israel and a half-breed, who uses this as an excuse and a reason to lord over us. And would to God that these people were under my hand and direction! I would remove Abimelech from over our heads, and I say to Abimelech with passion and contempt, 'Increase thine army, and come out and meet me on the field of battle, and I will purge this scourge and cursed upstart by force of arms.'"

CHAPTER 32

The Shadows of Mountains and Men

There were warnings and boastings added to a host of drunken cursing, all belittling the strength of the king. This was also to soothe the vanity of men whose guilty conscience had been offended. The words of Gaal traveled on the wings of scorn, and his threats of personal combat pierced the ears of Zebul, Abimelech's trusted captain, his only friend, the ruler of the city. Zebul was angered by the rash bragging and rabble-rousing of this foreign intruder. He was unwelcome, and Zebul vowed he would put a stop to the man's swagger. Zebul was Abimelech's eyes and ears, who was privy to the defiant pulse of the ailing city. He had risen up to be Abimelech's well-trusted chamberlain, of both policy and strategy. He immediately sent by night a courier, via a secret route, to the high plateau of Arumah, bearing news of this invader's challenge to the authority of King Abimelech. The parchment unrolled read:

Gideon: The Sound and the Glory

*Your Most Gracious Highness, King Abimelech: Gaal,
the son of Ebed, a former resident of Shechem, feels bitter
resentment toward you, Abimelech, son of Jerubbaal. His
bitterness revolves around a man of Israel taking the throne
in a city of Canaan. He has returned in the company of his
heavily armed kinsmen and has added fuel to the dry kindling
of mischief fanning the smoldering embers of sedition. He has
set the spark, inflaming the city to rise up against you. The
city has organized their men and weapons, while Gaal and
his league of ruffians hastily shore up cracks and breaches
with the trowel of discontent, fortifying the city walls against
you in open rebellion. Abimelech, my friend, and sovereign,
a warning: A frontal assault on the stronghold will reap only
a stale reward—that of a moldy blockade. Our success will
come from stealth, as when we attacked Ophrah. Approach
Shechem at the beginning of the second watch, covered by the
cloak of night. Lie hid from sight in the tall grass. The boulders
and trees of the field alongside the gate will be your shield of
invisibility. Most of all, be patient and allow the rising sun
to work the magic of your surprise attack. At first light, the
gatekeeper will be focused on his daily routine. There will be
no reason for him to think anything out of the ordinary is
about to occur. The inner courtyard will be exposed once you
are through the gate. Gaal and his followers will soon come out
and challenge you. I give you leave by my authority as governor
of this city to do what you deem necessary. I rely solely on your
discretion concerning how best to dismiss this rabble-rousing
bibber from Shechem.*

—Your captain and friend, Zebul.

Abimelech acted quickly upon the advice of his trusted friend. He assembled his people into four companies, surrounding the town in a scheme he had devised to overwhelm the foreign troublemakers. Abimelech and his host arrived at night at the start of the second watch. They lay in wait, concealed in the tall grass that bordered Shechem. Gaal's appearance at the entrance to the main gate had become part of his daily routine and was expected. He used the early morning to impress upon the men of Shechem his promise to be a friendly and agreeable king. He would call them by name, inquiring after their health and the welfare of their families. This was done to dispel any doubt that he was one of them and, thus, could be counted on as a true son of Canaan. In that very hour, Zebul made sure the gate was unbolted and open. His well-timed appearance made it clear that he remained loyal to the reign of Abimelech.

The sun burst through the open gate, blinding all who stood at the entrance to the city. Zebul lifted his hand in a bid to dim the glare—the shadow he cast over his face was a preset signal for Abimelech and his men to rise up. Four invisible armies appeared as if out of thin air. Gaal looked all about him, but his mind was unable to comprehend what was happening. His eyes were unable to adjust to the scene unfolding before him. Legions of armed men were rising up out of the dust. He turned to Zebul. "Behold, there come people down from the top of the mountains."

Zebul knew full well what was in store, for it was his plan that he was describing. He wanted Gaal to keep doubting his own eyes, knowing his hesitation would prevent him from pursuing a current course of action, thus sealing his doom. His words added fuel to Gaal's confusion.

"You see the shadows of the mountains as if they were real men . . . your eyes and your mind warn of your worst nightmare made evident in the flesh." Gaal was struck dumb. He was still suffering the effects of the previous evening's wine-stained corruption. He was unable to separate fact from fantasy. With time, Gaal was able to gather his wits about him. He focused in, trying to convince Zebul of the coming invasion.

"See? There come people down by the middle of the land, and another company approaches along by the oak of the diviners. We are surrounded by a host of ghosts from every direction."

Zebul, sporting a smirk and brimming with satisfaction, addressed Gaal with just a hint of sarcasm.

"Where now is your mouth? Were you not bragging just yesterday about how mighty you are and speaking words that belittled King Abimelech? Did you not say, 'Who is Abimelech, a man of Israel and a son of Jerubbaal? Who is he that we should serve him?' Is this not the people against whom you spoke hatred? Go out and meet him on the field of honor! Prove the words of your mouth in mortal combat, or be the coward that I believe you to be."

Gaal summoned his men, and his weapon was delivered to his hand. In the sight of all Shechem, he called forth Abimelech to personal combat. "We will settle the matter man to man!" exclaimed Gaal, and all agreed that Zebul was to be the referee. The fight was short-lived but savage. The years of wine and lawless living took their toll on Gaal's stamina, and Abimelech, after all, was a son of Jerubbaal. As the strength of the father so is the power of his son. Gaal was exhausted; his arms had the weight of lead, and his legs turned into quivering bands. His eyes blurred, affected by the sweat drenching his forehead. Gaal swallowed his words and his pride . . . to continue fighting was to die. Fear gave wings to his feet, and only his back was visible now, as he turned and ran for the gate. Abimelech was hot after him. Many were killed and wounded as they attempted to reenter the threshold of the city in the hope of finding shelter from the rain of sword and arrow.

Zebul called an end to the conflict. As had been previously agreed, no battle would take place inside the gates of the city, as long as he was governor. Zebul proclaimed King Abimelech to be the victor. He announced to everyone present that Gaal was a coward and that he and his men were no longer welcome in Shechem. He ordered them all to depart before the squawk of the next day's cock, or they would be turned over to King Abimelech to face the charge of rebellion and be sentenced to death. Abimelech was satisfied with the banishment of Gaal. The king Abimelech returned with all of his armies back to his stronghold at Arumah.

CHAPTER 33

The Assassin's Ax and the Fire of the Baal-berith

Hemor, Keret, and Hirvi choked back their disgust. Yet another failed attempt to have Abimelech's foot removed from their necks made them feel as if they had been fed a mouthful of feathers and dust! They immediately began to devise another plot. Keret spoke first. "We have to dispose of Zebul, Abimelech's trusted captain and tactician. Every move we make is immediately transmitted to him."

Hemor added a note of caution to the dialogue. "Zebul is the closest thing to a friend that Abimelech has, and if we slay him, we will inherit the king's fury. He will undoubtedly take revenge."

Hirvi weighed in next. "If we act quickly, before Abimelech takes notice, we can field all our forces, including Gaal, the House of Milo, and all of the Shechem to attack him. He will be at his citadel, celebrating his victory. He will not be expecting an attack so soon after his latest victory. With Zebul out of the way, there will be no one to advise Abimelech or give him any advance warning. We must act quickly, though. There is no time to hire a practiced assassin, so I will do the deed. I will visit Zebul with some new wine, making mention of some political conspiracy. In the privacy of his inner chamber, I will administer a fatal blow while we are all alone. My treachery will come at a time when it is least expected."

Zebul was at home, as was his custom at this late hour. His wife and children had long since retired to their pallets, and Zebul would usually have been alone, except for by accident or occasion Zebul was coaching young Sydyk, his apprentice, in the art of spying, late into the evening. Zebul was training him for the purpose of refining Shechem's political strategies. Sydyk was also loyal to Abimelech. The young apprentice was known for being fleet of foot and had shown shrewd promise in the shadowing of men. When an unexpected knock disturbed their secret conversation, Zebul directed Sydyk to an adjoining dark alcove. Hirvi appeared at the door with a skin of new wine. He offered a feeble apology for intruding without an invitation at this late hour. He begged for pardon but insisted on being admitted.

Zebul bristled at this insult to his privacy, saying, "What could possibly be so pressing that it can't wait until morning?"

Hirvi replied, "Please allow me entrance, Zebul, so I will not be overheard or misunderstood. There is a military adventure in the making that concerns all of the Shechem and the well-being of Abimelech."

Zebul sighed, opening the door. "In that case, you may come in, but be quiet, so as not to disturb the household, for they have all long since found slumber. Follow me to my private chamber."

Zebul offered a chair and two empty goblets, accepting the intruder's company and providing the comfort of his own hospitality. "Tell me about this pressing matter," he said.

Hirvi looked around before asking, "Are you sure there are no ears pressed against walls to overhear our conversation?"

Zebul shook his head, saying, "Speak on."

Hirvi continued, "Gaal is not making plans to depart. Instead, he has rallied his men and all of the Shechem, including the city of Thebez. They have agreed to field an army at dawn to surprise Abimelech in his stronghold at Arumah."

"Why have I not heard of this before?" Zebul asked, rising up, and standing over Hirvi. In a sterner tone, he inquired, "Have you any proof of these claims?"

Hirvi nodded briskly. "Yes, I do! Here. They are engraved on the blade of my dagger." Hirvi stood up, and in one fluid motion, he caught Zebul in the windpipe with his outstretched blade. Zebul gurgled and reached out to attack his assailant but soon crumpled, dead, to the floor. Sydyk had witnessed the murder of his mentor and sprang out of the shadows. Hirvi, taken by surprise, was unable to dislodge his dagger from Zebul's neck bone. While he struggled to remove his blade, Sydyk plunged his own knife deep into Hirvi's throat. Shocked at this turnaround of ill-fortune, his eyes ablaze, Hirvi reached the door and dropped dead on the threshold.

Sydyk cradled his dead master's head in his arms, grieving for the loss of his mentor; his hopes of receiving new wisdom and his rise in political ambitions had to be utterly abandoned. All that was left of his dreams was a puddle of blood seeping out the door sill. Sydyk knew that Hirvi's tale of impending invasion needed to be passed on to Abimelech . . . every minute could be counted for an hour. Sydyk knew the gates of Shechem would be locked down and guarded at this late hour. He would have to climb over the perimeter wall to make his rapid journey by night to Mount Gerizim. He could still reach the summit by dawn before descending down the far side to Arumah to warn King Abimelech. He just hoped he would get there in time to warn of the surprise and avert a crushing encounter.

The moonlight made the path up the slope glisten in the thin mist. A spectacular dawn broke just as Sydyk reached the peak. He abruptly turned to see the gate of Shechem open and an army of farmers and warriors being fielded in combat squadrons. Sydyk's dash to Arumah was sped up by the fiery alarm of urgency. The Arumah stronghold was roused by the yells from the panting cries of Sydyk, the spy. Abimelech, was awakened, and Sydyk was presented to Abimelech who was still wet from the privy.

"Your Majesty," he said, "it is with a saddened heart that I must speak to you of the death of Zebul, your captain, partner, and friend. If it is any consolation, my King, I killed his murderer in the same brutal fashion in which he murdered my mentor—with a dagger to the throat! There is a more pressing matter that has forced my feet to flee and my tongue to disclose that you are in the gravest danger. I have witnessed this day all the people who count themselves your enemies march through the gates of Shechem, where they were fielded into a formidable army. They are currently streaming to your palace. I have purchased a little time with my stealth and my speed, but time is at the core of your survival."

"My armor and my captains!" Abimelech shouted. "Awaken the people! We will counter their surprise attack with a full measure of our own shock. Their eyes will open wide in disbelief."

Abimelech's people gathered in great haste, waiting to receive direction from their chief and commander. Abimelech stepped into their midst to address them. "This day will confirm my right to be your king. With baptism by fire and terror, we will overwhelm their advance; we will then descend to Shechem and raze it to the ground. It is, after all, a place fit only for owls, jackals, and cattle. We will avenge the death of Zebul, my captain and my friend. They will know my fury. Their dying screams will be exquisite music to my ears. They will know pain and agony this day before they die. We will form three companies. I will take the first company to the head of the gap and lie in wait, unobserved. Let the advancing column of Shechem pass unharmed. The other two companies will lie in the blind on both sides of the depression, looking down from the ridge. On my command, we will all rise up with one accord. The cleft will serve as their common grave. We hasten at full gait to our destiny to ensure certain death for those who practice high treason this day."

As soon as Abimelech had led his company to the head of the gap to lie in wait, with not a moment to spare, Gaal and his people entered the ravine. They were followed closely by Keret and the House of Milo, with the balance of Shechem and a few men from Thebez taking up the rear. Between them, they had filled Abimelech's death trap. They were overconfident of victory, placing too much faith in an attack they had expected to be coming as a complete surprise. Abimelech signaled with the shofar, and all who were with him rose up and smote their enemy with a wrath-filled fury. To a man, their enemies fell dead. Blood trickled over the rocks, gushing out from artery and vein. The ravine had become a scene of devastation.

Abimelech was flush with victory; his men were stained red, their blades dripped gore, and their armor was smeared and splattered with a dark crimson dye. Abimelech gave his next battle command. "My company and I will rush the Shechem Gate. The other two companies will glean the fields surrounding the town. Leave no man alive. Then come and join us to finish the job."

All that day, the slaughter continued as Abimelech fought against the city. Some protested, giving an account of themselves, while others relented, accepting their fate. In the end, all who were found standing were butchered and hacked into small portions and pieces. Abimelech took the town and beat it down; there was not a roof or a wall left upright. Abimelech added a final touch to his vengeance: he seeded Shechem with common salt to poison the fields for a harvest of weeds, laying down the paving stones of desolation.

Fear gripped the remaining inhabitants who had escaped Abimelech's wrath. The grim reaper was in the streets. The only relief would come from the high tower of Milo, the security of the hold, the resting place of the Baal-berith, the Ephod of Gold. The tower was built on raised ground, both for protection and observation, forty rods from the center of town. All the men and women who were able scurried to the safe haven of the keep for shelter against Abimelech's ravenous onslaught.

Shechem lay in ruin, but very few of its inhabitants had been slaughtered. Abimelech inquired after the people, asking, "Where have all the people gone? Where have they hidden?" Sydyk had witnessed the desperate exodus of the townsfolk to the citadel of Milo, the cavern-keep of the Baal-berith.

Sydyk answered the king. "All the men have gone to their rock-solid hold beyond our reach. They have thwarted justice, adding to our wrath and all but stealing our revenge of insurrection."

Abimelech broke into a white-toothed grin. "There is a way, Sydyk! My father, Gideon, and my brother, Jether, spoke of the Tower of Penuel. It was here that my dad Gideon herded the men inside the hold before setting fire to it; in a blind rage, he wrestled the Tower down with flames of justice, and I will do the same. Set your company around the base of the sanctuary, and brace the door against any attempt to exit." Abimelech called to attention all the other people, saying, "Follow me to Mount Zalmon." Reaching the wooded skirt of the mountain, he took an ax in his hand. It was his father's ax, now his by birthright; he chopped down a branch from the nearest tree and then took it up onto his shoulder. Abimelech looked around, addressing all the people who were with him. "What you have seen me do, make haste, and do as I have done." The ax of Gideon, familiar in the wanton destruction of trees, was readily passed from man to man to get the job done. Some used killing swords to cleave limb and branch, rather than standing idle, for their blood was up.

A pile of hewn branches was placed at the base of the hold, piled to the height of the door. The green wood was doused with oil, and a spark was struck. The flames produced a thick, choking smoke, causing the men and women inside the hold to rush at the door, but it would not give way; it had been secured from without with a stout-beamed barricade. Someone inside the tower called out in desperation: "The Baal-berith will be our savior! If we can touch the gold of the ephod, it may yet shield us from cremation." The people of Shechem swarmed the altar, their bodies piled high, clawing and scratching to touch the ephod in the hopes of deliverance. Their screams grew increasingly louder until suddenly it all fell silent except for the crackle of flames that licked up to the heavens, causing the roof to fall in with a shudder. A thousand men and women died in the inferno, blinded by the ill-fame of a fallen idol. They died clutching for the golden idol in the futile hope that they would find relief from their torment . . . the snare of the Baal-berith continued to work its dark magic.

CHAPTER 34

The Bruising of Heels and the Crushing of Heads

Abimelech, his army, and all his loyal followers had battled and plundered all that day. Rest and refreshment were necessary. The stores of wine, bread, and raw meat were cooked from the glowing embers of what was left of the smoldering tower; the occasional flares from human remains sparked a long, dark shadow in the dead of night.

It was agreed to rise before the sun because the heat increased the rate of rot—the smell of burnt flesh sickened nostrils, even the noses of the most hardened stoics were insulted. All were anxious to depart from the open cemetery that was now Shechem. Abimelech addressed his three companies of professional killers. "We will encamp against Thebez! They have conspired against me and have sent men to war against my regency. Thebez is thirteen miles from here, just over the horizon. It is less than a day's journey. The city is known for the milling of wheat and barley into flour. They, too, have a high and secure tower that we will bruise and then topple to the ground."

Abimelech's great multitude of men-at-arms was expected in Thebez, and the townspeople feared a merciless massacre. When Abimelech's warriors were observed from the heights of their tower, it threw the people into a desperate frenzy.

Abimelech threw open the unguarded gate, finding no opposition—all the citizens of Thebez had abandoned their city and had barricaded themselves within the safety of their high tower. Abimelech fought to destroy the tower all day, going hard at the door with a makeshift battering ram. He bruised the heel of the threshold, but it would not give way. Abimelech stood ready, once more, to put fire to the structure; he was about to ignite the secure wooden door of the tower. Up above, people milled about on the upper balcony, watching as they were about to be roasted alive or to be assaulted by the sword and killing spear puncturing their secure womb once the outer hold was breached. One of the women high atop the tower's brim had missed her step and stumbled upon a piece of broken millstone. Stooping down, she hefted it with all of her strength. She raised it up, balancing it on the balcony rail, where she paused to find her mark. Finding it, she gave the millstone a mighty shove, allowing gravity and fate to do their easy work. Far below her, at the base of the tower, her rock found its perfect mark. Abimelech's head was crushed, cracking open with a brittle snap. He clutched at his skull, holding it together with the force of his hands, with blood gushing between his fingers and his brain exposed.

Abimelech knew he was a dead man. He could not bear the shame of being killed in such a manner, for he heard the voice of a woman calling out in jubilation, boasting of her aim, and shrieking with delight at how she had killed a ruthless despot.

Abimelech called out in distress. He was bleeding out—and black-ing out—and said to his young armor-bearer: "Draw your sword and slay me as a warrior king, so that I may avoid the ridicule of men from beyond the grave. I am king Abimelech and the son of Jerubbaal. Do this thing so that none can say that I was killed by a wayward stone, shamefully thrown from the dainty hand of a woman." The youth rose up and thrust Abimelech through the heart. Abimelech fell backward, hit hard, and broke open his splintered skull on the unforgiving cobblestones. When all the men of Israel who were his people, and even Sydyk, his captain of one Hundred, saw that Abimelech was dead, they surveyed the carnage; the eyes of their understanding quickly opened to a guilt-ridden regret. All departed, every man to his place. The reign of terror had come to an end. Thus, the wickedness of Abimelech, his cruelty brought against his father's house—in slaying his seventy brothers. And so, with a vengeance—evil was repaid to Abimelech's head. All the sin that the men of Shechem shared, God rendered upon them justice, and upon them all, it came to pass, the curse of Jotham, the son of Jerubbaal.

Genesis 3:15 And I will put enmity between thee and the woman, and between thy seed and her seed; it shall bruise thy head, and thou shalt bruise his heel. Selah.

Part Four

KIRATH-JEARIM

SHILOH

RAMAH

NOB

JERUSALEM

BETH-SHEMESH

BETHLEHEM

KHIRBET KHEIYAFA

(VALLEY OF ELAH)

DEAD SEA

MIZPEH-MOAB

ADULLAM
(THE CAVE)

KEILAH

GATH

MOAB

HEBRON

ZIPH   SELA-HAMMAHLEKOTH

WILDERNESS
OF MASON

CHAPTER 35

Eli's Coming and the Resurrection of the Baal-berith

Three years had passed and Israel continued to suffer under the cruel reign of Abimelech. It had also been three years since the departure of Jotham. Eli, meaning *elevation*, was a young and restless priest—a direct descendant of Aaron, and, therefore, an endowed Levite by birthright. He still had the ambition of youth. Being stuck as a chancellor of religious treasures at the house of God, high and away on Mount Gerizim, was not to Eli's liking. Eli was searching for an opportunity to be dismissed, for, by covenant and by written agreement, he could not just up and quit his sacred calling. He wanted to make his way to Shiloh, and to the Tabernacle, where the Ark of the Covenant resided and where a young priest could make his mark in this spiritual metropolis.

Eli and Uzzi, the chief high priest, were both aware of the Baal-berith, but Eli would possess it for himself, as a prize, to proclaim him worthy in the eyes of Shiloh. Eli dismissed rumors that the Ephod of Gold had become an evil snare to the House of

Gideon, cursing the death of seventy of his sons. He considered the testimony of young Jotham as fanciful and that Abimelech just had a ruthless temperament and determination to be king.

Eli coveted the ephod, wanting to take it into Israel's custody once again, so his people would benefit from its treasure.

Uzzi, the high priest, sensed that Eli was uneasy, so he inquired of him, asking, "What troubles you, Eli? You have been preoccupied ever since your journey to Shechem. Tell me about your concern, so we might put it to rest."

Eli frowned. "I have been troubled over the Baal-berith, it being in the hands of non-believers, whereas it should be a sacred treasure belonging to Israel."

Uzzi had considered the young priest's confession before he replied. "Eli, the Baal-berith was made with the highest intention, but its very fabric is cursed by all those who would embrace it. The ephod has become an idol of worship. It is best left alone and kept where it is housed. Think no more about this golden calf."

Eli would not be so easily dissuaded and responded with an argument he had been pondering. "It is not the object that has raised itself to idol status, but the beliefs of the heathens that give it power. It is merely a brilliant item of beauty if you do not give it power; it has none of its own."

Uzzi disagreed. "I believe the gold earrings of servitude have turned it into an evil snare. The gold of foreign gods is a sacrilege. I will not discuss this any further. Leave this icon of worship alone, and tend to your office! There is another matter that has come up before and again now. It is your failure to salt the meat used for sacrifice, which is a desecration of the offering. The salt represents freedom from corruption and decay; without the salt, the offering will not be accepted by the Lord, according to our ritual commandments. And every oblation of thy meat offering shalt thou season with salt; neither shalt thou suffer the salt of the covenant of thy God to be lacking from thy meat offering: with all thine offerings thou shalt offer salt.

The two men argued and would not be reconciled, until finally, Uzzi proclaimed: "Another such incident of disobedience, and you will be asked to leave permanently!" The two men parted, spiritually opposed from that moment forward.

Two weeks later to the day, the night sky over Shechem was ablaze. The sound of turmoil sliced through the serenity of the temple. The tower hold of the Baal-berith was blazing, and shrieks of horror filled the still night air. Uzzi ordered the gates locked and bolted against the overflow of screams and scourges.

A fortnight had passed with no tell-tale noise; Shechem was as quiet as wormwood in a graveyard. The smoldering embers of Shechem's Tower had been doused by a sudden rain and had been snuffed out for the lack of flame. Everything had been consumed. Shechem was still, except for the scampering of scavengers and the overflight of raptors. Eli departed without leave or permission from Uzzi, the chief priest. He dashed out of the high-walled confines the moment the gates were opened, and he rushed down to the scene of a horrible holocaust. The tower hold was wrestled to the ground, and all that remained was a curious mound where jackals, foxes, and vultures were feasting. The stench of death and rot choked Eli's nostrils, and he was about to depart when a single shaft of light reflected back off the pile of rubble and remains. There was an unmistakable glint of polished yellow peeking through the debris. Eli approached, and using a stick, he scared away the carrion-feeders.

He poked through the mound of the dead, and to his utter amazement, discovered that the Baal-berith was undamaged. It had been protected by the throng of bodies that had piled up around it. Eli was overjoyed and knew for a certainty that it was a gift from God. He freed the Golden Ephod and washed off the soot and the clinging gore. Eli hurried back to the temple mount and presented the Baal-berith to Uzzi, the high priest. Uzzi was immovable in his resolve not to permit the ill-fated icon to find rest on the temple grounds. "The Baal-berith will not find sanctuary under this roof! It needs to be destroyed before it causes any more harm."

Eli disagreed. "It was preserved from inevitable destruction, so I could find it and restore it to Israel."

This challenge to Uzzi's authority, in addition to their irreconcilable quarrel, left Uzzi no alternative but to dismiss Eli. "Eli," he said to his young disciple, "you will make your own way from this place! The door to this enclave is barred to you and to your idol of abomination. My words will tingle in your ears in the days to come. Be gone, and do not look back." Eli departed with his pride bruised but his prized Ephod of Gold intact. His excitement was matched only by his expectation—how would he be received when he arrived at the Tabernacle of habitation in Shiloh, the spiritual capital of Israel?

CHAPTER 36

Life in the Shadow of the Tabernacle

A gleeful Eli slid down the south face of Gerizim. It was only a short trek of twelve miles to Shiloh and the horizon. But it might as well have been on the far side of the world as far as priestly vows were concerned. Eli had been tightly bound to Mount Gerizim, as if with strong cords, until he had been released from his oath of obedience by Uzzi, the chief priest.

Eli sought out other Levites, and through them, he was introduced to men of position and standing in the Shiloh community. To these princes, he presented the Golden Ephod, a treasure belonging to Israel that Eli had managed to recapture. His backers were impressed. They provided him with elegant accommodation, a salary, and a tent wherein the Baal-berith could be displayed, in spite of it being a distraction to the tent of the Tabernacle of habitation and the Ark of the Testimony.

It wasn't long before a cult had settled in around Eli and the Golden Ephod. These cult followers supposed Eli to be a prophet and the Baal-berith a more acceptable substitute—and less demanding—than the covenants demanded by the God of Israel. The Baal-berith, as always, produced a bountiful revenue. Pilgrims from afar as well as nearby streamed in during the high holidays, many of whom were wealthy. They were very generous with their offerings when it came to petitioning the Baal-berith, asking that their wishes and desires be granted or pleading with it for healing many diseases and afflictions, as well as fulfilling the dreams that were brought before the Golden Ephod.

Eli was now a high priest with a new following and could now afford the trappings of wealth and position to which he had become accustomed. Eli knew that to be considered for the office of chief priest of the Tabernacle, a wife would be required of him. Taking a helpmeet was a necessary function to perform; in Hebrew law, a man was counted as nothing without a woman. The right mate was essential if he was to fulfill his life's ambition. The added blessings afforded by a male offspring would ensure his Levite legacy—it would also give him the opportunity to find favor with God.

Eli found approval in the eye of a young damsel. Elisheba was a Levite woman who worked tirelessly in the Tabernacle, and Eli found himself visiting the holy place as much to worship as to catch a glimpse of her stunning beauty. She had silky dark hair the color of midnight, her almond eyes were deep pools of desire, her waist was dainty, and her breasts were round, firm, and supple. He had by accident and timely fortune caught a glimpse of her ankle—it was well turned and held the promise of paradise. Eli was smitten. After one such visit, Eli attempted to engage her in conversation. He had asked around, finding out her name and inquiring into her family's social and religious standing. He was satisfied, the daughter of the reigning high priest, she would be more than acceptable, she would be a prize, she would be a dream come true. Eli caught up with her as she was leaving the Tabernacle one day after she had completed her duties. "Please excuse my boldness," he said. "My name is Eli, and I am a priest and a Levite. I would like to make your acquaintance, if possible?" The young maiden was flattered but was taken aback at Eli's boldness. "Such matters are to be arranged by the formal introduction," she replied, "and always in the company of Elders or matrons."

Eli produced his best frown. "A pardon is in order! Please forgive me. I am a stranger here, and I am not yet aware of Shiloh's correct social graces. I was the chancellor of temple treasures on Mount Gerizim until my recent move here. I intended no disrespect. What is the proper protocol I must follow to speak to you?" Elisheba dropped her eyes bashfully, and Eli's heart soared. "Permission must be sought from my father. If he deems you suitable, we may converse under the wary eye of his chosen chaperone. We are never to talk if we are not being supervised."

Eli, not in the least discouraged, inquired after her father. "Who is your dad?" Asking that of which he was already aware. "I would speak with him to honor the social protocol and to fulfill your wish for decorum. I would fulfill every desire you have." Elisheba smiled, and her cheeks grew rosy red. "My father is Phinehas, meaning *the bronze colored one* the chief priest of the Tabernacle, and keeper of the Ark of the Covenant. He sees visitors after the service on Shabbat. That is the best time for you to call upon him." She turned quickly and darted away. She blushed at the prospect of such a powerful and handsome suitor.

Eli followed Elisheba's instructions to the exact detail. He waited for the next Shabbat and then humbly begged for an interview with Phinehas. The high priest acknowledged Eli; then he paused, waiting for his caller to speak first. It was a manner he had learned over time, allowing him always to know the intent of a man's heart, and to take heed of how he proposed his cause.

Eli spoke. "I have seen your daughter, the beautiful Elisheba, and wish to talk with her. As you well know, she is a dutiful daughter. When I attempted to engage her in conversation—not knowing the local customs—she told me I could talk to her only with your permission and under the supervision of a chaperone you had chosen."

Phinehas nodded in acknowledgment of his daughter's proper behavior. "I am glad for this opportunity to speak to you, Eli. There is another matter that bears discussion before I will consider your request. I refer to your tent and your use of the Baal-berith of Jerubbaal for personal gain. A cult has formed around this icon, and it does not promote harmony within the congregation of God. I want you to work for me in the Tabernacle, Eli. I want you to fold up your tent and forgo the contributions and offerings you receive from this wanton exhibition. You may keep the ephod as your personal possession, of course, but you must contain it within the privacy of your home. If you agree to my request, you may court Elisheba, with my blessing. I sincerely hope you do comply with my appeal, for it would please me for you to become my assistant in the Tabernacle of the Most High God. What say you, Eli? Can I count you in? Do you wish to be on the Lord's side?"

Eli did not want to give up his flowing stream of income. Nor was he keen to forgo the mounting admiration received on account of his owning the ephod—praise and acclaim to which he had become accustomed. He weighed up his options: a beautiful woman to marry, and a highly respected position . . . it seemed a very powerful draw. And becoming an assistant to the high priest did, after all, put him in a position to become the most powerful man in Shiloh. Furthermore, he was a Levite, dedicated to the service of God. With all these good reasons to accept the offer put to him, the choice was made plain. He would forego the money! He would serve God. He would marry Elisheba. He looked directly into the eyes of Phinehas and smiled. "As for me and my house," he told the high priest, "we will serve the Lord." Phinehas embraced his future son-in-law, and with a holy kiss, he sealed the fate of both men.

The marriage of Eli and Elisheba was a gala affair, and all the Levites from the Tabernacle were in attendance. The most important people of the city were also present; the princes, elders, and high-ranking officials helped to celebrate the happy day with gifts and good wishes.

The union was a happy one, except for the strife that was bred by the presence of the Baal-berith in their home. After the wedding, Elisheba settled in happily. She was glad to be nesting and was still flushed with love but finally had to confront her husband. "Eli, my love, I have left my father and mother, and I have cleaved unto you. I am joyful for this, and such happiness I have never known. I do not want to disrupt this joyous feeling of bliss with an argument, but the Baal-berith, your prized temple treasure that you care for above all else, makes me uncomfortable. I feel uneasy knowing it is in your possession. Could we not perhaps have it melted down to release the gold and the gems? We could use the wealth to purchase an elegant new home."

Eli had not expected this troubling reaction from his bride. He had always taken pride in having custody of the Golden

Ephod and had likened it unto the second greatest treasure in all of Israel, surpassed only by the Ark of the Covenant.

Eli was quick to defend the Golden Ephod. "Elisheba, I love you! More than I ever thought possible. I will always strive to ensure your well-being and your happiness." Eli paused, not wanting to distress his wife but equally unwilling to part with his precious ephod. "The Baal-berith is stored in a private place, and I feel honored to have such a treasure as part of my personal collection. Please, my love, ask of me anything else, and I shall grant your wish. The beauty of the Golden Ephod has no comparison. Let us not speak of this again. I fear it will taint our joy with an unnecessary argument."

Elisheba, filled with love and wanting to submit to her handsome new husband's wishes, averted her eyes, dropping her gaze to the floor. "If this is your desire, my husband, I will be dutiful and submit my will to yours. I do, however, request that this Ephod is stored in a place separate from our home—not under the same roof. If we can agree to this compromise, I will not raise the subject again. I shall put my dismay to rest." An altar was fashioned in a small alcove in an outbuilding for the ephod's protection against the elements, and it was placed upon a pedestal. And so the matter was settled.

The work of the Tabernacle brought Eli and Elisheba many blessings, and Eli, being a likable fellow, was always sought after for his judgment and advice. Eli was favored by Phinehas, his father-in-law and the acclaimed high priest of the Tabernacle. He was favored for the careful manner in which he performed his priestly duties, but more importantly, Eli was supported by Phinehas for making his daughter, Elisheba, a happy mother of twin boys. Eli had honored his father-in-law by producing for him two jewels to place in the old man's crown—his grandchildren. Eli further acknowledged the high priest by naming his firstborn son, Phinehas, his grandfather's namesake. The second-born twin was named Hophni. Living in Shiloh was filled with religious ceremony and ritual. All of Israel made pilgrimages to partake in covenantal agreements on the high holidays and to fulfill their sacrifice of burnt offerings to the Lord God of Israel.

Phinehas and Hophni were known for their many toys. They were spoiled by their father and their adoring grandfather. The rod of correction was spared, and any penalty for their wrongdoing remained unpaid. They lacked the painful lessons that meaningful consequences follow every thoughtless action. The twins were held blameless. Their conduct was dismissed as normal; their misbehavior, merely as youthful hijinks. The brothers would often secretly steal time unobserved with the Baal-berith. They would wear the ephod in mock battles and in simulations displaying the sacred rituals of sacrifice. The twins soon fell into the evil snare of the Lord-berith. Lust of the flesh and the gluttony of their bellies became driving forces within them. The selfish pleasures they developed as teen-agers took root in the adult nature. They became the twins of lies and hostility. The boys grew to maturity in a loving and spiritual household, groomed to be priests and to serve in the Tabernacle. As young men, they were schooled in the ritual of the fleshpot and the three-pronged hook: to obtain the portion of boiled meat free of grease assigned to the Levites for their nourishment. The animal fat, the carnal craving of all natural desires, was to be contained within the bounds the Lord had made. This was a commandment to be strictly obeyed and performed without deviation, for the fat was burnt for a sweet savor to God and given up as a sacrifice.

Phinehas was pleased and found joy in his son-in-law Eli. The years passed quickly; Phinehas was physically pressed to continue his duties and responsibilities as the presiding high priest of the Tabernacle. Phinehas knew that a replacement needed to be named and trained in the fine details of ceremony and ritual. Phinehas fasted and prayed to God for permission to waive the rights of Abishua, his natural-born son, and so dismiss Abishua's birthright. Abishua had neither the temperament nor the desire to be saddled with such a demanding responsibility that was part and parcel of such an elevated position. Phinehas asked God, using the Urim and Thummim, when he attended the Holy Place in the Tabernacle. The permission of his petition was confirmed by divination. Eli and Abishua were summoned to hear the will of God. Phinehas embraced first his son Abishua with a holy kiss, and then his son-in-law Eli, and said, "Please sit. I have a message that concerns both my passing and the passing on of the keys of the High Priest. Please remember I have prayed and fasted in the Holy Place. The decision is correct in the eyes of God. Eli will be the next High Priest." He continued, "Abishua, please do not be upset; the weakness of health and the will of God has pronounced this decision." Abishua did not protest and seemed to be relieved with the decree. Abishua spoke up: "Father, this is the will of God, and I heartily sustain his ruling. Father, please, and for the sake of the ten righteous men, may I be counted in to make complete Eli's circle of ordination? This will help to confirm my support and will put any dissenting voices to rest."

Phinehas' authority was passed on to his son-in-law, Eli. Phinehas brought Eli unto the door of the Tabernacle of the congregation and washed him with water and declared to all in range of his voice, "I wash you with water preparatory to your receiving your anointings, that you may become clean from the blood and sins of this generation." Phinehas poured the anointing oil upon Eli's head and anointed him, to sanctify him. Phinehas then spoke the words of the blessing:

"Eli Ben Itamar: having the proper authority, I pour this holy anointing oil upon your head and anoint you, preparatory to your becoming a king and a priest unto the most high God; hereafter to rule and reign in the house of Israel forever. Eli Ben Itamar: unto you, it is given by my hand and by the holy priesthood that I hold, and in the name of the one true God of Israel—that I, Phinehas ben Eleazar, who hold the priesthood of the one true God, lay my hands upon your head and set you apart as the next high priest of Israel. I give into your keeping and stewardship, the Tabernacle of visitation and the Ark of the Covenant,with a promise and a warning: if you keep and maintain your charge, you will be blessed with long life—but the day that it is taken from your charge by force of arms, you will surely die. Remember this. Be watchful and attentive to the needs of the congregation—for they will look to you for direction and guidance, both in time-based judgments and for spiritual comfort—for the government shall rest on your shoulders. I seal this office and this blessing by the power and authority of the holy priesthood of God; and in His sacred name."

The ceremony concluded in the outer court of the Tabernacle between the brazen laver and the brazen altar. Phinehas turned to Eli and smiled and said, "Eli, it is time for your schooling to begin in earnest. Come follow me to the Holy Place outside the first door—the space set aside for the menorah, the table of shewbread, and the altar of incense. This instruction is for the preparation for wearing the holy garments. Eli, burn into your consciousness that exactly one day before the Day of Atonement, and not a moment before, you will enter into the Holy of Holies, and you must be free from all iniquity. You will be in the presence of Adonai, and He will not abide the least amount of sin. Your life will depend on both strict observance and purity to all His commandments." Phinehas brought Eli behind a curtain before the door of the Holy Place, and there was a cedar chest containing all the pure white and golden garments of the high priest.

"My son," Phinehas continued, "although you are very familiar with, and wear, these four priestly garments, it is given to me to school you as a part of the ritual of advancement.

"The holy garments are distinctive and essential; with deep meanings and endless consequences. The underbritches, of delicate, pure-white twisted linen, are in remembrance of Father Adam's apron of leaves—in an attempt to hide his nakedness from God— and that he had acquired the forbidden knowledge of modesty." Phinehas continued, "Next is the tunic of pure-white twisted linen, which represents the garment given to Adam when he was found naked in the Garden of Eden. Moreover, as long as you do not defile it, it will be a shield and protection to you against the power of the destroyer, until your work is completed upon the earth. The sash is four fingers wide and has a weave like the skin of a snake. It is thirty-two cubits in length and is for the atonement for the heart that dreams up wicked imaginations. Have the sash hang down to the ground, to atone for the feet that are swift to run to mischief. The great wrapping is a reminder to bind the laws of God continually upon your heart. Tie it about your neck. The miter cap of pure-white twisted linen is a head covering, showing the ultimate awe and respect for being allowed in the presence of our God with clean thoughts and pure intent. "This simple miter is worn by the high priest only once a year, on the day preceding the Day of Atonement, and only when entering into the Holy of Holies." Eli assisted Phinehas in his dressing—fixing a working memory of what would soon be Eli's routine duties. Phinehas then separated the golden garments, and handed Eli the sixteen-cubit length of twisted pure-white linen to form the High Priest's turban. Phineas lowered his voice to just above a whisper and said, "Eli, I will instruct you how to wrap this headdress to resemble a blossoming flower, which is believed to be filled with the spirit of wisdom—and this is to atone for the conceit of arrogance, and to be not wise in your own opinion. On the front of the turban, you will affix this gold plate that reads: 'Holy unto the Lord.' This is a reminder that God's will for Israel will be your first and most prominent thought. The plate will be attached to two sets of blue cords—one going over the top of the head and the other around the sides of the head at the level of the ears." After many failed attempts, Eli perfected his technique, gaining the reserved applause of Phinehas. "Well done, my son; let us now proceed to the blue robe worn underneath the Ephod. The blue is a reminder of the divine love of truth. The mantle is woven in a single piece. The opening in the center for your head to pass through is not cut or torn; the hem at the neck is folded over and can be likened unto a pair of lips. The wearing of the priestly robe atones for the sin of evil speech, gossip, backbiting, bearing false witness, and the evil-speaking against the Lord's anointed. The lower hem of the garment is fringed with small golden bells, alternating with pomegranate-shaped tassels of turquoise, purple, and scarlet wool.

There are two sets of thirty-six, or seventy-two—the number of letters in the sacred name of God. The average number of seeds in a pomegranate is six hundred and thirteen—the same number of laws given to us by the creator that protects us from the evil day. The bittersweet fruit also reminds us of the trials and joys from the consequence of choices; and so, too, his precious gift of life both here and next. The golden bells whisper your presence as you go about your duties—for you are blessed when you come in, and you are again blessed when you go out. If you neglect to wear this apparel, your life will be taken to maintain the balance. "Phinehas paused, as his legs buckled, and his speech became labored and slurred. Eli caught him on the way down and buoyed him up, and then immediately called out to the nearby priests, "Bring a chair and a cup of water—the high priest has taken ill." An old seat was hastily bought up, and Phinehas slumped down, and at first appeared as if his ghost had departed this life.

Moments passed with the weight of hours, and just as quickly, Phinehas' eyes opened and his head eased up off of his chest, and he said, "Why are all of you standing around? Have you no work to do!?" The relief of the old priest's revival was joyful to all who stood about him.

Eli said, "I am relieved you are still with us; you collapsed in my arms."

"Nonsense," replied Phinehas. "Sometimes it is how old men take cat naps. Besides, your instruction is not yet completed, and only then will God see fit to fly me away to paradise. Shall we continue?" Phinehas appeared spry and reenergized as he fished out the multicolored Ephod from the cabinet.

Phinehas exclaimed, "Beautiful, is it not? I think of its design like unto a backward apron. The colors are in a perfect weave with perfect proportions of blue, purple, scarlet, and gold thread throughout; on a base of fine, twisted white linen." Eli questioned, "Please forgive my ignorance, but why the many colors? Is that why Joseph's coat had so many colors?" Phinehas smiled a knowing smile and said, "That is a good question, and that is certainly a matter to ponder—but for now let us stay on point and on task." Phinehas shook his head and thoughtfully continued, "The golden threads connect the end from the beginning; it is all but one continuous round. Now know you this—that God wears a double bow upon his shoulder—and all the colors of the firmament are present. Each color has depth and a length of light, and so represents the vastness of His intelligence; this is because intelligence is the glory of God. There are also two sardonyx stones of red, black, and white; they are affixed to the Ephod at the shoulders. The stones are engraved with the names of the sons of Jacob from left to right in the order of their birth; this represents the government of God and of Israel. The belt, or girdle, of the Ephod, is woven in the same manner, and cinches tight around the belly—and it is placed over the navel—suggesting to the mind the need of constant nourishment to both body and spirit." Eli stood motionless as the eyes of his understanding continued to widen. The mysteries of God were unfolded like a scroll by the learned and esteemed High Priest. Phinehas paused and said, "Before I delve deeper into the details—do you have any comments or questions?" Eli bowed his head and announced, "Most knowledgeable High Priest, you have only whetted my

273

appetite for greater understanding, and by all means—that is, as long as you are able—please continue."

Phinehas then reached in and emptied the chest of its last Vestment—displaying the Breastplate of Judgment. Phinehas lifted the breastplate by its two golden chains and remarked, "This is made from the same weave and colors as the Ephod. It is folded over upon itself—forming a pocket or a pouch. The twelve stones are mounted in gold lattices that adorn the chest and cover the heart and lungs. This, too, is a reminder that the breath of life was given, and that the circumcised heart that pumps every drop of life-giving blood is a gift from God. Each gem has a signet engraved with the names of the sons of Jacob—and the colors are the same as the banners that marked each tribe's location. It was the time when every tent door faced the Tabernacle, as it rested in the desolate wilderness. There are six letters on every stone; the names that have less than six—such as Gad, Dan, Levi, Judah, and Asher—are filled in with letters from the names of the three patriarchs: Abraham, Isaac, and Jacob. The additions and subtractions render seventy-two letters in total, the sacred characters that encompass 'The Name' of the most high God. His name is what separates the creator from us—his creation."

Phinehas took several deep breaths in rapid succession. Eli could see that the old man was struggling to stay upright. A flush of color quickly reddened his face, and it seemed as if his eyes became sharp slits of determination. Phinehas threw his head back and stiffened his backbone with a warrior's resolve; he would at all personal cost finish Eli's mentoring. Phinehas, now renewed and revived, continued on and said, "When the need for an answer of national importance is required—then it is given to the High Priest to take before the Lord of hosts at the veil—directly before the Holy of Holies. Only one question at a time can be asked from the likes of governors, generals, and kings. The questions must be considered of the highest gravity and importance, thus requiring a complicated answer. You, Eli, as the high priest, will pose the question. Remember, only one question at a time can be uttered. And if the Lord honors your petition—light will radiate from behind the veil—striking the specific gemstones and illuminating them—so that when taken together, they will spell out the perfect answer."

Eli helped in the dressing, as his mind was whirring and this was the only way for him to stay focused on his lesson. Eli assisted Phineas in attaching the four golden cords. The top two chains were attached to the sardonyx stones on either side of the shoulders. The two cords at the bottom were to keep the breastplate from flapping when the high priest bent forward. Phinehas demonstrated its practical use when he leaned forward and sought a small script hidden in the shadows of the chest.

"What is that?" Eli eagerly inquired.

Phinehas unfastened the bag by opening its mouth and releasing the cinching of strings, and then poured out its contents and said: "Know this for yourself, Eli—for your life will depend on its dutiful inclusion. Describe to me what you behold."

Eli then pondered for a moment the mysterious objects and said, "Two stones, equally elliptical; one dark, one light, and about four inches in length." Phinehas, stressing their importance, explained, "These are the Urim and Thummim, the two seer stones—meaning lights and perfection. They are put into the Breastplate of Judgment, and they shall be upon your heart when

275

you go in before the Lord. Eli, you shall bear the judgment of the children of Israel upon your heart before the Lord continually." Eli had an outwardly puzzled expression that prompted Phinehas to say, "What is it, Eli? You seem to be bothered and bewildered."

Eli looked away, confused, and then asked, "Why the need for the two seer stones if answers are available from the Breastplate of Judgment?" Phinehas replied, "The very same question I had asked during my initial installation. The stones are placed over the heart as a reminder that Israel is always over God's heart. The Urim and Thummim, when exposed to the glory of God in the Holy Place, retain His divine spark. They can now be used outside of the Breastplate of Judgment for either discernment or revelations, or for simple answers to pressing questions by prophets, seers, or anointed kings. Well, Eli, does this knowledge satisfy your need to know? Yes or no?" Eli beamed as he held back a chuckle from the sudden burst of enlightenment and pronounced, "Yes, now it all makes sense to me. And thank you, most honored High Priest, for I feel closer to God for the knowing of these mysteries."

Phinehas was completely dressed in the golden garments, and both were prepared to pass through the portal to the Holy Place. "Eli," Phinehas counseled, "we will now attend to the washing of our hands and feet at the Laver, and thus, we can enter into the Holy Place, cleansed from the soil and dirt of worldly corruption and sin. Eli, I would caution you to never forget, or casually neglect, to remove the sandals from your feet—for when we cross over the threshold—we will be standing on holy ground. Eli, my son, it is time for you to receive additional training in the care and maintenance of all the sacred furnishings found in the very heart of the Tabernacle."

The two men entered into the holy place, and they were immediately bathed in the light of the menorah. It was as if the world outside no longer existed, and they had now entered into another dimension—the world of the spirit. Phinehas walked directly to the left, to where the golden lampstand stood, and said: "Eli, one of your duties is every day to trim the wicks and replace them when they are charred and no longer serviceable. Replace them with ripped strips—made from the worn priestly robes of pure-white twisted linen—and this fabric only. Keep the reservoir filled with pure beaten virgin olive oil at all times. The six branches represent the six days of all creation—and they all face inward to the center stem—which accounts for the source of all light and truth: the Creator. What do you see, Eli?"

Eli replied, "I see the branches of an almond tree."

"You have seen correctly," uttered Phinehas. "For this is how God watches to see that his word is fulfilled."

Phinehas then moved away from the brilliant menorah; crossed over to the opposite wall, and stopped in front of the acacia wood and golden-skinned Table of Shewbread—"The Bread of the Presence—" for it was always to be in God's presence. Phinehas turned and asked, "Teach me, young Eli, that I might know the depth of your understanding of this holy furnishing?"

Eli straightened up with a confidence born from his learned knowledge—for this was his regular ongoing assignment. Eli then nodded his head and said: "Twelve loaves are always present in the sight of God. They shall always be two rows of six each—and I put pure frankincense upon each row, that it may be on the bread for a memorial—even an offering made by fire unto the Lord. Fresh replacement shewbread is exchanged every Shabbat, and the previous offerings are then eaten by the priests—and only here in the holy place. Although the loaves are a week old, they remain divinely sweet and luscious. The table and the shewbread are a representation of God's willingness at friendship with his creation; showing that He has something in common with every one of His sons. It is an invitation to share a meal in communion and in an extension of friendship; representing God's willingness for a man to enter into His presence to fellowship with Him—and how His message remains eternally fresh."

Phinehas was pleased with this day's lessons and how quickly Eli absorbed his Levitical teachings. Phinehas then moved reverently over to the Golden Altar of Incense. Phinehas was drawn to the very front of the veil of separation, in his need to increase his nearness to God. Phinehas filled his nostrils with the aroma of the wafting incense before speaking; then he exhaled with the words: "We are to burn incense on the golden altar morning and evening. When the daily burnt offerings are prepared, we are to make sure that the fragrance censer is filled and fresh. The incense is to be left burning continually before the Creator, for a pleasing sweet savor to be carried upwards with our prayers. Eli, a simple forgetful mistake in the exact amounts, or an error in the required ingredients, will render an immediate verdict of death. God will not abide a strange fire to desecrate his altar. The four exquisite spices are: Stacte, because men's hearts are transparent to God; Onycha, to roar in a peal to His ear that beckons His attention; Galbanum, to open the channels of communication; and Frankincense, because He is the rock of our salvation. They must all be of equal weights and measures—for these are all the tears of our repentance; these and only these are deemed holy unto the Lord. Eli, the commandment is to never use the same formula outside of the Tabernacle for personal perfume, or you will be cut off from the people." A critical finger was extended to sharpen a point and directed at Eli from his renowned mentor. "Eli—the salt, the salt!" abruptly voiced Phinehas. "Failure to remember the salt will be more than a simple dismissal. This mistake, my son, is morbidly critical! The salt is a covenant with God in communion, sincerity, and purity in the fall from corruption. The salt, my dear fellow, is the element that changes corruption to incorruption, and thus confirms the promise of the resurrection. The salt in its course draws blood out of substance. A resurrected being is immortal and eternal. They are of flesh and bone, but not of blood; blood is the life—it is the stain of mortal beings requiring the bated breath of air. God's work and his glory are to bring to pass the immortal and eternal life of man—evidenced by the resurrection of the dead. The salt Eli—the salt of the earth—make no mistake."

Eli hung his head down with embarrassment, for the old priest had discovered his spotted past. Phinehas recounted, "Eli, you had neglected to apply the salt to the meat offerings after repeated warnings from Uzzi, the high priest on Mount Gerizim." Phinehas had compassion on his son-in-law and soon-to-be successor in the Tabernacle, and said, "I have given up all hopes of having a better past; I suggest you do the same, and let us move on with a perfect sureness in God." Both men agreed to put the past in the past and to press on.

Phinehas was keenly staring at the veil and seemed to be transported to another place and time. Then, in an instant, he rallied and became spiritually excited, with a twinkle in his eye, and said, "I have one last story to tell you that is sacred, secret, and, by all means, extremely confidential. Tell no one—not even my dutiful daughter and your loving wife, Elisheba." Phinehas continued, "It was at the appointed time and day for me to enter into the Holy of Holies. All that was commanded to do had been done and every detail precisely addressed. The sacrifices were dispatched, and the blood was sprinkled and spilled. I had discarded all the golden garments for the purity of the all-bright-white attire, and even my turban was replaced with a simple white miter cap. The pan of hot coals from the brazen altar was in my hand, and the perfect incense was prepared to sprinkle over the embers in the pan. I made my way through the veil of separation. It is two cubits deep in a hairpin maze of curtain hangings; this as a reminder of the twists and turns we encountered in the wilderness before arriving in the promised land.

When I entered into the Holy of Holies, I was met with the breathtaking vision of the Ark of the Covenant. It was richly aglow and seemed to have a light of its own with a skin of highly polished gold. The contents contained therein are two weighty stone tablets covered in the holy commandments deeply inscribed by the mighty finger of God. These are divine instructions imparted to Moses on Mount Sinai. Sinai means: *Bush in the clay desert—the place of enmity.* The commandments remain our beacon and our light so that we might navigate back into the presence of our loving Creator. Eli, if you abide strictly by their principles, you will not fail or falter in this life's uncertain perils.

A bowl of fresh 'manna,' or 'what is it?' also known as *The corn of heaven,* with the texture and taste of coriander: warm, nutty, spicy, and sweet orange-flavored. The manna not only fills the belly but it also guards against illness and plague. Remember

Eli—it was only one days' helping that was the required allotment. Hoarding was discouraged by worm and by rot. On the eve of the Shabbat, a double portion remained delicious. And this, Eli, is a reminder that God's word is fresh and alive, and to be feasted upon daily—and twice again on a holy day.

'And God created the rod of Aaron; also enclosed in the Ark; and He did so in the twilight of the sixth day of Creation. The scepter is representing the power of the priesthood, and an ever-lasting conduit to God Almighty. Aaron's rod put forth buds and produced blossoms, and it bore ripe almonds—an acknowledgment that the house of Levi were the keepers of the eternal priesthood. Eli, this is the very same priesthood we are commanded to honor. And please ponder that the rights of the priesthood are inseparably connected with the powers of heaven. Eli, sear into your memory that the powers of heaven cannot be controlled nor handled, only upon the principles of righteousness and with an eye single to the glory of Jehovah. 'Another of the essential elements found on the ledge in the holy place, a vial of anointing-oil, made of flowing myrrh, sweet-smelling cinnamon, fragrant cane, and olive oil—for a sweet savor to set apart the things God holds most sacred. And also be aware, young Eli, of the urn containing the sacred ashes of the red heifer next to the brimming pitcher of living waters. When mixed they create a barrier between the living and the corpse; between holy and unclean, righteousness and sin. It is a likeness of the coming judgment of the quick and the dead. Bathe your hands in the mixture before touching the Ark. Ground yourself in this ritual—or you will fall down dead."

Phinehas' eyes brightened, and his aged burden seemed lightened as he brought the knowledge of God back to his remembrance.

Taking a deep breath and renewing his vigor he continued, "There are two sentinels that protect the Judgment seat. The holy Sentries patiently sit on the lid of the Ark. Their golden wings are barely separated, and they are forever facing each other for a reminder that none can approach or ever pass through the narrow way without their permission. They are Jachin, who defends the right, and whose name means: 'He will establish'—and Boaz, who guards the left, and whose name means: 'Quickness.' And before you are allowed to approach the Judgment seat where God ruleth and reigneth forever, your righteousness will be 'quickly established' before you are granted access.

I sprinkled the perfectly prepared incense onto the coals, and the room exploded in a thick cloud of ghostly smoke, that instantly invaded every seam and stitch in the sanctuary. My sight could not penetrate the mist even to the length of an inch, and I struggled and strained to regain the smallest amount of vision. Then in the haze in the vicinity of the Judgment Seat, I perceived a thickening cloud where a faint outline appeared— a barely discernible silhouette. The image was whiter than its surroundings. A head and shoulders was supposed through the haze. There were shoulder-length curls as thick as a sheep's winter coat. I stared into the emptiness in the direction of the image for as long as I dared, and as of yet there were no facial features. Then suddenly two eyes burst open; they were burning orange and had a look of something hotter than fire. My heart stopped, and my breath caught in my throat. I had to look away. I felt that by lingering a moment longer, I would have crumbled into dust. Afraid and confused, I scrambled to find the pass-through back into the Holy Place.

Eli, that was my last encounter, and since then I knew my replacement was to be you—for soon I will fly away."

The days passed and finally, so did the old high priest, Phinehas. None was surprised that he had favored Eli, his son-in-law, in passing on the duties of the high priest of the Tabernacle to him—husband of his dutiful daughter, Elisheba, and father to his grandsons—his greatest pride: Phinehas, his namesake, and Hophni, the mastermind. Traditionally, the crown of the temple would have been passed on from father to son . . . from the flesh of Phinehas's flesh, and the blood of his blood—to Abishua—but it was not to be so.

Eli had attained his life's ambition and was now the chief priest of the Tabernacle. With widespread acclaim, he was also given the title of judge. He was the first to wear both crowns. Eli's first official act was to install his two sons for service in the Tabernacle. They would be priests of the threshold. They alone would allow or deny the local residents and the well-traveled pilgrims, who begged for admittance, to draw close to the presence of God. Their agreement or refusal would either admit or deny entry to those who they deemed worthy. The flesh pot was also given to the wayward brothers to administer, according to the sacred rites of their calling. The twins did not take to the expected humility of the priesthood. They remained light-minded and, scoffing at the religious ceremony, would rebel against the commandments. Hophni had a wild nature and pushed the boundaries of conduct and restraint. Phinehas would find courage in his brother's lack of consequence. He would participate in his brother's antics, which included bullying, to satisfy their sinful lust and gluttonous appetites.

Hophni hatched a wicked plan and shared it with Phinehas. "Brother, we have it in our power to eat our fill—but not from the bland, boiled, and tasteless meat of the fleshpot. Let us rather have our fill of the raw meat, succulent, and ready to be roasted. We will grow strong from the stolen bounty of choice cuts." Phinehas was, as usual, a willing accomplice.

The years passed quickly, and the twins remained unbridled in their passions. The extreme lack of control over them encouraged Hophni to keep scheming up new abuses, given their position of power. Hophni would whisper his lustful thoughts into Phinehas's ear. "Many women come here to serve in the Tabernacle. Are they not under our jurisdiction? We could easily have our way with them. Are we not men with needs? We can even use force if necessary when an opportunity is presented. The women will remain silent—their reputations will be more important to them than insisting on our punishment. Let us partake of these delicate flowers at our whim and pleasure."

Phinehas succumbed to his brother's evil plotting. "Brother, you are a mastermind. I, too, will partake of the ripe fruit of their virginity."

The twins defiled the Lord's offerings, and they mocked what was holy. Life went on uninterrupted, and Eli turned a blind eye to his sons' mischief.

Phinehas had to take a wife, for she had become pregnant by his all-too-casual and frequent, riotous womanizing. Phinehas was blessed with a son. He called his firstborn, Ahitub, who grew to be a man in the shadow of the Tabernacle: yet under the influence of the Baal-berith. The twins' carnal sprees with the women who assembled at the door of the Tabernacle was finally made known when Eli was frail and timeworn. For one reason or another, the outrageous behavior of the brothers had not come to his attention; and when he did finally try to interfere, he issued merely a light scolding. The use of a rod to straighten their backs had been lacking, and now he and they were much too old to attempt the folly of a beating. It would serve no purpose, and even be dangerous, as their evil could be easily turned back on the frail old man.

Notwithstanding—they did not obey the voice of their father—leaving no choice for the Lord but to slay them. A man came and scolded Eli briskly: "The Lord is displeased with you, and your house will be kicked to the ground. His sacrifice is made profane; yet you honor your sons, who are worthless in His sight. You honor them above God—to make them and yourself fat. The Lord says He will honor those who honor Him—and they who despise Him will He lightly esteem. The time approaches quickly when both your sons shall die on the same day. Your house and your descendants will be cut off. There will not be an old man in your house. They will all die in the flower of their age, and those who survive will beg to be restored to the priesthood once again."

CHAPTER 37

The Tingle of Ears, and the Ark Departs

The Philistines were at the threshold of Shiloh—that they might put all of the armies of Israel to flight. Messengers hurriedly brought news of the battle to the Elders—informing them that four thousand had been slain—and it was thought that the Philistines had gathered such force that they might be invincible. Agreeing to a plan, the Elders said, "We will send for the Ark, wherein the power of our God resides. It shall go before us, and this will inspire the men of Israel and strike terror into the hearts of the Philistines. We will fetch the Ark of the Covenant from Shiloh, and when it comes to us, it may save us out of the hand of our enemies."

The Ark of the Covenant resided in the Tabernacle—in the center place between two cherubim known as the Holy of Holies. It was under the hand of Eli, the high priest. His permission to remove the sacred relic was desirable but not essential. Aryeh, captain of hundreds, presented the request to Eli. "I have been sent to secure the Ark for the army of Israel. The Elders have instructed me to do so, that we may be saved from our enemies. The Philistines, thus far, have proven to be unbeatable. I pray, Eli, for your agreement that the Ark of the Covenant may go before the army of Israel."

Eli thought a moment before responding. "Without fasting and prayer, and the agreement of the Lord our God—removing His Ark from the Tabernacle seems dangerous and foolhardy. But if the Elders are insisting, I ask only that my sons, Phinehas and Hophni, accompany the Ark. As you well know, only Levites may handle the transporting of the Ark and see to its care. To any other person, contact will be deadly." Aryeh was relieved to have Eli's consent, for he was under strict orders to obtain the Ark, whether given Eli's permission or not.

When the Ark of the Covenant came into the camp, all Israel shouted with a great shout so that the earth rang out. The Philistines heard a great uproar coming out of the camp of the Hebrews and were puzzled as to its meaning. A lookout high above the tree line viewed the Ark, with its golden skin straddled on either side by two winged cherubim. There was no mistaking the Hebrew God box. The shock of its presence traveled quickly around the Philistine camp. Knowing that the box containing the mighty God of the Hebrews was in the enemy camp would mean certain defeat; like unto the plagues wrought upon the Egyptians in the wilderness. The Philistines lamented their loss as if it had already happened. The Philistine army general, Padi, heard their lament, recognizing their loss of will. He sensed the numbing cowardice spreading through his army, sapping the strength of their willpower. Padi climbed high above the cliff face so that every man could hear him. "Be strong and quit acting like frightened children. Start acting like men who have the courage and tenacity to win this coming battle. You are fearsome Philistines! Are we frightened by a box so small that it contains the God of the Hebrews and by the rumors of wash-women? Would you be servants to the Hebrews as they have been for you? Gird your loins and brace your hearts like men, and we will take the fight to them. We will prevail!" A cheer went out from the Philistine camp that challenged the resolve of the army of Israel.

The Philistines fought as if men possessed, whereas the Hebrews trusted the backing they had in having the Ark present. In their haste, no one thought to petition the Almighty for His permission or His grace—so when neither was forthcoming—Israel felt abandoned and shrank from the Philistine onslaught. The rout was complete; every man fled to his tent, and a very great slaughter commenced. Thirty thousand footmen fell that day. The Ark of the Covenant was captured. Phinehas and Hophni battled to protect the Ark, but they were mobbed—and they, too, tasted their own blood. The brothers fell into the dust, and the judgment of God was satisfied; the ears of Israel would tingle with the news.

A messenger left the massacre—a man from Benjamin—who was known for his endurance and great speed afoot. He ran to Shiloh, lifted by the speedy travel of bad news. He came to Shiloh in a punishing sprint with torn and ripped clothes; with smudges of blood and earth upon his face; still steaming from the heat of battle. Eli sat by the wayside watching in anticipation—as if for the return of loved ones. Eli's heart trembled, and an air of foreboding cast a dark shadow, for he sensed something was terribly wrong. The soldier fled to the town center. He blew the shofar of assembly, and all the people gathered to hear his news. The Benjamite runner was gulping for breath, which added to the dramatic effect. Finally, he exhaled his startling announcement. "We have been soundly beaten. The slaughter was great, and the Ark of our God has been captured by the Philistines." Upon hearing the news, the crowd's ears tingled. Some rent their clothes and put ashes upon their heads. There was wailing and gnashing of teeth, and a great cry went out as if they all howled with one accord.

Eli was ninety-eight years old. His eyes were dim. He could see the world now only in the thin twilight of shadows. The Benjamite messenger sought Eli out. It was proper that he did so, as Eli was the high priest and judge of all Israel. The Benjamite said to Eli: "I am he that came from the army, and I have come far from the battle with deadly speed and haste."

Eli asked, "What has happened, my son?"

The messenger paused, knowing that a fatal blow was about to be thrown. "Israel is fled before the Philistines, and there has been a great slaughter among the people. Your two sons, Phinehas and Hophni, battled mightily in the defense of the Ark and have fallen dead. The Ark of God has been taken."

When the messenger mentioned that the Ark had been captured, it was as if an enormous rock had struck the old man, and he fell backward, still seated in his chair. Eli was old and round. He fell uncaught— hitting the wooden gate with the full force of his breadth and weight—connecting it awkwardly with the back of his head. A loud crack sounded about his neck, and Eli, too, was dead. The glory had departed from Israel, for the Ark of God had been taken. Eli had judged Israel for forty years, and his esteemed seat was now abruptly vacant. Eli's grandson, Ahitub, the eldest son of the dead Phinehas, was bloodied in the battle. He, too, had fought alongside his father and his uncle, and he was valiant in the defense of the Ark. It was only through divine intervention—in the form of a crevice into which he had stumbled—that he escaped the reach of the Philistines. His life had been spared for some greater purpose. The people of Shiloh looked to Ahitub, and the care of the Tabernacle was thrust upon him. He was also given charge of his newborn—and recently orphaned—brother, Ichabod. Ichabod's mother was so distressed by the news of her husband's death that she went into premature labor and said, "I will name the child Ichabod, which means: *The glory is departed;* and with his name on her lips, she too departed this life."

The Elders delivered a message of warning to Ahitub. "Ahitub, our place here in Shiloh has become indefensible. We are weak and vulnerable. Most of our men are dead, our weapons have been blunted, and the Lord has forsaken us, He has abandoned His dwelling place at Shiloh—the Tent—which He had pitched among men. The Philistines, now in possession of the Ark of the Covenant, may very well desire the Tabernacle and all its fine and sacred furnishings as well. They could easily crush us at their whim, to take it from us, which would further add to our shame. We must depart. It has been agreed that Nob, in the outer parts of Jerusalem, will afford us safety from the Philistine horde—they will not think to venture there. We will build a new home there and a place of security for our Tabernacle as well. We can build a house for our God, and provide a place to house all our religious treasures, starting with your grandfather

Eli's Baal-berith. Let us make haste before we are massacred in our beds and the Tabernacle is brought to ruin, or even worse, captured. What tell you, Ahitub?"

Ahitub was baptized in the heat of battle. He knew the fierce resolve of the Philistine enemy and of their hatred for the Hebrew race; regarding them as livestock. They felt that the only good Hebrew was either dead or enslaved. The mantle of the house of Eli was full on Ahitub's shoulders, and he said, "I will do as the Elders suggest. I will prepare to make the move to Nob."

The Tabernacle was dismantled. All the gold and brass furnishings were secured—being a tempting target for raiders. The high priest's jeweled ephod had to be securely packed away, as it was not for display. It could be worn only by the high priest when entering into the holy place. Without the Ark of the Covenant, the tabernacle was reduced to a meeting place. The people of Shiloh would have to wait and pray for the Ark's safe return before glory could be found once again in Israel.

Ahitub was true to his word. A caravan of carts and refugees from Shiloh were quickly on the trail—a band of refugees fleeing from the fear of massacre—hoping to find safety and a new beginning in the rural settlement of Nob.

Ahitub's first order of business after settling in was to find a wife. Playing nursemaid to his infant brother, Ichabod, was not to his liking. A suitable spouse was quickly found, as most of the young men had been killed by the Philistines. The Tabernacle was reassembled, and the furnishings were sheltered from the elements. The congregation also needed a place to pray, but the Ark of the Covenant was not forthcoming, and God could not be discovered in his hiding place. The Tabernacle was erected for a shadow in the daytime from the heat—a place for refuge—and a cover from storm and from rain.

Ahitub had a dream—and in that vision—he was prompted to build a house of God, right there on the outskirts of Jerusalem. Ahitub told the Elders about his passion in council, saying, "Brethren, I have been prompted—and it has been impressed upon me to build a house for our God in the countryside of Nob. God has abandoned the Tabernacle; it is spiritually idle and still bound tightly with strong cords of punishment for the want of the Ark. We need a permanent place to pray and to petition for God's timely intervention for its speedy return—so that the Ark may be wrenched out of the hands of those who would taint our most precious connection with the Almighty."

The Elders agreed. "The Tabernacle without the Ark of the Covenant in the Holy of Holies is a sacrilege. All the sacred items of brass and gold, including the jeweled breastplate and the ephod of the high priest, must be safeguarded and protected awaiting the Ark's rescue. We leave this in your care and in your charge, Ahitub. We agree to sustain you in your efforts to build a house for our God in Nob. We will provide the needed labor and material to set your vision into stone and mortar—with an eye single to the glory of Jehovah."

CHAPTER 38

The Return of the Baal-berith, or the Ephod of Gold

Ahitub, having gained the necessary permission to build a house of God, was also granted what little resources were available from the new and struggling farming community. Nob had vast tracts of grasslands, with an abundance of sheep that clothed bare backs and filled many an empty belly. Ahitub entered into the work with great excitement. He pored over the sketches, adjusting the design and layout to perfection. When construction began, he often toiled alone, well into the dark hours beyond twilight. It was backbreaking work, building with stone and mortar, shovel and hoe; but the House of God soon started taking form.

Meanwhile, the Ark had been released by the Philistines. A plague of mice had burst open in the multitude of locusts and flooded the borders of Philistia. The grain stores and threshing floors were either consumed or spoiled in a sea of mouse droppings. There was no grain for bread or porridge; the needed bulk for proper digestion was now lacking. Philistia was obstructed with a widespread cramp from constipation. And try as they might with all possible stress and strain, nothing was gained but a rising tide of painfully swollen and ruthlessly itchy emrods. With no relief in sight, the Philistine princes counseled—standing up—and to a man agreed to send the God box back to the Hebrews—and immediately. It was hurriedly sent back to Israel with a gift of golden emrods *hemorrhoids* and golden mice; a peace offering to pacify the wrath of the mighty Hebrew God—in the images of the two plagues that had ravaged all the Philistine people—men, women, and children. They hoped that these treasures would satisfy the God of the Hebrews for their forceful capture of His Ark. The Ark of the Testimony was first carted back by kine or cows who had never known a yoke or plow. The lowing kine, flushed heavy with milk, were set at the crossroads of decision. Turning to the left it would lead them straight into the heart of Philistia; turning to the right and back to Israel would leave no doubt as to the Hebrew God's omnipotence. The cows stood dumb and unmoved until a sudden clap of thunder in a troubled sky put them into motion, and they flinched as if struck with a whip. The unpiloted cart wandered aimlessly to the unfortunate town of Beth-shemesh. Breaking the seal of the lid for a quick peek inside, the townsmen kindled the wrath of God and suffered many to die. The wandering Ark then found safekeeping of twenty-years in Kirath-ye'arim. The Ark was not coming back to Shiloh or to the Tabernacle of Habitation. The Tent of God was finally dismantled and stored away, fittings and all, in a free hold built especially for its safe keeping.

The years had also been spent recruiting young men for the priesthood of Aaron, thus ensuring a dedicated labor force for construction and for maintenance. The hold, or display chamber, was the first to be constructed—where Anatub could exhibit their only other temple treasure—the Lord of the Covenant, or the lord-berith.

A pedestal was built for the Baal-berith or the Ephod of Gold. Once again it had found the light of acclaim and admiration for the beauty of its jewels and gold. The dazzling artifact helped to enlist priests, both old and young; all were given linen ephods to wear. They were in the likeness of the Golden Ephod. That was the centerpiece of esteem and veneration, and the only temple treasure exhibited in the house of God. Ahitub was blessed with a son, whom he named Ahimelech—which means *brother to the king*. When still a toddler, Ahimelech worked alongside his father. He was suckled and weaned in the rituals and ordinances of a high priest. The House of God in Nob—its last stone set—now stood ready to be consecrated. The Holy place had been twenty years in the making. Saul, the newly anointed king of Israel, made his first decree, "Bring forth The Ark of the Testimony from Kirath-ye'arim—so that we might coax God out from his hiding place with our offering of a permanent home of mortar and brick." Saul arrived to celebrate its opening. The king was fresh from his coronation. Saul, the son of Kish, a Benjamite, came to witness the dedication and to bless the first Temple with his presence.

Ahitub greeted the new king with respect and appreciation. "Your Majesty, you honor us with your attendance at our small and rural temple. As the anointed king of Israel, I ask you to bless me and to bless this house of God." Saul was glad to grant the high priest's request. Displaying the office of his authority was as yet alien and unfamiliar. He was also unaccustomed to admiration, and the ritual helped to bolster his confidence and affirm his broad acceptance to the throne of Israel.

Ahitub knelt in front of the king, and Saul laid hands on the priest's head—and speaking in a deep voice, said, "Ahitub, I bless you and your future generations, who will see to the care and maintenance of this building. Blessed be the work of your hands in completing this construction for the glory of God. May all who enter here find peace, refuge, and serenity. I give you my blessing, as your anointed king, and in the name of Adonai, the one true God."

Ahimelech had come of age to fight for Israel. He was strapping and stout, for his youth had been spent working with rock and stone. Ahimelech stood close to his father, Ahitub, who was now withered and bent from years of grueling labor. He had been worn down to the very bone while fulfilling his love and passion in building a house of God in the wilderness. Ahimelech addressed his father, saying, "Father, I would like to show King Saul to the hold, where the Golden Ephod is displayed."

Ahitub responded. "That would be at the pleasure of the king, my son."

Saul was intrigued. "By all means," he replied. "I would like nothing better than to see this treasure of Israel that I have heard so much about. Lead on, Ahimelech."

Into the hold they went. Saul was taken aback by the brilliance of gold and jewels. "I have heard about this ephod for many years, but I was not prepared for its beauty and presence. It seems like a living thing and not just a religious vestment.

Ahimelech said, "It is magnificent, I agree. We also have in storage the high priest's ephod, worn by my father as it was passed down from Eli, my great grandfather. This sacred ephod can only be worn during temple ceremonies and only on temple grounds, whereas Gideon's Ephod can be called upon to travel. We also have all the gold snuffers, lamps, gold pomegranates, and brass fittings, which have all been correctly installed. The veil of separation spans the length of the inner chamber of the Holy place.The crucial holy furniture, the altar of incense, the shewbread table and the golden lampstand are all operational.The bronze laver and the altar of burnt offerings enhance the outer courtyard. We wait upon God to balance the scales of justice and to grace us once again with his presence."

The Ark of the Testimony retrieval from Kiryath Ye'arim was uneventful. It was with Jubilation that it was installed behind the veil of separation awaiting the return of God's presence.

Saul nodded his agreement. "First, we must secure Israel from the Philistines and all her enemies. Thank you for your hospitality and your magnificent work for our Lord and our God. We will speak again. Until then, good-bye, Ahimelech."

Ahitub, weak and exhausted from the lifelong ordeal of the continual building, finally did succumb to death and the grave. The mantle fell upon Ahimelech, now the chief priest of the Temple. Many men were recruited for the benefit of the community and the preservation of the House of God. They were all were given linen ephods to wear to celebrate the Golden Ephod on display in the exhibition hold.

The Philistine wars were relentless, and there was no letup from the carnage and conflict. Saul, true to his word, called forth Ahimelech—also known as Ahiah (or the king is my brother)—to meet him in the uttermost part of Gibeah, which is in the holy place Jarham—also called Migron. Saul requested him to bring the Ephod of Gold to help conjure up the hope of divine intervention. Saul set his chair under the pomegranate tree (the average number of seeds in a pomegranate is six hundred and thirteen, the same number of laws found in the first five scrolls that had been commanded by God). Gathered around Saul were about six hundred men—six hundred and thirteen exactly were the number of men. This was to signify that Saul was a king under the laws of God and of Israel.

The battle had not yet begun, but the army of the Philistines was close by, already in view, when a great quaking shook the encampment of the Philistine horde and roused all the people of Israel. The whole of the garrison shuddered, and the earth shook in giant slides of falling rocks and in the massive tumble of boulders. The watchmen of Saul, who were perched high above the fray, had an eagle's-eye view of the Philistine multitude, who seemed to melt away. They were stricken with fear and began beating one another down to the ground. Saul was still unsure of success but believed in the power and presence of the Ark. The Ark was now close at hand. Its mere presence could create an even greater enemy chaos. Saul shouted: "Ahiah (meaning 'brother'—as well as being Ahimelech's familiar name and the high priest at Nob)—"Bring me the Ark of God, let us ensure a most certain victory over the Philistine mongrels. Be quick about it! Sometimes battles rise and fall—and quickly turn—with the speed of shifting winds. Make haste!"

Ahimelech was painfully aware of what had happened the last time this diversion had been attempted. The results had been disastrous, and the Ark of God had been captured. He entreated

Saul; "Your Majesty, the last time my great-grandfather, Eli, agreed to this ploy, the Ark of God was captured. It resulted in the Tabernacle being vacated by the Almighty. With all due respect, my king, I would advise you to forgo such a request. I fear another insult to God will bring His great wrath against Israel."

While Ahimelech was speaking to Saul, the noise from the Philistine camp continued and then increased in volume. Saul looked at the priest. "Withdraw thine hand!" Saul had told Ahimelech to forego the order to bring forth the Ark of God from its resting place. Saul and all the people with him assembled themselves, and they came to the battle—and behold—every man's sword was against his fellows. Fear and confusion rained down from heaven, and the Philistines were greatly disgraced in the slaughter of their own forces. Selah.

Part Five

CHAPTER 39

Run and Stone a Giant

Living in Nob had its advantages: a wife, a warm bed, and regular meals served piping hot. Ahimelech looked after Nob's spiritual needs, and he also acted as a respected judge. Ahimelech dispensed justice among the communal farmers and shepherds for their minor trespasses, and on the rare occasion, a misbehaving priest who was in need of a scolding or a stiff slap on the wrist. Ahimelech had many duties, but he made the necessary time to sire a son, and he named the youth Abiathar. Abiathar was still a youth of fourteen years when Ahimelech was summoned to the Valley of Elah. Saul sought after Ahimelech and the Ephod of Gold as a way to increase his favor with God, and to improve his chances of obtaining spiritual support in this endless war.

Saul and the men of Israel gathered together and pitched their tents in the valley of Elah; Saul had set his battle formation in opposition to the Philistines. The Philistines stood tall on a mountain on the one side, and Israel stood tall on a mountain opposite to the one occupied by the Philistines, and with a valley between them. A loud cheer erupted from deep within the Philistine garrison, and there proceeded out a champion—the likes of which had never been seen or before imagined. The Philistine's name was Goliath, and he was a giant from the town of Gath. His height spanned over nine feet from toe to crown. He wore a helmet cast in brass that adorned his flowing mane and massive head. He was clad in armor, wearing a coat of mail that glinted and gleamed like polished fish scales—brilliant and bright. He stood boldly to rival the sun and menace a multitude of enemies; the weight of his armor was one hundred and twenty-five pounds—easily able to deflect the most vicious blows of ax, sword, or javelin's throw. Goliath had shin and neck armor to protect against the flight of arrows and to blunt the thrust of handheld weapons. The staff of his spear was like a weaver's beam: two inches round, and the sharpened head weighed fifteen pounds—it could shear a man in two. A strong man went before him bearing his shield; proclaiming loudly that Goliath was skillful in the murder of Hebrews.

Goliath stood at the base of the mount where it met the floor of the valley. The morning sun cast his shadow over the climbing landscape of the mountain, and it briefly doubled his size. Goliath spoke with a deep growl that echoed off the valley walls—causing hairs to stand on the back of necks and chills to fall the length and breadth of quaking backbones. He cried out to the armies of Israel in a booming blood-curdling roar: "Why are you here, and why have you set your legions in a hostile battle array? Am not I a Philistine, and you, the servants of Saul? I challenge you to choose from among you the strongest and most skilled warrior.

Let him come down to me so that we may battle—and if he can kill me in open combat, then we will be your servants—but if I prevail against him and kill him, then you, Israel, shall be our servants and serve us."

Goliath paused to test his effect and to allow the challenge to blister the ears of Israel. He then raised his spear and pumped the air with defiant cocksureness—and filling his lungs to double his thunder, he bellowed—"I defy the armies of Israel this day! Give me a man that we might fight together. Put me not to wait, as my patience thins by the minute, and your fearful delay only adds fuel to my brooding and contempt." Goliath's challenge was strongly felt by the Israelite camp, and it caused some breaths to catch and hearts to pound. Israel was dismayed and greatly afraid. They cowered in the shadows of fear and misgiving.

Israel and all the people considered Saul. Was he not, after all, the tallest man among them, possessing the largest frame? Saul stood head and shoulders over the host, and as a champion, he was celebrated for his bravery and endurance. It was rumored that he could kill a thousand men single-handedly. Saul had no equal in Israel, with either sword or spear. Thus, Israel murmured: "Surely he will go for us." Yet this sentiment was not openly expressed, for no one would dare to even suggest the death-defying act of man-to-man combat in the ear of their anointed king. Israel's battalions of footmen waited for Saul's reply to the giant's menacing challenge. Would their king engage this Philistine in a fight to the death? Saul had already crossed over from youth's relentless slide into middle age, but he was still as strong as he had ever been.

Gideon: The Sound and the Glory

He addressed his legions, saying, "I see this braggart for who he is, an Anakim ruffian, not a king or a prince. I refuse to fight a common thug! Present me with a Philistine prince, and I shall be most inclined to cut him into little pieces. Let us be patient. God's time is not our time. Ahimelech, our high priest, is among us, wearing the Golden Ephod. Let us pray and sacrifice until a champion who is appointed by God comes forth. This will give us time to reinforce our position and to stockpile our rations. Let us not forget that, sometimes, the best defense is the offense of patience and preparation."

Goliath cursed Israel for forty days, repeating his challenge both morning and evening. He kept up his challenge in the hope that he would wear down the morale of Hebrew resolve and that their valor would collapse into the dust, sealing their fate in the coming conflict. This cunning deception was a ploy to ensure that Israel would be routed and put to shame and that, once again, they would become servants and slaves. At dawn's first light, Goliath would be seen standing like a bronze statue, bold against the thinning shadows, costumed in his full battle attire. It was a devious design, played out to agitate and disturb the host of Israel during every waking hour. Goliath's ranting and raving remained a constant each morning, to be repeated at the close of every day. He would howl at the rising moon in a war cry of nightmarish aggression.

David was the seventh and youngest son of Jesse, the son of Obed, the son of Boaz. David was the seed of Jesse's old age. Jesse's youngest son was always burdened with the least pleasing chores and at everyone's beck and call. David spent most of his time among his father's sheep, often deep in the wilderness in the company of wild beasts. He suffered the heat of summer days and the chill of winter nights, pondering the vastness of creation. David's only physical relief, also a powerful source of protection, was the blaze of his fire, even on the rain-soaked nights. David's first source of warmth and comfort came from his burning love for God. David trusted first in God and then his sling above all else, and kept his script filled to the brim with five smooth stones. So accurate was his aim that he had slain a lion and a bear, crushing their skulls with the force of his blows. David was an expert with his shepherd's weapon, practicing both in daylight and in the gloom of twilight. He piled stone upon stone, starting out by smashing the largest, and then steadily decreasing his targets to ever smaller rocks, until finally, pebbles were smitten into fine powdered dust; rumor had it that he once struck a hawk when it was in the full flight of its dive.

Eliab, (meaning *"God is Father"*—and also known as Elihu, meaning *"My God is He"*), Abinadab and Shammah were Jesse's three oldest sons; who were obliged to follow Saul to the battle at Elah. David, being too young, was not yet invited—but tagged along from a distance to catch a view of how warring nations engaged in their battle formations. Upon reaching the front line, the brothers reported to their respective captains of thousands.

Eliab, having received his command assignment, turned to David. "David, this is no place for the likes of you! You are a youth of only fourteen years. You will only be in the way. War is a man's work and not a game played by boys. Your presence here puts your life in jeopardy, as well as ours. Besides, I'm sure you have pressing chores. Father is old, and the sheep need to be fed in Bethlehem. Be off with you!" David departed and did what was required of him.

Jesse called to David in the dark before the breaking of that fate-filled day, saying, "David, I need for you to deliver a bushel of corn, ten rounds of cheese, and ten loaves of bread to the captains of thousands that stand watch in the valley of Elah. We need to be compensated for these to pay our back taxes to Saul, so be sure to secure pledges from the wealthy generals. They must commit their promise to a future payment. Also, inquire about each of your brothers, as I am concerned for their health and welfare. Depart tomorrow, early enough for you to arrive at Elah before first light."

David rose from his bed with an air of anticipation and excitement. He gathered up his shepherd's bag with his trusted sling, but in his eagerness, he had neglected to fill his script with rocks, for his load was already heavy; he would dispense with the additional burden of stones. David looked at his father in the dark of the early morning and whispered the words, "I obey, father, and I will do all that you have commanded." David left the sheep bleating and baaing in the hands of a keeper, long before sunup. He put all the provisions into a carriage to overflowing and set out at a brisk pace to the field of battle in the valley of Elah.

Saul and all the men of Israel were in the valley of Elah; they were kept busy with bloody skirmishes along frontline trenches that both armies had deeply dug. The goal was to probe and defend, as both armies were evenly matched, each seeking to gain the slightest advantage. They were relentless in their search, looking for a breach or a gap to exploit, so they could destroy any distracted enemy caught off guard or just plain napping. Israel's nerves had been stretched thin by the back and forth of this stubborn standoff. Patience was at an end. It was time for the main event, a decisive clash of nations.

David came upon the front-line trenches as the sun rose to start yet another day of war and mayhem. The army of Israel was going forth to battle, shouting their war cry to bolster their strength and to unnerve the Philistine battalions. Israel and the Philistines had formed up along the now-emptied trenches in an effort to confirm that all were fully committed to a winner-take-all conflict. David let go of his cargo and placed it with the carriage handler. He then ran to find his brothers. David addressed Abinadab and Shammah, saying, "Father is concerned and is fearful of this battle's outcome. He sent me with rations for you and your generals that I might receive their pledges to relieve the press of back taxes." David was taken up short when the bluster of Goliath's blare overpowered the clamor of two armies.

For the first time, David heard Goliath's final challenge—the seventy-ninth crowing coming early in the morning of the fortieth day. Goliath spoke the same words he had spoken before, delivering his challenge with the same swagger and bravado as when he first provoked Israel and at every stab of the ear after that. The men of Israel, when they saw him, hearing his challenge yet again, backed away, for he filled them with terror. The soldiers of Israel said to David: "Saw you this man who has come up against us? Not a man but a giant, and he has come up counter to us to defy Israel. It has been promised by King Saul that the man who kills him and takes this evil out of Israel will be enriched three times. First with wealth; second, he will be given to marry the king's eldest daughter, the princess, Merab; and best of all, he will make his father's house free from all taxes in Israel."

David replied to the men that stood by him. "So, all this that you said, by the will of the king shall be done unto him who kills this man, and takes away this disgrace from Israel? And who is this uncircumcised Philistine who dares defy the armies of the living God?"

The men who stood close to David cried out once more. "All that was promised by Saul shall come to pass, and the victor will be heaped with praise. And the champion who vanquishes the Anakim Philistine will have the reward of riches, and his father's house will be free of taxes forever . . . and he will be betrothed to Saul's daughter, the princess, Merab."

Eliab, David's eldest brother, and the task master of the house of Jesse, was answerable for his youngest brother's pranks and his unwelcomed presence. Eliab approached the gathered mob just in time to hear David challenging the might of the giant, Goliath. When Eliab heard David's boast, his anger flared against his little brother's bragging. And he spoke harshly to David and said, "Why have you come down to the battle? When we talked last, I cast you out from this place of danger and death! It is no place for children. With whom have you left the few sheep that we so greatly depend on? Are they in the wilderness unattended while you are here sightseeing and causing discord? I know your pride and the mischief of your heart; you have left your charges and have come here only to watch the engagement of battle and bloodshed."

David felt the sting of his eldest brother's tongue. Eliab was still smarting from being passed over by Samuel, the prophet, in the anointing of his little brother, David. Calmly, David replied. "What have I done now? You have no cause to be angry with me. I have been sent by our father, Jesse, on an urgent errand to this place. You have no reason to be cross with me." David dismissed his brother's envy and turned quickly to another and asked again as before, "What is the prize for the killing of the Philistine giant, and how dare this uncircumcised heathen to defy the army of God?" Again, the reward was repeated and confirmed, exactly as it had been previously stated. The news of David's words was rehearsed perfectly and brought to the ears of Saul. Saul was as curious as he was impressed with this grand gesture and boundless confidence coming from an unknown stranger.

Had an unlikely hero been found in Israel? Could it be, Saul wondered, deciding to call for David to see for himself? "Bring me the one who has spoken so boldly against the giant and would be a savior of Israel. With all speed, relay to my captains of thousands they must prevent my army's forward advance. They shall wait in place for my further order." Saul thought, "I need some time to sort things out. Perhaps this is the miracle I have been praying for . . . a spark to rekindle Israel's dampened will to fight and win." The king's men found David in the heart of the crowd. He was informed that the king sought his presence, so David consented to the king's wish, and he was brought forth to King Saul's pavilion.

Saul was sitting on a makeshift throne, and standing next to him was Ahimelech, wearing the Ephod of Gold. David made his simple bow and looked down to the ground. Saul's hopes were dashed when he saw this youth of fourteen, a mere boy, and slight at that. His countenance was fair and handsome, even when dressed in shepherd's rags, but this child is no match, Saul thought, for the fearsome giant, Goliath. David, being unfamiliar with royal protocol, spoke first. Brimming with childlike enthusiasm, he said to Saul: "Let no man's heart fail or his countenance fall due to the crowing of this puffed-up infidel. I am your servant. Command me, and I will go to fight this Philistine marauder. Great will be his fall." Saul sized David up and down and then shook his head in disbelief, for the words that had been spoken were grander than the height of the giant that this simple, trusting, and innocent teen was insisting on defeating.

Saul addressed the fair youth. "Your name is David, is it not? You are from the little town of Bethlehem . . . and you would be a savior for all of Israel?"

David replied, "Yes, My King. It is as you say."

Saul smiled. Speaking kindly but with the insight of years from his close-combat experience, he said to David, "As much as I wish it were so, you would be unable to prevail against this giant Philistine monster. You could not best him in a duel to the death, for you are unskilled and out-matched. You do have the heart of a lion, and the strength of your will is that of a bear, but Goliath has trained for war since he was a boy. His skill and power fill grown men with terror and dread. David, you are overmatched."

David politely dismissed all of Saul's well-meaning but fear-driven advice before replying to the king. "I have kept my father's sheep in the wilderness all alone and have done so these many years. Once came a lion upon me, and once came a bear. Each in their turn took a lamb out from my father's flock, and I went after each one of them separately and was not afraid. I struck the lion and took the sheep from out of his jaws, and when the bear rose up to his full height against me, I caught him by his beard and struck him and slew him dead. Your servant has killed both a lion and a bear, and this uncircumcised Philistine shall be as one of them, seeing that he has defied the armies of the living God! The God Who delivered me out of the paw of the lion and the paw of the bear—he will also deliver me out of the hand of the Philistine. I trust in God enough to stake my life and my breath on the outcome."

Saul was moved by the youth's heartfelt declaration, and by his faith and by his deeds. "I agree. You shall be our champion and God's champion, and may the Lord be with you." With these words, Saul gave his blessing to David. Saul continued, saying, "David, you will have my armor, the king's armor, and you will have your own tent. Come with me, and we will fit you for the battle, a clash with a son of Anak. Little David, you have a faith greater than the size of giants." Hearing the shuffle of footsteps to his left, Saul turned his gaze upon the high priest. "Oh," said Saul. "My manners escape me in these trying times. Let me introduce you to our high priest, Ahimelech. He wears the Golden Ephod, in the hope that we might gain favor with God."

Ahimelech spoke directly to the fledgling who had taken on the mantle of the fearless warrior. "I am most impressed with your faith in God and in your resolve, David. I bless your efforts in His name. We will speak again after you have put away this evil from Israel." Saul and Ahimelech helped to dress David in the king's shining armor, fitting him with a helmet of brass and a coat of chain mail to protect his upper body. David wrapped around his waist the belt of the king's big sword, cinching it tight upon his armor. David was a pitiful sight in his oversized coat of heavy metal that hung loosely on his back, shoulders, and neck, making him look even smaller yet. Saul's armor was much too large, cumbersome, and restricting.

David said to Saul, "Thank you, my Lord, for this honor, but I have not been proven and I have not been trained in the use of such combat equipment. I cannot go with these trappings." David took the armor off, and putting it aside, he said, "Trusting in God means to be sure of the tools He gives us, as well as being sure of His timing." David took his leave, and Saul, having seen David fully dressed in his battle finery now realized what a hopeless attempt this would be, and his confidence in the youth started to rapidly shrink. Little David would fight a giant with a staff, a sling, and a shepherd's bag full of faith. David departed, and, on the outside of the tent, he found his staff where he'd left it and proceeded down the same path where earlier, he had crossed a fast-moving stream. Just over a ledge where the waterfall sings, there were five smooth stones all in a row, as if placed by providence or some unseen hand. Five was the number of the scrolls of the law, and it was just enough ammunition to fill his script or shepherd's pouch while leaving room for his hand to pluck out the perfect missile.

David was brightened by his find. Slipping the strap of his shepherd's bag over his head and shoulder, it rested lightly on his hip. David's trusted sling was clutched loosely in his hand, ready to receive its power from the whip of his wrist. The army of the living God and the Philistine mob together surrounded the rim of the valley. The winds picked up, and a bird of prey circled overhead, riding high on the hot updraft of contention. The banners and battalion ensigns were fully unfurled when little David came

314

into view. Everything went deathly quiet, except for the snapping of battle ribbons. David's reliable staff helped to steady his rapid descent to the valley floor below, bringing him into a swift and fatal collision with the menacing Philistine. Goliath squinted in the bright, early morning light. Far off in the distance, he could see a faint object scurrying down the mountainside. Could it be, he thought, the long-awaited Hebrew champion?

Goliath's spittle dripped from his lips with eager delight at the prospect of this long-awaited close-quarters combat. Goliath had time enough to prepare himself and stepped forward, his gigantic strides swiftly closing the shrinking gap between him and his would-be opponent. The man who carried his shield ran with all due haste, his gait short and shallow. At the last moment, he managed to overtake the giant, coming out in front of him, panting and gulping for oxygen. The huge shield was needed to attest to Goliath's magnificence, and also to ward off any wayward spear or arrow's flight that would hamper or threaten the giant's ability to maim and kill. David came into full view, now within earshot of the Philistine Anakim. Both men stopped, allowing the other to take stock of his rival.

Goliath looked down his nose at what seemed to be a mere youth. His face was flushed; his complexion was rosy red. The boy was dressed in shepherd's rags! The giant's ridicule increased tenfold when he realized the lad had no armor, spear, or sword . . . only a staff and a bag. Was this some kind of Hebrew joke? Goliath was furious at this blatant attempt to mock him. The giant was outraged. He growled at Little David menacingly. "Am I a dog that you come to me with a bag and a stick?" David's flesh-colored sling hung loosely at his hip and was almost invisible to the naked eye. Goliath continued with his railing against David. "I curse you in the name and by the might of Dagon, our mighty God of vengeance and retribution. Come to me, and I will give your flesh unto the fowls of the air and to the beasts of the field."

David had an unshakable faith and with all of his youthful daring, countered the giant's threat. "You come to me with a sword, a spear, and with a Philistine mongrel carrying your shield: but I come to you in the name of the Lord of hosts, the God of the armies of Israel, whom you have dishonored. On this very day, He will deliver you into my hands: and I will strike you to the ground. I will take your head off your neck, and I will serve up the rest of the Philistine mob of dead and rotting corpses. Feeding and refreshing the vulture and the eagle; jackals and wild dogs who will relish the feasting on Philistine flesh. Thus, will all the earth know there is a God in Israel! They will become a feast for carrion eaters. All who are assembled here will confess and confirm that the Lord is God, knowing He can save and defend; He can make dead or make alive without the need of sword or spear: for the battle is the Lord's battle, and He will give you into my hands."

All that was necessary to be said had been said. What more could be said? Goliath was enraged with this fiery pipsqueak's remarks, so he raised both his arms, increasing his already formidable height and menacing stature. He stomped the ground as he closed in on David, who started running straight at Goliath, charging the huge giant, who was steadily advancing toward him. David was vaguely aware of the Philistine army that stood at the giant's back, but his focus was on Goliath alone. Running at full tilt, David reached into his script and, with a practiced hand, chose an oval stone. It was smooth, with the perfectly rounded weight and girth, fitting into his sling like a hand into a well-worn glove. Still charging at the giant, the word "Genesis!" was heard in muted tones less than a whisper.

David whipped his sling, just as he had done so many times before. So quick was the spin that it was barely visible; he dug in. David bent at the waist; his arm and his wrist snapped the sling with an overhead throw. In his follow-through, he yelled out the word "Genesis," adding a name and energy to the Genesis stone. It flew to its target with unerring accuracy. The shield bearer made a desperate attempt to block the oncoming rock, but could not reach its height. The egg-sized stone sailed over the top of the screen and hit home just above the giant's eyes, sinking deep into the fleshy folds of his forehead. Goliath's knees buckled, and he fell forward upon his face, causing the earth to tremble. David had carried the day with a sling and stone, using the power of faith and his love of God. Goliath's breath was labored—knocked cold, but was not yet completely undone. David needed to fulfill the curse of his prophetic words and make his promise come true. He needed a sword, but he had no sword; there was only one sword that was available. David ran to the fallen Philistine and stood on his back. He took Goliath's massive sword, and using both hands, he removed it from its sheath. David raised it up over his head. With all his might, he bore down in a vicious arc and with three whacks separated Goliath's massive skull at the neck; all that remained was a headless corpse and the gurgling echo of the giant's final death rattle.

Everyone standing close enough to witness his twitching face and body was given a clear view of David's confirmed kill. The young shepherd boy raised Goliath's severed head by its pitch-black and blood-stained mane. David stretched tall so everyone on both sides of the mountain could see the victory of God made evident through the unshakable faith of a shepherd boy. God had confounded the mighty with the weak things of this world. The Philistines, saw their champion beheaded, and a little shepherd boy astride his back, wielding a massive sword and raising tall Goliath's severed head. David, then stepped forward threatening to attack, and suddenly, ten thousand spun on their heels, turned tail and ran in fear of life and limb. The men of Israel and of Judah shouted their war cry, coming out in force to pursue the fleeing Philistines. The distressed route taken by Israel's fleeing enemies lasted for many a blood-stained mile. Many were wounded as they scurried from one Philistine town to the next, seeking refuge but finding no amnesty from the murderous and merciless Israeli army.

David, still carrying the head of the Philistine as a trophy, went back up to the carriage keeper. To his dismay, he realized that his corn, his bread, and the ten rounds of cheese, given to him by his father was missing, taken no doubt by some passing infantrymen. He shook his head, thinking to himself that they must have been starving to commit such a crime. The mission he had been given by his father could not be accomplished without the food stuff to offset Saul's heavy taxes. David sat down on the edge of the carriage to think about what could be done. A thought struck him! He started considering the value of metal, brass, and iron . . . surely those pledges his father sought from the captains could be readily harvested from the disposal of Goliath's armor? Was it not his by right of conquest? David wheeled his empty carriage to Goliath's hulking corpse, where vultures had already started gathering, brought in by the smell of fresh blood. David stripped the body, taking everything of value that he could barter. David took the giant's belt buckle, his spear, and his sword. He even took the great shield that had been hastily abandoned by Goliath's armor bearer. It required three trips to the carriage to secure every inch of David's first spoils of war. He placed it all in his tent, the tent that had been given to him by Saul, the king of Israel.

Ahimelech entered David's tent. "All praise to you, young David. This victory of yours will be told and retold from generation to generation. Your name will always be on men's lips for as long as Israel survives as a nation." David lowered his eyes to the ground, and his ruddy complexion burned a little brighter. Quietly, he whispered, "It was not me, my Lord, who slew the giant; it was God. I was just confident in the outcome. It was as if I could see the end from the beginning, all glory to God in the highest." Ahimelech was humbled by the faith of this young stripling warrior. "Thank you for that, David the Giant Killer. If every Israelite could think like that, we would be invincible as a people." The youth and the high priest shared a smile, and Ahimelech addressed David once more. "Be that as it may, I have come to discuss another matter. I noticed that you set down all of the giant's armor here in this tent, and I am curious as to what you intend doing with it. Seeing as you could not fit into Saul's armor, you obviously won't be wearing it. What say you, young David?"

David, thinking that another party may perhaps try to lay claim to the armor, spoke quickly. "I claim this armor by right of conquest! My intent is to sell every item, even piecemeal if necessary, so I might give the pledges to my father. This is why I was sent here, as well as to report on the welfare of my three brothers."

Ahimelech nodded in agreement. "Yes. Of course, it belongs to you, unless the king would claim it for himself. But I know Saul. After the great feat you have accomplished this day, he would not quibble or even suggest such a matter. This booty is yours, and you can do with it as you see fit. Now, young David, the reason for my presence is that I would like to pledge against the sword of Goliath. I have a temple in Nob, a House of God, and I would like to display it on the wall behind this Golden Ephod's marble pedestal in the hold of treasures. I will wrap it securely in some oil-soaked cloth to preserve its luster, once I have washed off this giant blood stain." The high priest looked down to conceal his impish smile at the dead Philistine's expense.

David nodded his understanding, and Ahimelech lifted Goliath's sword, marveling at its workmanship. "This will be a perfect addition to our temple treasures and a reminder in Israel of a young man's unwavering faith." A bargain was struck, and a pledge was exchanged. Word quickly spread throughout the camp concerning the give-and-take promise of pledges in return for the store of metals piled high in David's tent. Nobles, merchants, and smithies quickly descended, and the armor was gone within the hour.

Saul could not believe in his mind what his eyes had beheld. Little David had slain the giant Goliath, the pride of the Philistine army. He inquired of Abner, his most trusted general, asking, "Whose son is this sprout? From what stem is his root? Who does this upstart belong to?"

Abner's forehead crinkled into a frown as he answered, "I do not know, My King, but I will find out, by your leave, Majesty." Saul dismissed Abner, who went immediately into David's tent. "King Saul demands your presence. Follow me." David took his trophy head and followed Abner back to Saul's pavilion.

"Well done," said Saul. "I see you have the giant's head with you. We will take it back to Jerusalem and display it for all to see and hear of our victory. You are a hero in Israel, young man, and everyone will want to know you. I neglected to ask when we first met—forgive me, but I felt you were going to be short lived—I need to know who your father is?" David responded, "I am the son of your servant, Jesse, the Bethlemite."

Saul, spied David with a new found respect; was this not the child who had received his anointing from Samuel the prophet to be the next king of Israel? Saul, considered to himself, "I need to keep this youth close at hand and help to curtail any future mischief. David, the giant killer could prove to be an even greater threat than was ever the fearsome Goliath."

David searched for his brother, Eliab, and finding him, said, "Brother, undoubtedly you have either seen or heard of my exploits?" Eliab nodded in disbelief, amazed at his young brother's incredible accomplishment. He had, finally, to concede that his little brother had been chosen by God. "I apologize for not believing in you, David. Please forgive me, my brother, so that we may put away our squabble, and I my sibling envy."

David hugged Eliab's neck, calling him Elihu, his familiar name, and saying, "I do forgive you, my big brother." They parted and David spoke of his news. "I have been invited to live with the king in Jerusalem, and to be his armor bearer. I will not be returning home just yet. Please tell our father I will visit him as soon as possible. And let him know that because of my victory, the House of Jesse has been made free from all the king's taxes, as this will please him to no end. Delight our good father with this mountain of pledges, received from the sale of the Philistine's weaponry. I hope it cheers him. Until we meet again, Eliab, I pray the Lord God keep you." David and his brother parted with a new understanding. They were more than just brothers now; they were also friends.

David and Saul entered Jerusalem after the great slaughter of the Philistines, and the city's women came out singing and dancing to help celebrate the victory. The women, in playful banter, whispered together and then sang in unison a song for all to hear: "Saul has slain his thousands, and David his ten thousands." Saul took great insult at hearing the song, saying, "They have credited David with ten thousand, yet they count me with only thousands! He has been anointed to rule my kingdom. Does he need to insult me as well?" From that day forward, Saul viewed David with an evil eye, regarding him as an injury to his vanity and his dynasty. The worm of envy, fear, and pride burrowed deeply into the mind, heart, and soul of Saul.

CHAPTER 40

The Life and Death of Sword and Bread

Seven years had passed, and Saul's hatred for David burned hotly; flaring into demands for David's swift destruction. The young David held his tongue and was wise in all his dealings. He never gave Saul any reason to mistrust him or find fault with his loyalty, and this increased Saul's anger, for there was no deceit in David. Jonathan, Saul's son, who would have risen to the throne if it had not been for the anointing of David, had put all his ambitions aside and had become David's greatest ally. Jonathan had made a secret pact with David. He took it upon himself to warn David, whose life was constantly in peril because of Saul's jealousy. One morning, the two young men were safe in the wilderness and free from spying eyes. Only David's loyal troop was in attendance, those men who saw to David's day-to-day routines or fought for his well-being in fierce and distant battles.

Jonathan said to David, "Go in peace, for we have sworn in the name of the Lord that between you and me and in all our generations to come, that we will be friends forever; but today, even now, you must not return to the city. You must leave from where you stand without delay. You and your league of men must travel beyond my father's reach, or you will be surely put to death this Wednesday before the sun goes down. You and your band must remain hidden for the next three days, while my father searches out every crevice and crack. He will relent three days hence on the Sabbath; then, and only then, will you have a moment's reprieve—for only by your dying will he quell his passion for your destruction."

David and his men hid in the clefts of rocks and in caves, traveling only by night. David's crew had no food and no weapons with which to kill game or to defend themselves. They were at the whims of chance and happenstance; seeking refuge under God's wing of tender mercies. Sabbath dawn broke late as the sun shone through a bank of clouds and discovered the house of God at Nob. David saw possible relief from the want of bread and their pressing need for weapons, and said to his men, "I know this place. I have had dealings with the high priest, Ahimelech, on the very day I captured the head of the Philistine giant, Goliath. Ahimelech is close friends with Saul, and Saul invites him to all the battles and royal events, that this priest might wear Gideon's Ephod of Gold. I must approach with caution, and alone, so as not to arouse fear or suspicion. I will signal you to join me after I have succeeded in my mission. I will make up some fanciful story about being on a secret mission for the king and that we had no time to prepare because of its urgent nature."

One of David's men responded by saying, "You are well practiced and pleasing with a lyre, but, as a liar, you leave a lot to be desired." All the men laughed. They needed a good laugh, and so did David.

David gave his men a final instruction. "Remain quiet and hidden here at the crossroads, and wait for my signal." David advanced along the winding path to the house of God, and there at the front gate stood Ahimelech. He was uneasy at the sight of David all alone, approaching him so early on a Sabbath morning. Ahimelech was afraid, for he knew David had lost the king's favor, and he did not want to be implicated in any disloyalty to Saul. Ahimelech had witnessed on more than one occasion Saul's increasingly evil nature. Ahimelech dismissed his usual, cordial greeting, and asked David abruptly, "Why are you here alone and without your band that is always at your command?"

David smiled his most disarming smile and said, "Ahimelech, be not dismayed. My crew of men is just around yonder bend. I did not want to approach in force and disquiet your serenity."

David signaled to his men, and they were quick upon the scene. David continued. "The king has commanded me a business to perform for his benefit, and I am under strict orders not to utter a single word as to the nature of our mission. Our departure was at night and our flight so hurried that we took no thought for bread, and now we find ourselves, with the lack of nourishment, all but starving. I cannot impress upon you enough the importance of our rush, for it is with the utmost urgency we attempt to benefit our king. I have been instructed to forego any further communication on the matter. Ahimelech, having been made aware that we are on the king's errand, I pray that you can give us what provisions might be available, even if only five loaves of bread or whatever else can be spared. That should suffice to sustain us while on the king's mission."

Ahimelech looked dismayed once more and shook his head, saying, "I have no common bread on my hand. This is the Sabbath, and there is only hallowed bread present, made fresh for today. I have twelve loaves still hot from yesterday's oven, and if you and your men have refrained from the company of women, I could give you the week's past shewbread for your feasting."

David replied quickly, wanting to show his relief. "To be perfectly honest with you, women have been kept from us for these three days—the precise number of days since we left to accomplish our secret mission. This makes the young men holy vessels and the shewbread as ordinary when it is eaten by them."

Abiathar, the son of Ahimelech, whose duty it was to see to the exchange of bread, gave them the holy bread that was taken from before the Lord. Abiathar drew out the fresh, hot bread from the heat of yesterday's oven—presenting the new shewbread before the Lord of hosts on the Table of the Presence, where the shewbread is always in the presence of God. David and his people were full and refreshed, and David thanked Ahimelech. After a moment's thought, he decided to press his advantage. "Ahimelech, one last question: under your hand, are there any hand weapons? Spears, swords, or even ancient bronze scimitars perhaps? I have brought with me no arms, not for myself or my men. We had no option but to leave in great haste on the king's most urgent business."

Ahimelech was surprised at such a request. "David, this is not an armory but a House of God. The only weapon here is one with which you are already familiar. It is Goliath's sword, the very sword I pledged from you in the Elah Valley. It is a temple treasure, wrapped in oil cloth to protect it from rust and ruin. It is mounted behind the Ephod of Gold. If you would have it, then take it, for there is no other I can give you."

David grew excited, for he had regretted many times his youthful zeal to please his father, wishing he had retained the weapon for himself. David grinned at his good fortune. "There is none like it! Give it here to me, and thank you for your kindness, Ahimelech. The wisdom of God has placed this weapon back in my hand." David, clutching the sword of Goliath, knelt before Ahimelech. His men, following David's example, also took to their knees. David looked up at Ahimelech. "Kind high priest, one last favor before we depart. I pray you, please, to enquire of the Lord, and ask for His blessing of protection for my people and me, and that He directs our path."

Ahimelech granted David's request for prayer. "I bless you, David, son of Jesse, and I seal your anointing with a consecration and a promise that you will find your way, and the Lord God will be your shield and your protection. Trust in Him always, and may you fill the measure of your creation and find joy therein. I say these things by the power of the holy priesthood I hold, and in the name of Adonai, our Lord, and our God."

David rose and hugged Ahimelech around his neck; then he departed with all his men for fear of being overheard and overlooked. They fled to Achish, the Philistine king, an enemy to Saul, and once an admirer of the kindhearted David—but all that was said and done at Nob was under the wary eye of Doeg the Edomite.

Doeg the Edomite was a regular visitor to the temple at Nob, for he was learned and was solid in the knowledge of God. Doeg was detained before the Lord in the breadth and depth of awareness, for his constant companions were study and learning. He was cursed with a longing for an elevated position, for he fancied himself as a diviner. Doeg was often sought out as an oracle, for he had been given the gift of discernment through his many hours of in-depth study of the Holy Scriptures. Doeg was often found in Nob due to the richness of its green pastures and his position as the king's chief herdsman. He often took advantage of the priests' learned stories and their stockpile of ancient scrolls. Doeg had ambition and detested his lot as a nursemaid to sheep, goats, and asses. He prayed that he would be raised up to the court and gain the ear of the king to become his prime minister. Doeg, seemingly in answer to his prayer to be given an opportunity to rise in rank and honor, had ventured upon the scene at the temple gate and had witnessed in detail, Ahimelech's betrayal of his king in the giving of aid and comfort to the fugitive, David.

David reasoned that Saul would not venture into a Philistine stronghold, risking death and defeat just to fulfill his need to extinguish his youthful nemesis, in spite of David having the rightful claim to being called "the Lord's anointed and future king of Israel." Saul would take all safeguards to sidestep God's petitions regarding David's anointing, to ensure his ongoing dynasty of Saul the Benjaminite king. David and his band of men were helped by the people of Israel as they wound their way to the borders of the Philistine territory. David presented himself at the gate of Gath, begging for admittance and an audience with King Achish—in the hope of smoothing things over—that he might obtain a grant of pardon and a needed sanctuary from his constant need to evade Saul's death sentence. The servant of

Achish, hearing David's name, asked, "Are you not the David who is king in the land of Israel? Did they not sing one to another and dance, flattering your incredible feats, saying, 'Saul hath slain his thousands, and David his ten thousands'?"

David was taken aback, for they were speaking of him killing ten thousand Philistines. David became sore afraid and was filled with a dreadful worry. The fear that King Achish would seek revenge melted his heart and jangled his nerves. David fell down to the ground, scrabbling and scratching at the doors of the gate like a madman. David's saliva dripped down in pools of drool that fell upon his beard. Achish observed David's strange behavior, and to his servant he said, "Look! Can you see that this man is mad? Why have you brought him to me?" Achish respected and liked David but could not be seen to be giving the killer of so many Philistines comfort and aid. David was also an enemy of his enemy, Saul, and in this way, he could dismiss David while keeping his honor intact. Achish said, "Have I need of madmen that you have brought this fellow to play the madman in my presence? Shall this fellow come into my house? Cast him out from among us!"

CHAPTER 41

The Murder of Prophets and Priest

D avid quickly put some distance between himself and Gath, and his panic slowly subsided. He did not look back, fearing that King Achish might change his mind and that revenge would suddenly be upon him. David made his way with pressing speed to the remote cave of Adullam. There he lingered in the wilderness and felt encircled at every approach, for each path he attempted was beset with peril in the form of liars, snares, or enemies. David had grasped the sad fact that no friend had compassion for his soul and that he could find neither relief nor refuge. Wearily, he dropped to his knees, praying to the Lord from the depths of his depression. "Oh, God, hear the words of my mouth and know the meditation of my heart, that it be acceptable in Thy sight. O LORD, my strength, and my Redeemer—I am brought very low, and my heart breaks. Deliver me, Oh Lord, from my tormentors. For they are stronger than me; bring my soul out of prison that I may praise Your name and that Your righteousness shall surround me like a warm blanket, and that You will deal with me from Your endless bounty of love and grace."

David rose up and felt inspired to send for his brethren and all who were in his father's house. David foresaw the peril they faced due to the treacheries of Saul. He had become impressed that Saul planned to use as leverage, the lives of David's family, to accomplish his overriding obsession—the destruction of David. Saul hoped to use the House of Jesse as a wedge against David. David's parents and all his brothers came to him, and they were glad for the reunion.

David turned his thoughts to the benefit of his family, and almost immediately the weight of the world lightened; he found, in its turn, the favor of God. His courage and his outlook began to brighten; David again was in the service of the Lord. He had regained a spiritual glow; it shone through his physical being and was revealed in everything he did. David attracted an army of men who were either in distress, in debt, or in some way disconnected. This army of lonely and deprived beings gathered themselves together to be in his service and to share in his anointed presence. David became a captain over them, and there were about four hundred souls in all.

David found solace and comfort in the company of his family, and he recruited his brothers to train his army of misfits and to take a leading role among them. His mother and his father were frail and already of advanced age. The cave was cold, and it chilled their old bones. David knew it was just a matter of time before Saul would find his hiding place, for Saul had spies and informants who received a hefty compensation for any hint of David's whereabouts.

David honored his mother and his father and, therefore, felt the need to seek out a safe harbor, where he and his family would find relief from the constant threat of invasion. David went then to Mizpeh, to the watchtower perched on the highest peak, and from there all movement of man or beast could be easily detected. The king of Moab had been in an extended conflict with Israel and had a network of informants and spies, so that nothing escaped the wise king of the all-seeing Tower of Moab. David and his four hundred rebels and all his brethren made the trek. David's great-grandmother, Ruth, was a Moabite, and he was counting on family ties of blood to provide a safe sanctuary. David continued onward into Mizpeh in Moab. He asked for and was granted, an audience with the king. David made his plea to the king, asking him to give asylum to his aged parents; putting him in remembrance of Ruth and the importance of family. "I ask that you let them come to you and be under your protection until I know what God would have of me."

The king said, "Your parents are welcome here in my stronghold, as well as you and all your men—for your enemy is my enemy—namely Saul. Now, go and fetch your parents and my distant cousins. Have no fear while you and yours are among us, as safety and nourishment in abundance will be forthcoming."

It was a small step, but David felt a divine momentum and welcomed this opportunity for a breather. It gave him time enough to wait for the Lord's direction. David followed the king's directive and quickly returned to Adullam. He said to his father, Jesse, and his mother, Nitzevet, "Good news! We have been invited to Mizpeh, to the all-seeing tower of the king, and we can enjoy his protection in Moab. Good food, warmth, and safety will be made available upon our arrival."

The journey was comfortable as it was uneventful; every step increasing the distance from the threat of potential danger. David introduced his parents and all his brothers to the king. "Your Majesty, we come before you to thank you for your generosity and your protection against our common enemy. Thank you for inviting us into the family of Moab. My men are used to hardships; so to lessen your burden they will remain outside the walls of the citadel."

The king replied. "Welcome, my honored guests. Please make your wishes known, and be sure to take your rest. A place is being made ready for you, David, secure in the hold. Have no fear while you and yours are among us."

The Lord, in His time and in His way, sent a prophet unto David; it was Gad, brother of the prophet Nathan. Gad carried a message that was to be delivered directly to David, and to no other, from the hand of the prophet Samuel. Gad was to seek out David in Moab and had been commissioned to find him before the wrath of Saul could catch him unawares and unprepared. Gad, upon finding David, said, "Stand no longer in the hold of this watchtower. Saul knows of your location and that of your recruited army of exiles, debtors, and discontented rabble. Saul views your presence here as proof of your attempt to incite an armed uprising; your continued presence here places everyone around you in harm's way. Depart and return to the land of Judah to fulfill your anointing as king of Israel." So David left with his brothers and all of his followers, knowing full well that Saul would not commit himself to a hostile invasion of Moab if he, David, were no longer the prize for such a risky expedition; thus ensuring his mother and father's safety from the assaults of Saul's blind determination. David left for the thickets of Hareth, affording him and his people some protection from spying eyes and before Saul could home in on his current whereabouts.

Saul's spies whispered in his ear that David had recruited an army of followers, and that, with the House of Jesse, he was plotting and planning in the Mizpeh watchtower with the assistance and blessing of the Moabite king. Saul convened a council in the uppermost part of Gibeah, on the mound of a hill where he resided among his fellow Benjaminites, as was his custom. Saul held court at Ramah, or the holy place called Jarham, and it was directly under the pomegranate tree. Saul was a king who ruled under the canopy of God's six hundred and thirteen laws: (the average number of seeds in the bittersweet fruit that is the taste of life, and so, too, the taste of the pomegranate). Saul held tight to his spear, his scepter of authority, and used it to make a point either in war strategy or when he was displeased with a servant's lackluster performance. Saul rose up to his full stature and height, so he could make eye contact with all the men who stood before him. "Hear me now, my fellow Benjaminites. Will the son of Jesse give every one of you fields and vineyards and make you all captains of thousands and captains of hundreds? He will not do what I can do for all of you, for I am one of you, and he is not. He will see to his brethren from the tribe of Judah! So then, why have all of you conspired against me? There is not one here who was brave enough to warn me that my son Jonathan had conspired with David, the son of Jesse. And there is not one who laments on my behalf, for he would have advised me that my son had stirred up my servant against me, to lie in wait, as he does this very day . . . is this not so?"

All of Saul's servants looked at each other in disbelief, for none could fathom the depths of the king's fear and madness. Not a sound passed anyone's lips for the dread of a spear, thrust in punishment, for a misplaced utterance. Doeg, the Syrian, who had been set over all the herdsmen of asses, stepped through the confused silence. "I saw the son of Jesse coming to Nob. He had conspired with Ahimelech, son of Ahitub, in front of the house of God, and Ahimelech inquired of the Lord for him. He also supplied him with shewbread and with the sword of Goliath, the Philistine." Doeg spoke words that devoured Saul's mind and laid the foundations of mayhem and carnage.

Saul rose up, his face turning blood red with rage. "I will deal with this highly regarded traitor! I will make an example of him, his house, and all who serve with him. I will send a chill throughout all of Israel; I will have them know that anyone caught giving aid or comfort to the son of Jesse is an enemy to the king and will be dealt with in a manner that draws blood and brings terror! Give me a messenger, for I have a dispatch in need of rapid delivery to Ahimelech, the son of Ahitub, at the house of God in Nob. Tell him the king awaits his presence in Gibeah, in the holy place, Jerahmeel (also known as Jarham and Ramah), under the pomegranate tree. Tell him to bring his entire house of priests, for the king and all his chieftains desire his participation, and demand his immediate submission. Tell him to make haste, for we await his speedy arrival; delay or defiance will be regarded as high treason."

Saul turned to address his chief servants. "We will eat the noon feast of meat with an abundance of dark red wine while we wait for this traitor, Ahimelech, under the cool canopy of the pomegranate tree. We wait right here for him and his house of criminal co-conspirators."

Saul's messenger made it to Nob in double-quick time—the house of God being only a few miles away. Saul's runner found Ahimelech in his residence and said unto Ahimelech every word as it was told to him by King Saul, adding nothing and omitting nothing. Ahimelech then asked, "Was there nothing else?" The messenger again repeated, word-perfect, what he had said before, and then asked, "What shall I say to the king? Will you quicken your steps to agree to the king's urgent request?"

Ahimelech responded without further hesitation. "Certainly, I will comply! Tell the king I will gather up all my priests, as a hen gathers her chicks, and we will journey forthwith to the holy place as the king has commanded me." The messenger left as quickly as he had arrived, on his way back to prepare the king for the coming of Ahimelech.

Ahimelech felt uneasy about Saul's unusual and demanding request. He said to his son Abiathar, "I wish you to stay behind to guard the House of God in my absence. To leave this place empty of all humanity would be a sacrilege. Remain alert and be wary—I feel unsure about Saul's request for my presence. He has become unpredictable and violently temperamental.

Abiathar looked curious. It was not like his father to be troubled. "Do you foresee some evil that lies before you, father?"

Ahimelech shook his head. "It is probably nothing; just a feeling of anxious misgiving. I will not wear the Ephod of Gold. You will remain behind to protect it back on its pedestal and in the safety of the hold."

Abiathar responded cheerfully. "I will keep an eye on the ephod and on the crest of the hill. I will stay in the shadows until you return at sundown. Be not concerned about my welfare, father—I can take care of myself. I am no longer a child."

Ahimelech hugged Abiathar's neck. Before he departed, he said to his son, "God be with you!"

Abiathar called back to him: "And with you, father."

Ahimelech and his house of eighty-five priests dressed in their best linen ephods and journeyed to Jerahmeel—the holy place under the pomegranate tree. The assembly moved quickly, moving silently to their uneasy meeting with the king; not a wayward word passed between them, for they walked with an inner peace lifted up in prayer and meditation.

Ahimelech and all his house presented themselves at the foot of the king. Saul looked around the crowd of guards who quickly formed a semi-circle completely surrounding the unwary priests. Then, looking down his nose, he said in a gruff voice, "Can you hear me now, son of Ahitub?"

Ahimelech answered the king, saying, "Here I am, My Lord, as you had commanded. Your faithful and loyal servant."

Saul rose up out of his chair and pointed his spear at Ahimelech. "Why have you conspired against me? You have fed, armed, and then blessed the son of Jesse! You have given him bread and the broad sword of Goliath, the Philistine brigand. You also inquired of God for him that he should rise against me. He lies in wait for me this very day, and in his hand, he has the sword that will kill me. Secured by you . . . This is treason, priest!"

Ahimelech could sense the king's irrational fear, and from the profound depth of his innocence, he answered the king.

"Who is more faithful among all your servants than David? Who is also the king's son-in-law? He comes and goes at your command and does your bidding with never an objection or a complaint. He does not conspire against you, and he does not speak ill of you. David is always honorable in your house in or out of your presence, my lord. If I have committed any crime, it was the crime of innocent belief. David said he was on a secret and urgent mission for your benefit, and he insisted he was unable to divulge the nature of this commission. He told me that he and his people had left in such a rush that they had neglected to bring bread or weapons. It was at this point that I inquired of God for him and his men's well-being so that they could serve you more thoroughly. Be this charge far from me: let not the king attribute an evil intent unto me, your most loyal servant, or to all the house of my father. For your servant knew nothing of treachery. I acted in good faith."

Saul's eyes glazed over, and sweat poured off his brow. His crown slipped to one side, and he said, "Which lie am I to believe? All I heard were excuses and pleadings to save yourself and your father's house alive. You shall surely die, Ahimelech, you and all who are in your father's house will suffer a traitor's death this day, and I swear it." Saul swept with his menacing spear at all his servants gathered about him at heart level, and in a low growl, he gave the order. "Turn, and slay the priests of the Lord. Yet they hid this crucial evidence from me, and for that blunder, they shall all be put to death. Their deaths will serve as a blaring example, causing all of Israel's ears to tingle. Let it be known that anyone who helps the son of Jesse, even unknowingly, will feel the full force of my savage fury."

Not a sound was uttered. No one took a step forward. Who would slaughter the innocent? Shielded by the garments of the holy priesthood, wearing the ephods of their commitment to God, especially here at the Jarham, the holy place . . . better to suffer the wrath of Saul than to bear a curse from God for the murder of his holy men. Not one of the servants would put forth a hand to fall upon the priests of the Lord. Saul was distressed and dismayed, for his command had gone unattended, and he was merely unheeded by all his trusted chieftains. What could he do? He could not kill them all, in spite of the fact that murdering the lot of them did cross his mind. He turned to Doeg in the hope of saving face; the Edomite would be less concerned about a curse from God and would be more likely to curry favor with the king. Saul tossed his spear into the hands of Doeg. "Turn you, and fall upon the priest." Doeg turned on the holy flock, and in a rapid progression, he thrust and then withdrew, without pause or remorse, Doeg mercilessly stabbed through Ahimelech, and the eighty-five priests who wore the linen ephod.

Their blood stained the grass a blackish-red hue, and the chieftains looked on at the overwhelming carnage of Doeg's one-man slaughterhouse. The chieftains held tight to their sword hilts, waiting for the moment that Saul might very well spur this rabid Doeg against them. The hours passed grimly in the slaughter of innocence. Saul was pleased with his butchery and found favor with Doeg, his only loyal chieftain. Torches were lit to give light and bring shadows, to complete the massacre. Saul glared at all his servants. His eyes were decidedly dark; like a feral animal on the prowl, he growled, "We are not through, and this I give to you, my faint-hearted servants—the opportunity to redeem yourselves in my sight. Nob, the city of the priests and the descendants of Shiloh, will come to destruction by your hand, and every living thing will cease to breathe this very night. Doeg will command in my stead while he holds firm my spear of authority. Do not test me on this. I need to know of your absolute loyalty. Now, be off with you!"

Doeg had found his place—second only to the king, and in charge of all the Benjaminite chieftains. Doeg was in the lead, and all the torches blazed hot against the night sky as the throng approached the crest of the hill that wound its way down to Nob and the House of God. Abiathar viewed this torch-lit mob from an upper room in the temple and quickly snuffed out all the lamps, showing no sign that anyone was in attendance. The House of God appeared empty; a few footmen quickly scouted the premises, only to confirm that the enclave stood unoccupied. Abiathar was well hidden in the dark shadows, watching and listening from his hiding place. He overheard a disturbing admission as two footmen searched through the dark, torch-lit passageways of the commune. "This is a waste of time. Did we not see with our own eyes how Doeg killed Ahimelech, the high priest, and all of the eighty-five priests who wore the ephod? Let us join Doeg to finish this night's work. Let us take part in the massacre of Nob that we might redeem ourselves in the eyes of Saul. Besides," he added, "this place of the dead is eerie. I feel like I am being watched by ghosts. Let us depart."

Doeg and his troop of chief servants were merciless. Their blood was up, and they slaughtered everything that drew breath. They mangled men, women, and children, even sucklings still on the nipple. They killed all the oxen, asses, sheep, and goats, and everything caged in the coop fell that night—to the point of the sword, and the edge of the blade.

Abiathar watched the slaughter from an upstairs window, and he could hear the screams of women mingled with the death bellows of oxen. The unnerving upsurge from the foul deeds of slaughter grew louder. He knew that Doeg would be back to ransack the House of God before long and to burn it down to the ground, leaving no stone unturned. Abiathar considered finding David, knowing that if he could find him, he would, at least, offer him some protection. He thought about what he could provide David to curry his favor. The Ephod of Gold! It was still down in the hold. It would be sought after by Doeg as a prize for Saul. It would also be of great value to David.

Abiathar thought about how to handle the situation in which he found himself. "I can wear the Ephod and ask God to guide my direction and show me where to place my feet. Trusting God, I may find salvation from Doeg and his blood lust, and I may find David before it's too late." In the dark, and in his dire desperation, Abiathar put on his linen Ephod and prayed: "Direct my steps by Your word, and let no iniquity have dominion over me. I trust in You, Lord, with all my heart, and I lean not on my own understanding; in all ways I acknowledge You, and You, Lord, shall direct my feet."

In the silence that followed, Abiathar thought he heard a still, small voice say "Keilah!" His first thought was that it had not been his voice. He knew now—in his heart and in his mind—where to go and which road to take. To secure favor with David, Abiathar donned his linen ephod for travel and protection against this night's unbridled mayhem. He would bundle the Ephod of Gold with strong cords—resting it on his shoulder. He would present it to David as a token.

Abiathar, in the cover of night, crouched low—presenting a subtle profile. Upon reaching the crest of a hill and being too far away to be detected, he looked back—only to witness a roaring blaze—signaling the holocaust of Nob. In the fire's silhouette, there was a cart caravan, filled to the brim with spoil and artifacts. The Tent of the Congregation and all the holy furnishings were destined for Gibeon—to curry favor, and to help salve Saul's unbridled madness.

CHAPTER 42

The Falling-Down Affliction

David and his army of outsiders were but a little while in Judah and found temporary relief in the wooded thickets of the Hareth Forest. A word of distress had gone out concerning Keilah, a city of Judah, and now word had reached David. It was said that the Philistines had fought against Keilah, and they had robbed the threshing floor of all life-sustaining provisions, leaving the people to starve for want of a deliverer. This was David's tribe, and his brethren were under a blockade of starvation. Could David and his small army of misfits overcome the Philistine onslaught? David inquired of the Lord, asking Him for direction, so he could relieve the sufferings of his comrades. "Shall I go and strike these Philistines?"

The Lord answered David sharply, as He did in all of David's righteous petitions. The Lord said, "Go and strike the Philistines, and save Keilah."

David gathered up his people and his family and addressed them all. "Men, friends, and brothers, are we not outcasts in

Israel? We have been given an opportunity to redeem ourselves. I have inquired of the Lord, and we are to go to Keilah. We are to strike down the Philistines, who have robbed and spoiled the threshing floors of Keilah. They are currently laying siege to the city, waiting until the people are weakened from hunger and the specter of famine that they might go into Keilah unchallenged to commit murder, rape, and plunder. The Lord has given it to us to stop them!" David's men grumbled at his proposition, questioning if it truly was God, who had proposed to send misfits into battle against a stronger and well-proven adversary.

Eliab, Jesse's eldest son and David's older brother, spoke up for the crowd of vagabonds. "We are fearful here in Judah, not knowing when Saul will discover our whereabouts to attack us in our sleep. After all, we are simply a pack of distressed debtors. With all due respect, little brother, what makes you think we could prevail against a battle-hardened army of Philistines?"

David pondered the fear-driven lack of confidence displayed by his people, and to be fair, offered them a solution to their doubt. "I will risk the wrath of the Lord. I will inquire once more if this is in fact what He would have of me, and of us. I will ask that He informs me of His will so that I can relay it to you with absolute certainty. I will confirm His words to dispel your doubt, given that we are thinly trained and a poorly armed band of desperate vagabonds and malcontents. Knowing God's will, we may forge ahead on His behalf, to save Keilah. Using us, His weak and uncertain people, to act in faith and to trust His word, everyone in Israel will know that the victory belongs to the Lord of Hosts and that there is a God in Israel."

David inquired of the Lord yet again, saying, "Lord, forgive me, for I am a weak and foolish man. My people wallow in doubt and misgiving. They need to be reasoned with and to be assured that we follow Your omnipotent will and not mine. Should we go to Keilah to defeat the crowd of Philistine infidels?" And the Lord answered him, saying, "Arise, go down to Keilah; for I will deliver the Philistines into your hand."

David and his motley crew proceeded to Keilah, encouraged in knowing they were on a mission from God, and that they could trust in Him rather than their old and rusted swords. Most of them, in fact, carried pitchforks, slings, and staves. David scouted the approach to the city, finding that the citadel walls were tall and formidable, and every portal covered with iron bars. The Philistines were encamped before the city gates. They were waiting on the ache from starvation, hoping it would eventually grease the high doorways' starving hinges with the specter of famine, and force a desperate opening.

The Philistines had robbed the threshing floor and had secured all the grain before surrounding the city. They had denied access to all life-giving provisions to the now despairing and starving people. The Philistines had prepared for a long siege, bringing cattle in abundance to ensure themselves of fresh meat, while tormenting the inhabitants with the tantalizing aroma of roasting beef. David and his brothers took turns in a constant vigil, by day and through the night, keeping a watchful eye on the Philistine encampment, hoping to find a flaw in their defenses. David's army was a mile away, lying low in a ravine, waiting for David's return. David took the middle watch. It reminded him of the endless nights alone, guarding Jesse's sheepfold. It was an hour before dawn when David stirred his brothers from their fitful slumber. He covered each of their mouths in turn to avoid any accidental outcry, whispering to each as he went: "I have found a weakness within the Philistine strategy. Tread lightly, and keep silent as we make our way back to our men in the canyon. I have a plan that I will disclose when we reach our hiding place."

The sun was fresh when David and his brothers made their way back to the cleft. David gathered his anxious men all about him before he began to speak. "I have found a way to conquer the Philistines with their own meat-eating gluttony. They have brought their own destruction with them, the seed of which lies within their herd of cattle. These cattle are guarded by only a few men, and most fall asleep just before sunup. They are the key to undoing the whole of these overfed trespassers. We can approach the guards in the dark, eliminating them one by one with the silent cut of an assassin's knife. Our next goal will be to cause the cattle to stampede straight into the sleeping Philistine encampment. We can accomplish this objective in one of two ways. First, we can either ignite the dry grass with hot sparks from firebrands nestled in clay pots, frightening the dumb brutes in the direction of our enemy's encampment. Or second, with a mighty blast from the sacred shofar, we can charge them into the slumbering Philistine horde. If the wind does not cooperate in spreading the fire in the needed direction, we will forego the flame by using the clanging of swords and the shofar—to drive them into the midst of the Philistines—still fast asleep in their tents." David looked around at the circle of men gathered around him. His plan was greeted with disbelief and then with enlightened smiles, in the short quick nods in the compliment of a muffled cheer of agreement.

"To further ensure our enemy's destruction, we will shoot a blunt arrow—carrying a message—into the middle of Keilah, advising them to launch a fire-arrow in the direction of heaven, one hour before sunrise. This will be a signal to set our firebreak—or to lash out into a crashing noise that will unnerve the sleeping herd into a charging runaway frenzy. The message we send to the men of Keilah will inform them to be ready to open their massive gates—so that their army can follow hot upon the heels of the rampaging beasts, who will start the slaughter with their pounding hooves and slashing horns."

The band of vagabonds and brothers-in-arms were excited by David's plan and felt a renewed trust in God. They now had a plan that was divinely inspired; with every chance of great success. David, feeling encouraged by the progress they had made, clenched his fist to stress the importance of precision. "Our timing is critical! Our brothers and sisters starve. They are entombed in their great walls and iron-barred gates. We strike tonight."

A bowman set off so he could approach the wilderness side of Keilah in stealth. The wilderness side was the Philistines' least guarded area. They had concentrated their forces on the gates and on the walls facing the approach to the city—this to ensure that no one could exit out and that no food baskets could enter in—or any messages at all could travel along the length of ropes or cords.

David attached a hastily written note outlining his instructions. He fixed it to the arrow's shaft, praying it would find its mark in the hands of the chief captain. David turned to his men and gave his final instructions: "There will be no talking, sneezing, or coughing during the approach. Each footfall must be carefully measured, for the slightest sound could mean death to us all. If we die, the Philistines will surely capture Keilah—a strategic foothold with which to menace all of Judah. Enemy weapons will be plentiful after the beasts have gored and crushed. They will be lying about on the ground. Secure the weapons, but do not adorn yourselves with enemy armor or enemy helmets, as you might be mistaken for a Philistine by the men of Keilah in their rush to battle. My brother, Eliab, is well practiced with the horn of shofar. He will sound a blast to raise the dead." David turned to his eldest brother; smiled, and winked.

Turning to his other brothers, David continued. "Abinadab, Shammah, and four others will carry the clay pots filled with smoldering firebrands. They will also be responsible for starting the clashing and clanging of noisy swords. If the wind remains constant, and the dry grass is set ablaze, we will file behind the curtain of fire until it breaks on the barren landscape one hundred yards from the entrance to the gate. By then the cattle will have done their worst. All this will depend on the skill and the stealth of our assassins, and how well they accomplish their secret art of silently cutting throats in the shadows. We will attack in the darkest hour, the hour before dawn. As soon as the bulls begin their charge, we will fall in behind this dual shield of fire and steers. God-willing, the army of Keilah will meet us on the battlefield. Now, let us pray for divine intervention."

David and his army of unlikely heroes knelt down on even ground. David bowed his head to pray. "Lord, we have come to this place as you have commanded, and we ask Your guidance and protection. You are our high tower and our buckler, our shield and our scepter. Blessed be the LORD, our strength, who teaches our hands to war, and our fingers to fight: that we may prevail in Your invincible service this very night."

David stood up and said a few final words. "Men, take your rest and be at ease, for we will venture out during the middle of the second watch. Remember, patience will count just as much as courage! We align ourselves with silence and shadows."

The rest of the righteous soon became evident, made plain in a chorus of snorting and snoring. The rousing was orderly, and the men had confidence as if the battle had already happened. They felt that their victory was a foregone conclusion, and all they had to do was go through the motions.

The assassins were subtle as they slowly inched their way on their bellies through the underbrush. One by one, the outpost guards met their end with a muffled death rattle. David and his people found the favor of God. As they approached the sleeping herd, the wind was at their backs and moving in the desired direction. This was crucial, as it would obtain the greatest effect, creating thick, choking smoke and scorching fire. Every nerve jangled and every heart pounded while waiting for the confirming arc of the fire-arrow, launched from deep within the stronghold's center. The time was at hand, and the moments played out, every second an eternity. All eyes focused on David in the dark. David was in doubt. Had his message been received? If so, had it been understood? Would the men of Keilah comply? Should they retreat, hoping to find safety in fear and misgiving, or should they keep trusting in God? David could not wait another minute to make a decision. If they lingered, the sun would rise, and they would be discovered, losing the advantage of surprise. David filled his lungs and rose up. He would trust in God and accept his fate, come what may. Before he uttered a single word, the fire-arrow raced across the horizon, and the battle was on.

The firebrands ignited just as the winds picked up, fanning the line of fire into a running blaze. Eliab speared the ears of the docile herd with a mighty blast from his shofar horn, and the noisy swords were also employed. David's four hundred men lined up behind the wall of fire in columns of four. The cattle collapsed the enemy tents. Many were trampled as they rose up from their beds, and others were gored with pointed horns while fleeing from the charging fury. The gates of Keilah opened wide as the cattle charged on every side, and the army of Keilah hungered to join the fray, slashing and stabbing at the Philistines in a frenzy of slaughter. David and his army of four hundred, the least likely of champions, saved the inhabitants of Keilah. A feast was in order, and the cattle were rounded up. All of Keilah had meat to eat, and some beasts were sacrificed on the altar of God in thanksgiving for providing a savior. Philistine wine, claimed in the spoil of war, overflowed in bottomless cups, adding merriment to a night of tales and toasting. David and his people were proclaimed as heroes for confirming that there was a God in Israel.

The governor of the city addressed David, saying, "You and your family, and all who are considered your people, are officially received as our honored guests. You may stay as long as you will, secure in our protection from the ravages of the world. You will find safety behind our great gates of iron and our tall walls that reach to the sky."

Abiathar, the son of Ahimelech, fled to David in Keilah, directed there by God. Hoping to curry favor with David,

Abiathar came down, and in his hand was the Ephod of Gold. David was impressed with the lavish vestment. "I had seen it only once before, resting on its pedestal in front of Goliath's sword that hung on the wall in the house of God at Nob." David invited Abiathar to a private dinner, for they had much to discuss and needed the privacy. David sat and inquired of Abiathar, "How is your father Ahimelech? He has always been kind and generous to me."

Abiathar looked down, and sadness was visible on his face. He looked up at David and said, "I have news that carries both a harsh and ruthless warning. Saul had my father murdered, along with all eighty-five priests who wore the linen ephod. And as if that was not bad enough, he raised up Doeg to be his most trusted chief captain. Saul ordered him to massacre everything that drew breath in Nob: men, women . . . even suckling children and all the livestock were put to the sword. This was done to send a chill through all of Israel. Anyone found giving you support or bringing you relief from hardship, whether knowingly or innocently, will be treated as the king's enemy. They will be dealt with in a like and merciless manner. I alone managed to escape, due only to my father's cautious protection, and by the grace of God."

David shook his head, sinking down into his chair, real in his despair. In confirmation of his guilt for the lies he had told, realizing now that many had died, he asked Abiathar's forgiveness. "I knew the day that I approached the House of God and saw Doeg the Edomite lurking about, that he would inform Saul of my whereabouts. I have caused the death of your father, Ahimelech, all who were in his house, and the entire city of Nob. Please forgive me, Abiathar, for my trickery. I was desperate, unarmed, and starving, and I took advantage of your father's generous, innocent and trusting nature, solely for the benefit of my men and my own selfish ends."

His appeal to Abiathar was readily accepted, and Abiathar said, "With certainty do I forgive you, David. You could not have known the dire consequences of such a simple ruse for bread and weapons to secure your protection in the wilderness. Nor can you be held accountable for a madman's obsession with trying to guarantee his own dynasty, no matter what the cost. He sees you as violating the legacy he hopes to leave, and is angry that, through being who you are, his own son, Jonathan, whom Saul loves as much as he hates you, has turned against him. Saul greatly fears you."

David found peace from the pardon of sin and offered refuge to the man who had granted it. "Abiathar, stay with me, and have no fear, for he that seeks your life also seeks my life. But if you agree to abide with me, my new friend, you will be safeguarded; this I pledge to you on my oath and honor." Abiathar was glad for the invitation of a safe haven after his dreadful experience. Being the friend of the Lord's anointed could only bode well for a young man's future prospects.

Abiathar looked down and shook his head, wondering how to express his secret. Finally, he looked up, mumbling to David: "There is something I must shamefully admit to you."

David smiled kindly. "Do not overly concern yourself, no matter what, no matter how cruel or how rude, for we are friends now, and your secret will abide in me alone and forever. We can overcome any obstacle. I have deprived you of kith and kin, both friend and family, and I feel obligated to secure your well-being, as I have already promised. Speak to me, my friend."

Encouraged, Abiathar whispered shyly to David: "I have the falling-down disease. I sometimes dribble on my beard. I scratch and scrabble on wooden panels, walls, and doors. Sometimes, I fall to the floor, and I quake so uncontrollably that it strikes fear into all who are around me, causing them to flee. Some think it an evil spirit." Abiathar looked into David's eyes, traumatized at having to bare his soul but wanting to be honest with his new friend. "I wish not to burden you, and I don't want to have you succumb to the illness for being in my presence."

David smiled. He said to Abiathar, "Is that all?

Abiathar, feeling insulted, gave a sharp reply. "Why do you make light of so grave of an affliction? Do you ridicule me, my lord?"

David, in a show of compassion, extended his hand to Abiathar's shoulder. "No, my friend. Please excuse my inappropriate remark. You see, I suffer from the same affliction. My family knows, but not another soul has been told. We keep it as a family secret, as it occurs only infrequently, in the moments of stress and sometimes at moments of rest. Please consider, my friend, that you are in the most renowned of companies. King Saul is also afflicted with the falling-down disease. His episodes are even worse than mine, which leads me to believe that the illness might become more severe as I age. I think his behavior is affected by his constant headaches. Be that as it may, as far as you and I are concerned, we shall be lifelong friends. Being thus afflicted as we are, we will keep this to ourselves, and treat it as our secret bond."

Abiathar was relieved and even pleased, for they shared a common reality. "David, I have something else I need to impart, and this only to the anointed king of Israel." David's interest was keen and with his hands motioned his friend to continue.

"My father was concerned about the security of the Tabernacle and all the holy furnishings in his care. Many had been made aware of our location, and he feared a breach from thievery or its loss from confiscation and sale. An evil spirit fell upon my father soon after you had departed, filling him with dread and misgiving. There was also Saul's vicious aggression to collect war taxes. This was done to feed the demands of his insatiable army. My father feared that the temple would be ransacked of all its gold, precious metals, and gems. "My father was disappointed and dismayed that God dismissed his temple offering. He claimed that Jehovah wanted a house of cedar, and would not reveal His face, and instead remained in His hiding place. My Father also determined that there must have been some evil lurking under the surface, and that our God does not abide the least amount of sin. Ahimelech then ordered the Ark brought up to the house of Abinadab in Gibeah for safe keeping. We were about to secure the Tabernacle of the Congregation and all the holy furnishings in a secret vault, just before the massacre. Doeg had seized all things valuable—to deliver his blood-stained plunder to Gibeon—and what seems to be with Saul's permission and blessing. Abiathar took a moment to collect his thoughts, looked David squarely in the eyes, and inquired, "Do you know how to pitch a tent?"

"I do—I am a shepherd, lest you forget, and I have had the luxury of stitched skins as a covering in sudden downpours. You puzzle me, Abiathar."

Abiathar, with a renewed boldness said, "My Lord, when you come into your own, sitting upon the throne in Jerusalem, you can pitch a tent and restore the Ark of the Testimony. You, David, as king of Israel, can make a whole out of what once was broken. And so, the Ark of the Covenant will be lodged in the city of David. Your Booth will house this most glorious treasure, until an enduring sanctuary of stone and cedar is made ready and is pleasing to our wonderful Creator." David put his arm around Abiathar's shoulder and kissed his cheek with a holy kiss for his service to him and to the struggling nation of Israel.

David's exploits, and his part in the vast slaughter of the Philistine garrison—along with his legendary rescue of Keilah with an army of debtors and malcontents; aided by fire and stampeding cattle—quickly spread abroad to all the coasts of Israel. The news was relayed to Saul and confirmed by outpost spies. Saul was delighted at the prospect that his prey had been caged. He rallied all his people to go down to Keilah to lay siege to David and his fledgling army. Saul stood in the midst of them and said, "Men of Israel, God has delivered the son of Jesse into my hand; for he is shut in by entering a town that has gates and bars. The people of Keilah will be weary from their recent encounter with Philistine brigands, and I am, after all, their king. They will give up this usurper without an argument, for they will not want to know the sting of my outrage and suffer hunger and extinction, so help me God."

CHAPTER 43

The Passover of the Ephod of Gold

David knew that the twin horns of rumor and gossip
would quickly prick the ears of Saul. He also knew that
Saul would find any excuse to attack him. David's misgivings were
soon realized when given a report by a breathless messenger: Saul
was gathering his army and would destroy the city of Keilah to
ensure David's destruction. David called upon the priest, Abiathar,
saying, "Bring me the Golden Ephod, so I may pray to the Lord
with authority." David put the vestment on. He stretched his arms
toward the sky and said: "O Lord God of Israel, hear the words of
my mouth. Your servant has certainly heard that Saul is planning
to come to Keilah to destroy the city for my sake. Will the men
of Keilah deliver me up into his hand? Will Saul come down, as
your servant was told? Oh, Lord God of Israel, I plead with you
to give your servant answers to these questions."

And the Lord said, "He will come down."

David pressed his inquiry and asked again, "Will the men of
Keilah deliver my men and me into the hand of Saul?"

And the Lord said, "They will deliver you up."

Having prayed, David knew what he must do. He called Eliab and his other brothers, who were captains of hundreds. Abiathar, the priest, was also summoned to a war council, and David spoke to them all: "I have heard Saul is preparing his army to invade Keilah, in the very same way the Philistines originally had attempted. The Philistines failed due only to the Lord God's inspiration and through our valiant efforts. I have prayed in earnest to the Lord, and He has confirmed that our presence puts Keilah in dire jeopardy. They will hand us over to Saul to save themselves and to protect their city. If they choose not to comply with the king's wishes, it will make our recent victory hollow because Saul will destroy this town. He will undo all the good that we have done. He will make the inhabitants of Keilah suffer a bloodthirsty massacre, as was enacted in Nob. Saul will do this just to capture me so that I trouble his imaginings no longer. We must depart!"

Eliab answered, saying, "I agree with your decision to leave, but where can we go? Every door is closed to us, and we have an additional two hundred men to care for, bringing our number to about six hundred men. With so many empty bellies to feed and so many men in need of weapons and provisions, maybe we should stay and put up a fight. At least, then we will be finished with this endless flight."

David pondered his eldest brother's counsel before replying. "Staying does not bode well. We put ourselves behind iron bars. We will find ourselves in a high-walled cage. Our best defense is the ability to stay one step ahead of Saul—the bird on the wing is a harder kill. We will leave for the thick brush of the wilderness. I will mention neither our direction nor our intended location to a single living soul. We will abide for only a short while at any given locale and in various strongholds. This will frustrate and exhaust Saul, for, in time, the Philistines will become a more pressing matter. The wilderness I have in mind is dense and heavily wooded." The council agreed to a man. They all stood up and departed into the safety of the thickets of Ziph.

Saul's ears were pinched with bad news. David and his men had escaped from Keilah, and the only news he could scrape together was that David had headed off in the direction of the wilderness, with not a word as to his actual whereabouts. Saul did not inflict Keilah, but he did consider revenge for the city having harbored the fugitive son of Jesse. Saul kept the pressure on—hunting David every day—but God put a veil between Saul and David, and David was not delivered into Saul's hand. David found a stronghold in the mountains of Ziph, and to further secure his secrecy, he empowered a ghost battalion captained by Eliab, his eldest brother, who had a striking resemblance to David. Eliab was often mistaken for his youngest brother, which greatly enhanced their intentional deception.

Eliab and his men traveled to other strongholds and stayed only long enough to give a false trail to David's sanctuary. When Saul was alerted, he and his men approached the supposed location, only to find that David and his legion were long since gone, reportedly being seen on the other side of the mountain or deep in the dark and murky forest. Saul's intelligence gatherers were flooded with hearsay and rumor concerning David's whereabouts. He was perceived to be everywhere, but in fact, he was nowhere to be found. This turn of events only helped to scorch Saul's burning obsession. He was convinced that a widespread conspiracy was being kindled against him. Saul's outrage was further fueled by the growing strength of David and his followers, aided by the love of Jonathan, his spellbound son, who was, after all, the rightful heir to the throne of Israel.

Jonathan, son of Saul, would forgo the honor of being the future King of Israel because of his love for the anointed, David; Jonathan loved David even more than his own life. Jonathan always remained in contact with David through a secret go-between, and in this way, David stayed one step ahead of Saul's evil designs. Jonathan longed to be with his best friend. He yearned to give him comfort and to assure him that his father's obsession would not prevail against him by casting a long shadow on his hidden wilderness stronghold. Jonathan hoped to protect his friend from the menace presented by his father. Jonathan journeyed by way of a secret passage to avoid the ever-watchful eyes of his father's loyal informants. He took extra precaution to ensure a secret meeting with his soul-brother, David, in the forbidden forests of Ziph.

Jonathan and David embraced when, at long last, they came face to face. David's burdens seemed to lift when Jonathan demonstrated genuine warmth and kindness to his dearest friend and comrade. Jonathan, to reassure David, and to dispel his misgivings, said, "David, my friend, have no doubt that you are on the Lord's mission, and reside in His strong hand and outstretched arm. Fear not: for the hand of my father will not find you, and if found, he will not be able to close his tight fist around you. You shall be the next king over Israel, and this also my father, Saul, knows. Although he knows this very well, he is still attempting to sidestep the will of God."

David and Jonathan made a covenant with the Lord. They knelt down upon equal ground, agreeing that all men are viewed the same in the sight of God. They prayed. David said, "Lord, bless me and my friendship with Jonathan, son of Saul, with an undying love—and that I may always agree to hold him dear and in the highest esteem come what may—in the bright light of day and life or in the dark foreboding death of night."

Jonathan said, "I, too, hold David in the highest regard and agreed by pledge to comply with David's lawful anointing as king, and to be forever on his right side."

Both men rose to their feet, and each hugged the neck of his like-minded brother; having renewed their covenant of civil devotion and the undying loyalty of blood brothers. David stayed in his stronghold in the thickets of Ziph, whereas Jonathan returned to his home in Gibeah, before he came up absent and forced to bend to his father's will and have to explain his sticky web of wandering.

Eliab was subtle in keeping up the deception of his ghost battalion, but it was just a matter of time before David's secret lair would be uncovered. The Ziphites were hunter-gatherers and knew well their primeval forest—every rivulet, run, and cleft. Soon enough, David's location became known to them, yet they tolerated his presence, glad of the barter in traded goods brought to their forest by David and his men. The relationship began wearing thin when there was nothing left to sell, and the army of David was slaughtering all the wild game. A council of Ziph chieftains was summoned, and they agreed that David and his army needed to depart from their hunting preserve before all the game was gone, as this would leave them and their families facing a winter of famine. What else were they to do?

Just then, a well-regarded old man who was long in the tooth, stood up at the council fire and said: "Have you not considered that we can rid ourselves of these hungry trespassers with no loss of life or limb? In other words . . . ," the old sage winked, ". . . we will lose no parts, for doing our part. We can gain at the same time a reward of good favor from a grateful king! It has long been known that David is a vexation to Saul's reign and to his dreams of establishing a long-lived dynasty. Saul will be eternally grateful if we are to notify him of David's presence. He will surely reward us with land titles and bags of gold." The council nodded their agreement, grateful to have in their midst what they considered the wisdom of the aged.

A body of Ziphites journeyed to Gibeah to present themselves to Saul. Their spokesman bowed his head low, stressing his humility, and then addressed the king. "Your Esteemed Majesty, it has been made known to us that you seek the son of Jesse. We are here to inform you that David hides in our forests and strongholds in the hill of Hachilah, which is on the south side of Ziph, also known as the dreary desert or Jeshimon. David has been very cunning. His brother, who closely resembles him, has been employed in moving a portion of David's army from stronghold to stronghold, never staying more than a night and a day in one place, so as to confuse any trackers. David has gathered about him nearly six hundred armed men, more than we are able to subdue. We propose, O King that you and a portion of your army come down to Ziph with us to satisfy the longing of your soul. We will do our part in delivering up to you this dangerous rival, David, son of Jesse. We will deliver him into your waiting and eager hands."

Saul was overjoyed in seeing that there were some in Israel who were not in a conspiracy against him, and that they would aid him in his desire to capture the son of Jesse and to ensure his swift execution. Saul believed David's death would finally ease his own mind. He also felt it would secure the kingdom for Jonathan and all his descendants. Saul smiled, for he was giddy with joy. "Blessed are you," he nodded to the spokesman, "and all of you." He looked to the men of Ziph. "Blessed of the Lord are all of you; for you have taken compassion on me and my house in your efforts to destroy my most dangerous enemy." Saul leaned into the crowd of men and said, "You, men of Ziph, go, I pray you, and prepare to make certain! Have no doubts as to his hiding place. I would know where he stands and where he sits. Be sure there is no mistake concerning his whereabouts. I want to know exactly where he is to be found. Interview those who have had their eyes on him; gather together firsthand witnesses who will insist as to his exact location, for I have been told that he deals in subtle trickeries, which you have now confirmed. I have merely been chasing his brother, who only resembles him in likeness. I was being led astray by whispers and rumors of sightings in and out of steep forest strongholds, and all for naught!" Saul shook his head, pacing as he spoke.

"David mocks me and ridicules my best attempts to capture him. I need you to secure the knowledge of all the territories where he lurks and hides. When you have gathered all this intelligence, come back here so we may proceed with certainty. I will go with you and put an end to this outlaw and his mockery. If David is not where you say he is, or if he has fled my snare—by all that is sacred, it will not go well with you. If David and his men remain in the land, I will continue to seek him throughout the thousands of strongholds, crevices, and hiding places in all of Judah!"

The men of Ziph agreed to the commands of the king. They left for their forest home, to scout out and to confirm the exact site of David's concealed dwelling place.

Jonathan had made it his concern to learn all the mischief that his father was planning to commit against his best friend, David. Jonathan had overheard his father's newest scheme of enlisting the Ziphites, and he promptly sent a secret message to David. Jonathan's messenger outran the men of Ziph. His message detailed their intended betrayal, making David and his men aware that Saul's impending net was deftly cast and would capture the unwary.

David received Jonathan's well-detailed dispatch in time to move his people to the wilderness in the plain of Mason, on the south side of Jeshimon, also known as the south shore of the lifeless desert. The men of Ziph were downcast to find that all traces of David had vanished. They had given their pledge to deliver this crafty nomad, David, son of Jesse, and all of his men into the waiting hands of their bitterly impatient king. The men of Ziph straightaway recruited their very best scouts and trackers to sniff out David's location over rocky ground and mountain passes. David's new stronghold was quickly disclosed, and his resting place was just as hastily conveyed back to Saul. The men of Ziph were not inclined to take any chances by incurring Saul's displeasure or enduring the possibility of brutal punishment for broken promises. They told Saul that David had departed Ziph and was now down in a gorge across from a rocky division or

Sela in the wilderness of Mason. This was the most clear-cut information regarding David's hiding place Saul had been given since the onset of his hunt for his crafty contender.

Saul was hoping for relief from the constant agony he felt over the near miss of his javelin that he had replayed in his mind a thousand times in a futile attempt to relieve his torment from a near hit outcome. Twice he had failed in his attempts at killing his youthful tormentor. Saul was quick to gather up his chieftains and footmen. He was not going to let this golden opportunity slip through his fingers once again. Saul pursued after David in the wilderness of Mason with great haste, leaving the borders of Israel undefended.

David was glad of the timely warning sent to him by his dearest friend, Jonathan—yet he and his men were faint for lack of game. The wilderness of Mason was sparse, and the wilderness of Ziph was all but used up. There was nothing left to trade, and all the gold and silver had long since been spent. Eliab then said unto David, "My brother, the men are weary of this cat-and-mouse strategy. It will be only a short while before the Ziphites curry favor with Saul and start tracking our every move. And another matter, even more pressing, has made itself painfully apparent to all of us."

David, who had been staring at his older brother, suddenly interrupted him, "Speak out, my brother, for I know already what you are going to say—but it needs to be said out loud."

So Eliab continued, "The men have exhausted all the local game, and our purse is as empty as our hollow stomachs. We suffer a lack of salt and provisions, causing tempers to flair. Some speak of departing and stay only because they have nowhere else to go."

David pondered Eliab's words carefully, for even his own girdle had begun to droop for its lack of girth to fill.

David summoned Abiathar to bring forth the Ephod of Gold, and he did so in his hand. He addressed the priest, saying, "Abiathar, I am in need of wealth to sustain my army. Without the needed gold to obtain weapons and provisions, we are all but lost." Abiathar made as if to speak, but David put up his hand to prevent him from making an utterance. "I have talked to God, and He has been gracious to me in our communication. I have come to the conclusion that no bejeweled vestment is actually necessary or needed to speak to God. I believe that it is an affront to God to put such store in gold and silver trinkets. This ungodly treasure has a history of death and violence. It has been a snare to all who have come into contact with it, and its value to me has finally been reduced to its weight in gold and the value of its jewels. These will fetch the price of food, salt, and shoes, and will help to replace our old and broken weapons with new and useful ones. No graven image is required to hear the word of God; only a contrite heart and a righteous desire to do good, and in so doing, they proclaim the greatness of our God."

Straightaway, and without hesitation, Abiathar said, "For the greater good, I agree to your wishes, David, as the Ephod of Gold's history, when reflected upon, is tainted with snares, murders, and mayhem to all who have possessed it. Let us pluck out the twelve stones to ensure that the Twelve Tribes thrive with you as our king, and then pass the ephod through the fire." And as a token of my undying loyalty to you David, my Lord and my friend, please accept my linen Ephod to bind us forever to God and to Israel."

David was greatly heartened by his agreement and the expression of his respect. "Abiathar, thank you for your electing to choose this righteous path. You will be rewarded for your generosity of spirit. You will be my high priest in all of Israel, and will remain so for all the days of my reign."

The jewels were pried loose, and the fire was quickly stoked with makeshift bellows made from a bull's bladder. Before long, the breastplate and all the golden thread started melting into a shiny puddle of molten yellow.

Saul approached at the near end of the mountain. Across on the other side of the mountain, there was a Sela or a yawning rock gully that separated Saul from his quarry. David was alerted to Saul's invasion, making a hasty but futile attempt to escape the king's forces. David feared Saul, for he had encircled the mountain, and no route promised a safe getaway. At the precise moment, the last thread of the Ephod of Gold dissolved back into the pool of its raw element, Saul's victory was snatched from his grasp. A messenger approached Saul, his message filled with the urgency of life and death. "Your Majesty, the Philistines have invaded! They threaten all of Israel, and there is none to withstand them. Your kingdom will fall . . . only your presence can save the nation."

Saul was confounded by the message, and feeling compelled to respond, he was forced to withdraw, leaving David for another day. In bitter frustration, Saul called the place, "Sela-hammahlekoth" or "the rock of separation or escape."

David was free to flee, and now, with gold and precious stones enough to feed and provide for his army of six hundred, he went unmolested to the strongholds of En-gedi. David was convinced that a brighter future for him and Israel was about to commence.

And so, the legacy of Gideon remained, but the Ephod of Gold was put through the fire and thus ended its evil snare. The ephod found its way back to being of maximum service to God in the purchase of food and in the obtaining of arms. These necessary provisions were all that were missing to ensure the crowning of David, the shepherd boy, future king of Israel. Selah.

Amen and Amen. The End.